LOWISH, S

THE LAST TRUMP OF
AVRAM BLOK

THE LAST
TRUMP
~ *of* ~
AVRAM
BLOK

F/353197

SIMON
LOUVISH

COLLINS
8 Grafton Street, London W1
1990

William Collins Sons & Co. Ltd
London · Glasgow · Sydney · Auckland
Toronto · Johannesburg

BRITISH LIBRARY CATALOGUING IN PUBLICATION DATA

Louvish, Simon, *1947–*
The last trump of Avram Blok.
I. Title
823 [F]

ISBN 0-00-223462-9

First published in Great Britain by Collins 1990
Copyright © Simon Louvish 1990

The extract from 'And Death Shall Have no Dominion',
from *Dylan Thomas, Collected Poems 1934–52* (Everyman's Classics),
is reproduced by kind permission of Dent Publishers.

Typeset in Linotron Bembo by
Rowland Phototypesetting Ltd, Bury St Edmunds, Suffolk
Printed and bound in Great Britain by
William Collins Sons & Co. Ltd, Glasgow

In Memoriam:

JOHN FLETCHER
RAKETLA TSEHLANA

Always laughter in the dark

'I ain't crazy, I just don't give a darn.'

DAFFY DUCK

'Would you like a fuller knowledge of the truth?' asked Herr Trippa, 'by pyromancy, by aeromancy – much esteemed by Aristophanes in his *Clouds* – by hydromancy, or by lecanomancy, which was most celebrated of old amongst the Assyrians and attempted by Hermolaus Barbarus? In a basin full of water I'll show you your future wife being rogered by two rustics.'

'When you poke your nose up my arse,' said Panurge, 'don't forget to take off your spectacles.'

RABELAIS: Pantagruel

'The soul is the prison of the body.'

MICHEL FOUCAULT:
Discipline and Punish

I

Inferno . . .

THE COMING

The Primal Scream
Blok strides across the earth in seven-league boots, his head above the clouds . . .

No, he crawls upon the earth, with the rest of us, postponing the day he's ploughed under.

What else can we expect?

The Madman Cometh
Avram Blok, ex mental patient and ex patriate, arrived at Heathrow Airport, London, after abandoning his Homeland and his home city, Jerusalem, on March --, 1983. Chance meetings led him to be offered a post as assistant to the editing tutor of an educational establishment named the London College of the Cinematographic Arts. Some time later the College became bankrupt and, in the twist and twirl of events, Blok eked out his life for a while in a cardboard box by the Charing Cross Embankment. But two years later he found himself hitchhiking upon the Scenic Highway 1 along the coast of California, where he was picked up, just above the Ragged Point, by a middle-aged all-American couple named Mr and Mrs Arnold Joy, who were motoring north from Los Angeles in a Chevrolet station wagon pulling a large white trailer laden with all their earthly goods and chattels, to re-settle in Carmel, a small town which had recently elected as its Mayor a film star specialising in manly individualism and the armed chastisement of wrongdoers.

'And where are you headed, young man?' asked Mrs Joy, after Blok and his rucksack had climbed in the back seat.

'Big Sur,' said Blok. 'I am visiting a dying old man who was once a giant of the motion picture business. I had a friend who was going to drive me up there, but I lost him in Los Angeles.'

'Everybody gets lost in Los Angeles,' said Mr Joy, whose face was made of home-made apple pie. 'Pretty soon it'll all go under. It's all down in the Scriptures, boy. Voices, and thunderings, and lightnings, and an earthquake, and the seven angels will prepare to sound. There will be hail and fire mingled with blood, and the bottomless pit and the smoke of the furnace. But those men with the seal of God on their foreheads will be saved. Revelations, 8 and 9.'

'But they too, who have the seal, will be tormented,' Mrs Joy reminded him. 'They should be tormented five months.'

'But their torment will be as the torment of a scorpion, when he striketh a man,' countered Mr Joy.

'That's why we're going to Carmel,' said Mrs Joy. 'It's far enough from the Fault.'

'You can walk the streets without getting killed,' said Mr Joy. 'Air's pure. The people are friendly. People genuinely care about their mind and body. It's a good place to wait.'

'This old man you're visiting, is he a relative?' asked Mrs Joy.

'No,' said Blok. But he could not explain why he was undertaking the journey to the ailing Irving Klotskashes, king of the Fifties' shlock movies and alleged former Elder of Zion.

'The Day's coming soon,' said Mr Joy, 'you can bet your bottom dollar.'

The afternoon was beginning to fade and the mist beginning to roll down the hills towards the great Pacific breakers. Out to sea waves broke on protruding rocks upon which seals slapped their flippers and barked. Further out, the trace of a whale's nostril could perhaps be glimpsed, briefly, in the spray. Down the cliff, a community of failed businessmen, living in prefabricated huts on a ledge, awaited orders from the Sun God Ra. They were dressed in white robes, with silver dollars wrapped round their foreheads by means of orange headbands. Their eyes were closed as they deflected their gaze inwards, to their souls, each attempting to find the inherent nothingness that, it appeared, lay at their core. Mrs Joy turned towards the back seat and extracted a paper bag of fruit from a wicker basket. She handed her husband a banana and

14

Blok an apple, red and shiny. Sitting back, she peeled herself an orange.

'And where are you coming from, young man?'

★

Where indeed . . . ?

'THE WEST!' Three years earlier, Asher Katzman taunted Blok, 'What the fuck are you doing here? What sucks you to this territory? Is it the Fleshpots? The Good Life, Prosperity, Freedom? The tall towers of wealth, the gilded cage, creature comforts? The double duvet, fitted carpets, three-piece genuine leather, lamborghinis and latex, contact lenses, cosy body warmers, water purifiers, portable cappuccino machines, ionisers, personal computers, hip pocket calculators, answering machines, travel kettles, foldaway solariums, blood pressure monitors, golf-ball holders, pierre cardin gladstone bags, dental buffs, travel clock radios, teas-mades, filofaxes, personalised labels, spud-u-like and macdonald hamburgers, kentucky fried, szechuan cuisine, chicken bhoona, lasagne and linguine, storage organisers, videocassette recorders, designer shirt wallets, foldaway filing cabinets, social security, supplementary benefits, cold weather allowances, pierre cardin djellabahs, luggage wheels, hide-a-pocket moneybelts, early warning burglar alarms, pet grooming kits, sonic pest repellers, hosiery mates, DIY worksuits, beard trimmers, electric toothbrushes, personalised hydraulic drain cleaners, heraldic paperweights, car boot tidies, homes in the country, garden conservatories, automatic cat feeders, futons, omega watches, bacardi rum à la baba and the forty million thieves, I Gambled 13p and Won 56,783 Pounds In 5 Years, I Was a Two Hundred Pound Overdraft Weakling, I Was a Failure Until I Was My Own Van Gogh, the old masters, the new mistresses, better sight without glasses, needleless acupuncture, self-improvement through self-hypnosis, self-knowledge, self-denial, self-acclamation, tune in and turn on, find yourself, lose yourself, find god, lose pounds around your midline with yoga, yoghourt and yodelling, keep your own live poultry in the inner city, think slim, think young, think rich, think powerful, megalomania made

15

easy. Just relax, and let it all wash over you. Success or Death, the misery of ages. Is that what you came here for, Avram?'

Shucks man, naow ah doan't know . . .

'Or is it the politics, Avram?' Asher continued. 'The whiff of Parlielementary Freedom? Democrassy? Magna Carta? Futons never never shall be slaves? You wish to be one of them, *ne c'est pas, mon ami*? A master of his own castle. The proud owner of a tattered but authentic birthright, waving in the winds of stormy seas? Tradition, Empire, Westminster Abbey, raven beefbeaters in the tower. Mouldering roots of a once great tree eaten away by dreck and mildew. Ah, the Royal Horse Turds, Ma'am! The unicorn up the lion's arse. The woolsack, the honours list and the old school tie. The Prince (no Paupers need apply). There'll Always be a Waiting List. Lord Blok, slavering for the day of his Residency, freeing him from the obligation to report every three months to the police station like a thief of bicycle spares. British Passport holders this way, kikes, wogs and coons over there. The master, not the slave. The high, not the low. The whitewashed, not the shvartze chayeh. Pardon me, but you hardly look the part, with that swarthy, downmarket keister. A Turkish Cypriot, at the very least. I see you sweltering vainly in the booths of Petty France, sent back to the genetic whirlpool. So what's wrong with going back where we came from? The sun! The shore! The tarry beach! Blue skies! What fuck do we give for Wars, Oppression, the unalterable cupidity of the Masses, General Underdevelopment of the Brain? What have you gained, what have you gained, miserable bugger, by your rush to Freedom? What's *your* excuse?'

Anything for a life . . .

The hell you say!

'Or is the Arts, Avram? Arse and Craft! Le Culture! The Opera, the Ballet! Ah, wasn't Pederasto profound? And Cuntomova, divine! Have you seen Gielgud in *The Penetrated Arse of Capitalism* at the Theatre Downstairs? The Dancing Ayatollahs at the Brixton Square House? The Sandinista Pipes and Drums Tour? The very latest scream of the culgarde! New Fascism at the Progressive Arts. Albanian Cubism at the Round House. Vertical Images at the Horizontal Gallery. Lucien Krafft-Ebbing shows selected pieces of his psyche in hologram lasers. A full retrospective of

Schicklgruber's Paper Cut-out Animation (Weimar period) at the National Film Theatre. Is that what you flew over the oceans to swallow, Avram, tell the truth now! Vroom, vroom, vroom, over the Mediterranean Sea, the Italian Boot and Alsace Lorraine? The Merry Hives of Windsor in Uzbek at the Garrick? No Sex Please We're Castrated? 'Masterful . . .' the *Sunday Times*. 'I would have fallen off my seat had I not been nailed to it . . .' *Marxism Today*. Or is it the beat of new, vibrant sounds that you want to savour first ear? Dave Palooka and His Squeaking Fish, live at Crouch Hill Town Hall. Rock, Soul, Reggae, Rap, Ska, Skoo, Skum . . . Sarah Toad and Her Singing Tadpoles. Jabavula and the Shebeens. Repo Woman Slash Band. Heresy and Skull Funk. Or how about this: 'no funk, no soul, no hip hop, just pure wank off guitar solos, none of your girly goth guff, bring your own crash helmet for the dance floor.' Yeah! Yeah! Is that your fucking bag?'

★

You never can tell, as, on that dour English March day, Blok stepped off the M--m Airlines flight from the Holy Land on to the concrete of the United Kingdom, under the grey sky, the drizzle and nonchalant faces, the stretched corridors and walkways carrying him past the names of global flight destinations imprinted in inverse order on the walls: Zanzibar, Yokohama, Xanadu, Washington, Vladivostok, Uppsala, Tulsa, Singapore, Rio de Janeiro, Potsdam, Oporto, Nice, Mexico City, Lichtenstein, Kinshasa, Johannesburg, Istanbul, Helsinki, Geneva, Fukuyama, Everglades, Djakarta, Celebes, Bokhara, Alahabad. Exotica that way, pushed up against the long, suffering Aliens' line, the heavy breathing of the Unwanted, the microscope scrutiny of outcaste documents: the Government of India requests, the United States requires, the Republic of Gabon pleads. Customs men and women, neat and scrubbed, in Ariel washes whiter than white uniforms, like sailors who have never seen the sea, hovering alert for illegal burnt offerings, declarable totem poles, unregistered dependants or diamonds stashed in coat linings, crushed into shirt pockets, bags of heroin and cocaine concealed up rectums, nostrils, vaginal cavities, colons.

17

'Have you been here before, Mister Blok?'

'In 1972. This is a new passport.'

'And how long do you intend to be in the United Kingdom?'

'Just a few weeks.'

'And what is the purpose of your journey?'

'Visiting friends.'

A likely story. Grey X-ray eyes gaze under blonde eyebrows into his brown semitic peepers. Madame Albion Sees All. Your secrets will be wormed out, sir, do not fear. Nothing is ever lost nowadays. Every shred of information, every hint and rumour can be retrieved and endlessly replicated, the dead shall walk, and talk, answering questions, helping us with our inquiries. But Blok merely returned The Gaze with the blankest stare he could manage. The X-ray eyes sheathed.

'Next!'

Out, carrying his single, unexamined suitcase, The Gaze aware it contained nothing but the merest shreds of evidence of a comprehensible past: faded underpants that might yet serve a short while, three shirts, two extra pairs of corduroy trousers, four of socks, one of sunglasses (!), a bar of soap, a comb, a small towel, a Clifford D. Simak novel, a copy of *Newsweek* magazine: 'Is God An Alien?' An ancient guide to the United Kingdom: *Time Out's Book of London, 1971.* An equally decrepit and faded programme for the New Cinema Club, circa October 1972: *Quiet Days in Clichy, I Am Curious Yellow, Eldridge Cleaver, The Grape Dealer's Daughter, Millhouse, The American Dreamer, Even Dwarfs Started Small, Diary of a Shinjuku Thief.*

Wraithlike, he joins the flow of passengers and luggage parading past the eager eyes of persons of all races, colours, genders and creeds trusting to the resurrection of love. National Westminster Autobank. Bureau de Change. The Skyshop. The cabbage whiff of new worlds, guttural trundling of Cockney and West Indian porters. Security guards, alert for new and old crimes. The cluttered, confused commingling of Arrivals and Departures. Ah! Way Out, Taxis and the Underground . . .

Hatton Cross, Hounslow West, Hounslow Central, Hounslow East, Osterley, Boston Manor, Northfields, South Ealing, Acton Town, Hammersmith, Baron's Court . . . magic names foundering in the queasy air of the crowded, rattling carriage. Nevertheless, nevertheless . . . Thundering down the tunnel, merging with the crowd, following the exit signs past dimlit tiles, he flows up the long liftshaft of Russell Square Station, towards Bed & Breakfastland, out of the shadows, into the half light of yet another Blokkian dawn . . .

★

1983!

A quiet year, for most, on the global scale. Only four major wars proceeding, Afghanistan, Iraq and Iran, Angola, Eritrea. Minor skirmishes continuing in El Salvador, Chile, Guatemala, South Africa, Lebanon. Polish demonstrators for Solidarity clashed with police enforcing Unity. In Paris students clashed with police, obeying a fading genetic heritage. In Beirut many people were killed by car bombs. The Soviet Union called for a nuclear-free Europe. The secret Diaries of Adolf Hitler were found in West Germany but soon after proved to be fake. In Ethiopia millions of people starved, in the eye of TV lenses. In Colombia a large town was destroyed in an earthquake. In Bangladesh 60,000 people were made homeless by floods. In the United Kingdom the extreme right-wing Government of Mrs Margaret Thatcher* was about to call a General election. Her principal opponent was the aged candidate of the Labour Party, who walked his dog in the mornings on Hampstead Heath and had been a youthful firebrand long ago. The outcome was not in serious doubt, only the scale of progressive defeat was in question. (And what else do you expect, Avram?) Meanwhile, the Russians continued to send cosmonauts into space, to orbit the earth, round

---

*Margaret Hilda Thatcher: the daughter of a Conservative grocer in Grantham, a small town somewhere in the centre of England, she had gained the leadership of the Conservative Party and later of the Nation by a combination of political acumen, unyielding fanaticism and, it was alleged, the aid of a group of secret service officers, who had put paid to one former Prime Minister, Harold Wilson, by accusing him of being a Soviet spy and to another, Edward Heath, by revealing him to be a wet liberal bleeding heart in disguise. Her extended period in office was to be distinguished by a shrinkage of civil liberties and a substantial expansion of lucrative financial speculation, combined with a consumer boom.

and round and round, little slavic meatballs patrolling the exo-
sphere to the sound of celestial balalaikas, while Blok slowly rose,
in his crowded lift, hemmed in by his random segment of humanity, clanking past dark iron shaft ribs cleaned, in the dead of night,
by council men in overalls and nosemasks, wielding air hoses and
thick brushes and pans . . .

The solid masonry of the Big City, as Blok travels on the top
deck of a red double-decker bus, occupying the front window
seat, a joy only the exile Anglophile can realise fully, sailing above
the mundane world. The crowd, appearing at first as an anonymous mass, undifferentiated bits crumbled off a soggy lump, as
only slowly separate identities emerge, facial features flitting by
below, the tops of heads, bald, thatched, fuzzy, the bright plu-
mage of last year's fashions, aimless migrations, hum, babble and
clip-clop of feet, the still grey sky, the monochrome buildings and
bright shop windows, ebb and flow, time and tide, trickle and
twitch, mutter and mull, mill and murmur, the silent shout, boy,
ain't that city got rhythm, the old story, the gliding cliché. Blok
dips and makes an effort to merge with it, to ride the gently
bucking bronco. I am one of the pack. I am everybody. I am that
mythical nothing. Who me? A component of the eternal flux of
commerce. The buzz and fuzz of market forces. The wealth of
nations. I am but a comma in the learned treatises of social
theoreticians. I have no history and no past again and no future,
but the rocking amniotic present. I shall not be born out of this
womb. The incinerated child eventually shuns the fire. I am the
stuff of nonsense, a mere ball of fluff in the upholstery of consumer
man. Eventually I shall procure my own colour TV and video and
three-piece suite and family car and mortgage and put out the cat
promptly at twenty-three hundred hours, and read nothing but
the popular tabloid press: BABY, 1 YEAR OLD, SNIFFS
COCAINE. TALE OF THE JESUS EGG THAT WEPT. LOVE
LIFE OF RUNAWAY BAZENJEE. MAN FROM ATLANTIS
FOUND IN PUB BUST. SEX VICAR'S NIGHT OF SHAME.
Yea. I shall belong to the senseless. I will merge. I shall conform!

Lulled, he falls asleep on the bus, succumbing to:

The Vortex (Blok's First Dream):

Born again nevertheless and despite protests, he squeezes out of the vaginal cavity amid a storm-tossed sea. Passport stamps pressed coldly to his buttocks, he crawls, off the immigrant ship, through Arrivals, merging with a seething mass of humanity, a multitude dressed in costumes of all known eras: pantaloons and turbans of the medieval orient, periwigs of Louis Quinze Versailles, Salonikan porters, Volga boatmen, Edwardian flat straw hats, Prohibition tuxedos, top hat, white tie'n'tails, flowing gowns, crinolines, corsets, chastity belts, shapeless schmutters of the *shabab* of all nations, the lower classes, the sans culotte, the mob, khaki uniforms of Everybody's Defence Forces, bashi-bazouks, centurions, Biblical hordes dressed in cardboard. The contorted faces of Hieronymus Bosch. (*Ship of Fools, Ecce Homo, The Ascent of Calvary, Christ Crowned With Thorns, Carrying the Cross.*) But as he stands, reeling in the pungent reek of halitosis, he now notices that they all possess surplus eyeballs, watching him suspiciously from collar buttons, jacket pockets, open flies. They turn upon him, demanding instant visas. He runs, stumbling across the great hall. Pudgy, purulent fingers clutch at his pyjamas. He reaches the exit, marked, in many languages: NO SMOKING, NO SPITTING, NO CRACKING OF SUNFLOWER SEEDS. But his way is barred by a phalanx of individuals he recognises as an assortment of his ancestors, who have, it appears, poured out of his genes. Shaking their fists and kaftans, they proclaim themselves to him: Yisroel Belzheim, of Szeged, seller of glue, bespoke clothing and rubber goods; Dov Baer Gold, the Rabbi of Törökszentmiklós, his uncle's grandfather's uncle; his mother's grandmother Rosa, who gave his mother her name; Yehezkel Blok, registered Bratislavan mohel, direct progenitor of Papa, and Nehama, his spouse. Epikoros! they shout at him. Blood is Blood! Flesh is Flesh! You can't keep a good Jew down! His parents, Baruch and Rosa, buffeted in the mêlée, Mama pulling Papa's wheelchair out of the way.

A small group of the friends he has left behind rush forward to try and stay the onslaught, spraying the hordes with cans of mace: Long-suffering Avi, red-haired Esther, and Shuli, and no-longer-young Yissachar, assistant editor of Holyland Films and later

21

sidekick of the mogul Adir Kokashvili, tossing his eyeballs in the air and catching them. 'Listen Avram,' he says. 'You have a right to break even. You gotta knock 'em dead out there.' He claps a piece of paper with a scrawled address upon it into Blok's palm, and turns away. A resilient female cry sounds from above. Blok looks up, astonished at the spectre of Victoria Happenstance, revolutionary par excellence, Friend of the Oppressed and unrequited love of previous incarnations, swinging upon a glass chandelier. Her great blonde mane dazzling in the lights. She shouts again: 'Play the game, *kafirboetie!*' The crowd pushes him back, pressing their familiar faces up against him: old inmates of asylums, a skinned lamb, a great Pig with sunshades, under a yellow canopy, with a mangy, bandaged black cat, curled upon the massive corpse of a fat man with a fez crawling with roaches hoisting the skull and crossbones. Angrily, they throw their spare eyeballs at him, which crunch painfully on his forehead, arms, shins. He falls, crawling among the scattered loose eyes bursting beneath him as he trawls desperately forward amid the stench of unwashed feet, pulling on the chain of the giant plug which he finds in the centre of the hall. The multitudes cry and struggle as they are drawn inexorably down the hole. He replaces the plug, shutting off their cries, rising to his feet amid the cavernous litter of torn leaflets in wet vomit, the chandelier swinging empty above him. He strides out of the hall, into the Strand, and the throb of London traffic. He flings his hand for the Number 9 bus. It draws up, and he climbs aboard, to the top deck, taking the empty front seat. The Cathedral of Saint Paul looms before him.

'You OK man?' the bus conductor twangs.

A scroll of the law flaps slowly and ponderously across the overcast grey sky.

He gets off the bus, walks back, up Fleet Street, turning into a narrow alley between warehouses with trucks unloading massive bales of paper, ready to print tomorrow's obfuscations, up Holborn and High Holborn, along the tall commercial buildings, with the crowd, the red double-deckers inching past like brightly painted ocean liners, faces buried in newsprint pressing by, the photocopy shops, newsagents, electrical goods, office furniture, the circling hub of Holborn Station,

above Kingsway, below Southampton Row. The human cascade.

He fingers the two London addresses Yissachar, in Tel Aviv, had given him, before he had set out for the International Airport. On his first day he had telephoned both numbers, but had drawn a blank. People move on, change lives, destinies. He discards these umbilical links in a wastebin, amongst used Cola cans and abandoned *Evening Standards*, and walks on, towards Russell Square. A man should go forth, alone. Though he would have to find a longer term sanctuary, examining what might be a last option, one more echo of the dreamed past . . . It, too, appears barren, but, nevertheless, a chance meeting opens the door . . .

★

'. . . *Amandla!*'

'. . . *I'm here* . . .'

'. . . *not you Amanda, sit still* . . .'

'. . . *have another of these continental crisps* . . .'

'. . . *the time is near* . . .'

'. . . *the times are far* . . .'

'. . . *put hair on your chest* . . .'

'. . . *Mayibuye!*'

'. . . *small sausages in the kitchen* . . .'

'. . . *became a Black Muslim long ago* . . .'

'. . . *well, he could hardly have become a white one* . . .'

'. . . *Goddammit! who's in charge of the booze* . . . ?'

'. . . *the fatted calf? Meat for the chopping block, my boy* . . .'

'You have met my friend Avram Blok? You don't remember . . . ?'

'. . . *ah, but if it hadn't been for the coup* . . .'

'. . . *thirty pounds an ounce? I could have died* . . .'

'Stamford Hill, wasn't it, ten years ago . . . ? Gottverdommen!'

'. . . *I haven't touched a grain since the Seventies* . . .'

'. . . *memories? It's all we have of her, poor Victoria* . . .'

'. . . *Walter! what happened to the boerewors?*'

'. . . *still some taramosalata* . . .'

23

'. . . *of course, we do remember them all* . . .'

'E, Avram, over here, meet your compatriot, Asher Katzman, another exile from the Promised Land. And let me introduce you to the lady of this, ah, memorial, our fair maiden here, Jacqueline. She is our, ah, departed sister Victoria's sister . . . Jackie, this brother here is Avram Blok . . .'

'. . . *and Kaunda said: I want that man's balls on a plate* . . .'

'. . . *then he cried* . . .'

'. . . *he always does* . . .'

'. . . *the tears rolled down his cheeks* . . .'

'. . . *they always do* . . .'

'Good to know you, Avram. Walter here tells me you and Vicky were friends, back in '68 . . .'

'Yes. I was really, uh, staggered to hear about . . . I'm very sorry . . . ah . . .'

'. . . *ah, c'est triste, c'est très triste* . . .'

'. . . *Defunct Imperialism, my boy* . . . !'

'. . . *an osteopath, in Luanda* . . . ?'

'. . . *Mboya, he was the man* . . .'

'Well, I only knew her when we were small. We grew up in different worlds, she with our Dad, Max, in Oxford, I was brought up in the States, in Kansas . . .'

'Kansas, can you believe that, Avram? Notice that Yankee accent, my boy . . . is that a place for a native English mem-sahib. . . ?'

'. . . *another minty stick, will you* . . .'

'. . . *the booze! Who's in charge of the booze* . . . ?'

'Mein Gott! Asher is at it again . . .'

'. . . *cheese snaps* . . . ?'

'What have you been doing all these years, Avram?'

'Our Aybraham has been in the Holy Land, have you not? Leading his people out of bondage. Trying to sell them the virtues of the True God. Jehovah, my friends, no imitations!'

'That's nothing to do with me, Walter . . .'

'. . . *O tempura! O Morris Minor* . . . !'

'. . . *the Abbey National, of course* . . .'

'. . . *busted on the Central Line* . . . ?'

'Ah, our Aybraham is modest. He declines the priesthood.

When was it you were here last? '73. . . ? Man, you can't believe how time passes. Edward Heath! Good Lord, can you believe that? Now we look back to that man with nostalgia! Can you beat that? Not to speak of old Wilson!'

'Vietnam . . . the Committee of One Hundred . . . Bertrand Russell . . . Canon Collins . . . Grosvenor Square . . . the LSE . . .'

'When Savimbi was still a Marxist . . .'

Memory lane. Memory lane. After drawing a blank with Yissachar's two addresses, Blok had taken a red London bus northwards, to the old abode of Victoria Happenstance, the Seventies' hub of his own remaindered echoes of meatier times, in Stamford Hill. But the house whose number he remembered belonged to a Hassidic family, who had bought it, unoccupied, from an estate agent, in 1978. Blok returned south, continuing to wander the West End streets aimlessly, half resolved to the abortion of his entire escape plan, and the premature use of his return ticket, when, by the random luck of his wanders, he came across a group of South African exiles, standing on a picket line outside the South African Embassy in Trafalgar Square, unfurling banners of defiance at the door of the Republic: 'FREE NELSON MANDELA AND ALL POLITICAL PRISONERS NOW!'

A familiar black face behind one of the shaken fists. Mutual recognition across the years: 'Avram Blok! I cannot believe this!'

'Walter! My God! It's been a long time. How have you been? Do you know where Vicky is?'

'. . . reading Guevara's Guerrilla Warfare on the bus . . .'

'. . . Consciencism? My God, who could forget . . .'

'. . . bayonet practice in Queen's Park . . . ?'

'. . . golden years . . . golden years . . .'

'. . . man, you can say that again . . .'

Then Walter had to tell him the sad news: 'Your old friend Victoria Happenstance is dead. It happened just one year ago in Zimbabwe. She was poisoned by an Elixir of Life. She'd gone back to her old profession of Anthropology after she broke up with the Black Panther, Wellington Frog. He became a Black Muslim and wanted her to convert. Now he is publishing Islamic Books in Memphis. A millionaire, can you believe it, Avram?'

'Well, so many people have changed . . .'

'I haven't, as you can see. Have you, Avram?'

'Well . . .'

'It's really lucky we came across each other now, Avram. Would you believe it? There is a gathering in my house this Saturday. A sort of memorial after one year – we were not able to gather for her funeral . . .'

Chips and crisps and hors de combat. Garibaldis and dips. Scattered crumbs and dabs of alcohol pools –

'. . . I never use heroin. It leads to harder stuff . . .'

'. . . Albania! That was last year's tour . . .'

'. . . we saw a tin of peas, in a museum . . .'

'. . . in a glass case . . .'

'. . . the Albanian pea . . . !'

'. . . cocksucking? It's a matter of taste . . .'

'. . . nothing but rice and barley water . . .'

'Hey,' Walter stretched out a hand to a passing sojourner, 'here is our Mister Katzman again! Asher – I want you to meet a compatriot of yours. Avram Blok, this is Asher Katzman, the sole representative so far in our little circle of the chosen people, amen!'

'You know this nigger, too?' Asher waved a half empty whisky bottle at Blok's nose. 'This coon, this ignorant blackfellah, this kaffir wog, this octaroon?'

'Ah, you yidlas have such rhythm!' said Walter, pouring himself his own dram.

'I just can't believe Victoria is dead,' Blok shook his head. 'It doesn't make sense. I always hoped . . .'

'Entropy,' said Asher. 'Everything whittles and rots. Hair falls out. Bellies sag. Pimples, warts and carbuncles appear. Cancer tumours grab what they can. Did you fuck her?'

'No. She was a great friend . . .'

'Friendship or love. I remember those arguments, when I was four years old. Which would you rather have? Later your pecker reduces you to reason. Do you believe in platonic romance? Don't bother to try and guess the answer. There is a new disease in San Francisco which will bring back the whole shebang. Meanwhile we have to keep crawling. Say when.'

'When.'

26

'You can't survive on cissy rations. I fucked her, but she was stoned at the time. She had special fields to graze in. Scorched earth now. Shma Yisrael. They buried her out there, did you know? Only the family were present, old Max Happenstance and Jacqueline. She wanted to be planted in the Orobo hunting grounds with the old matriarchs and spirit mediums. Having drunk deep of Nepenthe, she succumbed. In old Zimbabwe lay me bones.'

'At least she died happy, among people she liked, not in this dull and drizzly land . . .'

'. . . Margaret Thatcher's Britain . . . !'

'. . . the New Jerusalem! our green and pleasant land . . .'

'. . . just the thought of burning the body . . .'

'. . . it's an old Orobo rite . . .'

'. . . the Bama-Fulani . . . still traces of Animism . . .'

'. . . in Islington . . . ?'

'. . . so many plans, ideas . . .'

'The gnashing of teeth, the tearing out of hair,' said Asher, 'a year late, but nostalgia never dies. Do you know she had become very fat, and waddled? It was something in the Orobo diet, they say. I never saw her like that, but Walter had some Super-8 reels. The wonders of Reversal film. The original fades – but look at the reprint she's left us: Jacqueline Happenstance! But salivate in vain. She is of the true reversal persuasion. I'm amazed she's even donned her gumboots to come here. She is one of the main dykes of Cheetham Common. You know, the little Dutch boy who stuck his finger in? Or was his name Kannitverstan?'

'I like Jacqueline,' said Walter. 'She is a real fighter, like Vicky.'

'I never knew there was a sister.'

'She is the old man's daughter by a mistress, you see. Family secrets, *verstehen*? Thus the Kansas connection. Nurtured by country cousins . . .'

'She looks like Vicky come alive again.'

'It was the father who was the large blonde,' said Walter.

'Genetics is bunk,' said Asher, firmly.

The anniversary wake swirled mustily. Walter's wife, Annie, moving sveltely among the assembled guests, bearing the bowls of dips, savouries. The table still laden with dry roasted peanuts, cashews, prawn crackers, a hot pot of red stew. Paper plates and cups . . .

'. . . yes, remember them all. Difficult times, difficult times . . . But people really believed then that you could make a change . . .'

'. . . the time is near, comrade, the time is near . . .'

'. . . you have to spit death in the eye . . .'

'. . . and get out of the way when he spits back . . .'

'. . . Afrika!'

'. . . Amandla!'

The past has died again. Long live the present. The Kansas blonde smiles at Blok from her cross-legged perch on Walter's sofa bed, across the room. He ignores all present advice and past experience and merely allows the free flow of his dreams. But they are unable to hold, and break up, in the hubbub. And nevertheless . . . and nevertheless . . .

Later they remained, the five of them, among the party flotsam of paperware and full ashtrays and bits of sausage and crushed salt sticks and butts ground into the carpet. Asher stretched supine on the sofa bed, Jacqueline perched on its arm, Annie and Blok slumped in the two armchairs of the Willesden Green semi-detached's ground-floor living room, while Walter, the man of the house, tried to stack the bowls of dips in the kitchen. His voice filtering through, amid crashes and bangs.

'E, Avram, it's good to see you. We thought you had been lost in Yidlaland. This corpse out there on my sofa is a refugee we picked up in your stead. He used to make documentary political films. But look at him now! A piece of baggage. Weren't you in the film business once too?'

'I recorded sound for a while,' Blok disclosed. 'And I spent some time, in Israel, reading scripts for a producer. But there was no point . . .'

'Scripts are bunk.' The supine Asher spoke in a gurgle, through his stomach, without moving his lips. 'Life, unscripted . . . Stream of the unconscious . . .'

'Selope! Come back before you break all the dishes. We can do them later.'

Walter walked in, carrying the washing-up cloth. Later he

explained to Blok, 'We call each other by our genuine names now. Why be colonised, even in Willesden Green? We've had enough of these Anglo-German names. Walter, *mein Gott*! You know what that means? It means the ruler of an army.'

Certainly inappropriate. 'You remember J.D.?' he remarked to Blok, sitting by Annie, who seemed to have retained her colonisation. 'You met him with Victoria here, in '72. He is representing the movement in China. And Zeph, the Thin Man, remember? He rejoined the armed struggle and was blown up by a bomb, in Dar Es Salaam, in the summer of 1980.'

'No easy walk to freedom,' said Jacqueline.

'Unless you take the chaffeur-driven limousine.' Asher raised himself with difficulty, gazing imploringly at Annie. 'Whisky, for the love of Allah!'

'Get it yourself,' said Walter. 'This is Maggie Thatcher's Britain. You can't expect to scrounge off the State.'

Rolling off the sofa, Asher crawled over the carpet flotsam towards the low table with the bottles. Blok, seated by it, poured him a tot.

'Thank you,' said Asher. 'All Israel are brothers. Absent friends.' He toasted the dead guest of honour. Silence, and the re-run of memories.

'Ah, its a sad way to meet old friends,' murmured Walter, trying to light a pipe, 'but good comes of bad.'

'I think I'll have another whisky myself,' said Jacqueline.

Blok measured out another glass. His finger gently touched hers as she took it, but no electrical charge seemed to pass.

'Do you live near here?' Blok asked, nevertheless, no charge for trying.

'Our Jackie lives in a tent on the moors,' said Asher, 'next door to an American Air Force base. She wants to rid the world of nuclear weapons by singing Pete Seeger ditties and hanging out unwashed socks on the fence. Am I right or am I right?'

'You better believe it,' said Jacqueline.

'I like nuclear weapons,' said Asher. 'They're firm and manly. They have a real kick. They're made to fuck the universe.'

'That would be some orgasm,' said Walter, sucking desperately.

'Why don't you come and visit us, Avram?' said Jacqueline. 'It'll show you what really goes on in this country.'

'Rum, sodomy and the lash,' said Asher.

Later, he explained further to Blok: 'Jacqueline lives in a tent with a Vest German called Frida, the obersturmbahnfrau of disarmament. They lick each other's cunts and splash around in galoshes, shouting slogans at sex-starved Yank soldiers. Sometimes clergymen and Hare Krishnas come to join them and sing peace songs and cut through wire fences. Our Jackie served an apprenticeship with anti-nuke groups in the U.S. of A. She is wanted for mail fraud, biting a National Guardsman on the thigh and hammering a hydrogen bomb with a mallet. I merely give you unbiased information, comrade, to save you agony, frustration and grief.'

But Blok encountered no signs of this aggressive militancy when Jacqueline invited him, on a lacklustre Saturday afternoon, to accompany her to the West End of London to view a movie entitled *The Meaning Of Life* by a British comedy team. Later they sat in a coffee shop in Old Compton Street and agreed that the movie's overblown production values might have reduced rather than enhanced its impact.

'I liked the talking fish though,' said Blok.

'Talking fish are always a plus,' she agreed.

They swam around their goldfish bowl for a while silently, stirring their cups.

'Asher told me you don't go out with men,' said Blok.

'I go out with friends of all genders,' she said softly. 'But I prefer to fuck with women.'

'I had two girl friends who ran off with each other,' Blok revealed, 'in my previous life. Or rather, one was the girl friend of a friend, really.'

'People go their own way,' Jacqueline said.

The rain poured outside while about the round long tables artists, post-bohemians, neo-punks, spivs and loafers sheltered among the chocolate éclairs. Blok's ancient *Time Out's Book of London* had been no use to him, and he had given it to Walter, who had stacked it, to Annie's outraged gaze, on one of the high piles of defunct ephemera weighing down the living room shelves. Blok had told Walter he had taken a Bed and Breakfast in the swathe of Russell Square. 'That is insane,' said Walter. 'You will stay here. Jackie has the spare room but she's only staying a week. We can pull out the sofa bed. It's a sturdy piece. Joshua Nkomo slept on it once.'

Those were the days. The rain continued to fall. Jacqueline and Blok walked in the wet. From Old Compton Street, past the everlasting *Jesus Christ Superstar*, up past the bookshops of the Charing Cross Road. Foyles, Books Etc., Waterstones, Collets International. *The Complete Works of Yuri Andropov*, latest General Secretary of the Communist Party of the Soviet Union, a slim volume in the window.

'If I were the head of the KGB . . .' Blok murmured. But he did not complete the thought. Omnipotence did not beckon. Instead an Iranian student solicited their signatures on a petition denouncing the crimes of the Ayatollah Khomeini. Jacqueline listened sympathetically and scrawled her name. Blok, reluctantly, took the proferred pen and wrote: 'Johannes Kepler, Hotel Belvedere.'

'How long will you stay?' Jacqueline asked him. 'What are your plans?'

'What are my chances for political asylum?' he asked.

'Nil,' she said.

'I thought so,' he said. But nevertheless . . . nevertheless . . .

★

'I have your measure, Avram,' Asher challenged him at breakfast the morning after the wake, expropriating Walter's Sultana Bran. 'You don't have to tell me, I have my crystal ball. Don't bother to correct me if I'm wrong: I see a disillusioned mug, escaping the cat's cradle of a supposedly renascent nation that has gone off its head. Inflation, wars, oppression, general incompetence. The boy can't take it. He runs for the hills. The Lebanon War. It tears away at his conscience. Great tears fall to sog his old boots. He remembers a time when it was all so pure, so innocent, so redolent of a bright future. He cries out: Why have you done this to me, pascudniaks!? Why have you fucked up my life? But the grass is

31

greener elsewhere. It grows and twirls. A beanstalk, it surpasseth its roots and reaches the skies. Eagerly our Jack climbs up it, hand after hand, foot after foot, reaching for the etherial regions. Sanctuary! Sanctuary! he cries, throwing open the doors of the cathedral. The priests look down at him with grim, wary faces. He crouches down, hiding his lack of foreskin with his calloused, bleeding hands. Sanctuary! Sanctuary! They hold out the collection box. He stretches his palms out in mute supplication. Perhaps this time they will not wallop him over the head with it. Am I right or am I right . . . ?'

'I cannot deny it,' Blok said.

Walter away to his job at the local library. Annie to her post as a ward sister at Hampstead Hospital. Jacqueline still snoring the wake off above. And Blok's feelers still in the future.

'I thought I'd see if I could earn a little cash somehow, and stick around . . . sound recording somewhere, I don't know. I thought I had some contacts, but . . .'

Asher buttered a slice of Mother's Pride and cut himself a hunk of Cheddar cheese. The sun had parted the clouds a little to reveal in the garden a welter of old boxes, bicycle frames, pram wheels, crates of empty wine bottles, an old fridge, a dead washing machine, piles of cut branches, weeds bursting out of plastic bags, a row of old disembowelled cinema seats.

'I know,' said Blok. There was no need to mention the issue of rents, recessions, rejections, of four million bodies and souls out of work, stretching out dole queues, lives wasted not as the reserve army of the State but as its punching bag. The morning paper's headline pointing at the future: 'SNAP SPRING ELECTION FOR MAGGIE?' But he spelled it out, yet again: 'This is Margaret Thatcher's Britain.'

Nevertheless, the Monday after his outing with Jacqueline, Asher took Blok to see the Director of the film school at which he eked out his living as a tutor of hopeful young cineastes: the London College of the Cinematographic Arts, otherwise known as LOCCA, a large warehouse at the backside of Drury Lane, brimful to its labyrinthine sixth floor with aspiring artists whose names might or might not, one day, be inscribed in lights in the cinema marquees of the world or in the invisible dots of television. 'These are people,' said Asher, 'who have yet to fail. Let us put up a brave face at their ecstasy.' The students hopped, skipped, jumped up and down the steps of the institute, carrying camera cases, cables, tripods, lights, viewfinders, or just their hopes, in tense, fluttering hands.

'There might be a vacancy,' Asher told Blok, 'not in the Sound Department, the main qualification for which is a tin ear, if not absolute deafness, but as an assistant for the Editing Tutor, Bill Flint. You'll like him, he's a gent of the old school. Only here for the beer, exercise your rights, join the Red Revolution and so on. The job is usually reserved for an ex-student, but we can say you did a stint in the Homeland.'

'I have done a spot of editing . . .' murmured Blok, recalling perhaps his days of hanging out-takes of New York hard-ons upon hooks on plastic bins, many many moons ago.

'Whatever you say here, don't tell the truth,' said Asher. 'This is the castle of illusions. Just get a foot in at the bottom of the ladder. Don't worry about the effort to climb. That need will not arise.'

He ushered Blok in, past a cud-chewing secretary with spiked hair, on the second floor, a small reception area with walls covered with cork notice boards bearing witness to mundane agonies: 'FERNANDO, PLEASE CONTACT THE BURSAR URGENTLY', 'CHRISTINE, MY KINGDOM FOR YOUR CHEQUE', 'PHILIBERT KOCH – FOUR BIG ONES CASH ON THE NAIL', 'JOCK WOON – YOUR MANNA OR YOUR LIFE', 'ARISTOFANOUS D. – THE METER IS TICKING', 'TWENTY STARVING (to which someone had appended AND BLIND) STAFF TO FEED', 'NO KWACHA OR YUGOSLAV DINARS ACCEPTED', 'GET THAT DEAD WEIGHT OFF YOUR POCKET', 'TIME'S UP!' 'NO IOUS', to the file cluttered office of the incumbent director of the College, a heavy-set thin-haired florid-faced gentleman slumped behind a desk strewn with application forms to which polaroid mug shots were attached.

'Oh my God, it's the Jews!' he cried, as Asher entered, making the sign of the cross with his fingers.

'Drat, forgot the nails again,' said Asher. He introduced the

33

newcomer. 'Avram Blok, this is Henry Gibson, our Führer. Don't worry, they only let him out once a week.'

'Ze bells! Ze bells!' The director threw his arms up over his head, upsetting a paperweight. He recovered swiftly, straightening his tie over a soft grey waistcoat. 'Sit down, if you can find an electric chair. There, Asher, that one has just been wired up. You know this criminal, Mister Blok? Asher Katzman? The law can only be one step behind him. I tore up three telegrams from Interpol only yesterday. So what can you do me for this time? Are you a candidate, Mister Blok? You look a little mature, if I may venture to presume, to start to flower in our humble greenhouse . . .'

'My friend would not dream of dropping his hard-earned cash as one of your registered convicts,' said Asher, 'but he is an ideal choice for the Editing Assistant's post, if you haven't yet found a victim.'

'So reduced is he in circumstances?' asked Gibson, swivelling to fix Blok with a languid stare of bottomless compassion sunk in the deep green of eyes enlarged artificially by his thin-rimmed thick spectacles. 'My heart goes out to you. What are your bona fides? Have you carried out at least six contracts for the Mafia? Have you participated in the Hopi blood-rite? Have you eaten live worms and spent a night locked up with a member of a Trotskyite organisation in the Great Pyramid of Cheops?'

'I have worked in the film business,' said Blok. 'Sound recording. Some editing. Reading scripts.'

'Don't read any of our lot's. You'll go blind. Have you had lunch? I'm starving. Let's escape the queue of predators eager to rend my flesh for my failure to supply their money's worth even if they don't pay it. Fórm a shield around me and let's go. *Avanti!* Don't look back, or we shall all be turned into ammonium nitrates.'

They walked, and Henry Gibson staggered, waving his arms, through the narrow streets of a revamped Covent Garden, milling with tourists in search of ersatz ephemera, knick-knacks, fashionable shoes and schmutters, art galleries, French restaurants for businesspersons and new coffee shops straining to be à la mode in a mode of shifting urban sands.

34

'Ah! What all this used to be!' enthused Asher. 'Did you ever know it, Avram, then? The old fruit and veg warehouses, the hustle and bustle of real commerce, cockles and mussels, alive, alive O. Hitchcock shot one of his last films here, did you know? A man who strangled women with ties. Ah, nostalgia! And now look at it: fart galleries and shops selling plastic frogs and cardboard mice, nutburgers, packaged incense and pot noodle dispensaries.'

'One Messerschmitt raid and we'd be rid of the lot,' Gibson oozed melancholy. 'It's all gone, Asher. We are the last mastodons, mooning for the palaeozoic.'

Plod, plod, plod. Gibson led them, by an invisible ball of thread, through the modern maze to a small Italian restaurant in a side street off Leicester Square, where he exchanged light banter with the waiters of the 'Hey Luigi, *come sta*?' vein. Dishes clattered noisily in a recessed kitchen and a warm aroma dispelled the dank grey chill of a typical London spring.

The Tutor's Lament:
'Where can I get a new Nagra?' he asked Blok and Asher as they waited for their order, sipping water. 'Where can I get a replacement for a cracked Steenbeck prism? Where can I find an Arri 35 blimp? Where do I get a sky-pan free of charge? How do I replace a broken Moy head by tomorrow afternoon? What do I do about seven reels of cod western lost in the Humphries bath? How do I get the Venezuelan government to cough up four unpaid sets of fees? How do I save an Iraqi student from the Baghdad draft? Do you happen to have a condenser microphone stuck in your coat pocket? What do I do about the chronic lack of toilet paper in the college WCs? How can I teach rubber numbering to people who can't count to five, let alone ten? What can I do about complaints of sexual harassment in the fifth term? What is the difference between script and mental breakdown? Who can you think of who might want to steal four thousand foot of Standard Academy Leader? Where can I find cheap Brutes? Do you have a Synchronising Pulse Separator? What can one do about demands for teaching of Feminist Semiotics and Deconstructionist Aesthetics tic tics? Should I ban the use of fisheye lenses? Should one replace staff who

are dead? What are we doing to introduce ongoing ethnic media contextualisation techniques at a nonverbal level? Should I introduce creche facilities for disabled perverts? Who do you know who can lecture on Helical Scan Head Configurations to the third and fourth term? Why do we not run courses in braille? A man from Texas wants to know.'

Henry Gibson bowed his head as the weight of the world bore down on him, pressing his nose almost into contact with the plate of spaghetti napolitana which the waiter slid below his lips, steaming his spectacles. Outside, traffic swirled in the maze of junctions leading west to Piccadilly Circus, north to Euston, east to Fleet Street, south to Trafalgar Square and Whitehall, palaces of power, treadmills of tradition, the delight of the red double-deckers, anonymous cars chasing the nirvana of parking spaces, pedestrians hugging coats tight against the usual chill, hurrying past the international news-stands, the Chinese restaurants, the first- and second-hand bookshops, the names of legend on theatre marquees, pornographic emporiums and delicatessens of Soho and cigar stores bringing a whiff of true old times . . .

And Blok knew that in this city of refugees where even its natives were scattered by the broom of progress, reduced to bitching over their losses in pubs, the city of nouveau riche and oldeau poor and a culture blossoming in its own manure, the city whose alleys and streets he had once walked both in innocence and sheer despair, the wandering pin in the metropolitan haystack, space odysseys and internal iliads, pigeon shit and burger stains, now as then, then as now, as he tore up that past buried in spirit medium graves and confined dreams, scattering it in Westminster Council bins, turning his back on his face and resolutely facing the rear, advancing along his routes of withdrawal, he knew that in this centrifugal place which flung one out to infinitely proliferating peripheries, he could, with luck, achieve the goal of his escape from bondage: to blend and disappear into the mass, unharassed, undisturbed, invulnerable to expectations. And yet, the old distractions: hopes, desires, itches, yens, terrors and trepidations. The slight difference between One and Zero. Birth or miscarriage, the aborted embryo swimming in formaldehyde . . .

Nevertheless, rotating in the new womb, leaving the Russell

Square chrysalis behind, stretching his spine in the warm acceptance of exiles to whom nothing need be explained: A vegetable needs roots, Avram, but human beings?! As Walter/Selope puffs his pipe alight at last and Annie sits slumped, in Willesden Green, after a day of medicare and hard graft with the Hampstead stricken, in the pitter-patter of April showers over the flotsam in the garden, brooding, inevitably, at the plight of the oppressed left behind, the countless fallen and falling of the womb continent, the faded cradle of Man and Woman . . . Despite Asher, forbidden thoughts of Jacqueline. I have warned you, Avram! You are merely stockpiling grief. But she departed, renewing her invitation for him to wander up, no obligation to buy, to the protest camp at Cheetham Common, poised at the gates of Imperialist power, the nuclear font of the Phallocracy. Held back, nevertheless, by the happenstance of his fortune, as he accepted the post offered by Henry Gibson at Asher's bequest ('You look like a good honest chap, m'sieur Avram, take this broom, the latrines are over there . . .'). Indeed, there should be new security, should there not, for Blok, as he prepares to step forward on to the stage of the new act of his drama, tragedy, comedy, masque, burlesque, farce . . . On with the fucking show, Goddammit!

★

Persona Grata (London, 1983):
Avram Blok: Tourist, tripper, emigré, conceived Budapest, Hungary, born on the high seas, en route to Palestine, 1946. New Israeli Citizen No. 345763 (1948). Education: Yes. Abode of Youth: Jerusalem. Army Service: Well, yes. Reserve Service: General exemption. History of Mental Health: Moses Klander Asylum. T--t State Mental Hospital (demob. 1978). Passport No. 1654798K. Validité prorogée: 15.7.86. Tous Les Pays. Renouvellement: Non. Exit stamp, Ben Gurion Airport: 23.3.83. UK Visitor's Visa No. 4536799. Colour of hair: Brown. Colour of eyes: Brown. Distinguishing marks: None. Domicile: Willesden Green, followed by West Hampstead.

Orde Clapper: Head of Camera Department, London College of Cinematographic Arts. Ex-Head of Min. of Ag. & Fish Film

Unit, 1943–8 (Freshwater Division). Gainsborough Studio: 1948–53. Lighting Credits: *The Baize Pyjama* (dir. Forbes Blush), 1948; *The Gentlemen's Room* (dir. Alberto Cavalcanti), 1949; *Tally Ho, Gracie* (dir. Lazlo Szjimelweiss), 1949; *The Return of Captain Bligh* (dir. Cecil Meridew), 1950; *The Lusty Wench* (dir. Otto K. Poodle), 1951, etc. Head of Milk Marketing Board Film Unit, 1954–8. Consultant, Borgnine Opticals Consolidated, 1958–63. Author of: *Some Observations Concerning the Mitchell S35R (Mark II)*, 1965.

Annie & Walter(Selope) Dhlamini: Exiles from the Republic of South Africa. Members of African National Congress (Sophiatown Student Branch), from 1958. 1964, sought asylum in Tanzania, a newly independent African nation. Entered Britain in 1966, became members of the Ad Hoc Action Committee Against the Rivonia Trial. Found employment in the Social Services. Later travelled as political delegates in Western and Eastern Europe. One son, studying engineering in Sweden, one daughter, returned to work in Africa. Hobbies: Walter – collecting junk. Annie – ignoring it. Ambivalent views of the old methods of the struggle (total non-violence versus armed struggle). Encouraged by mass protests of recent years. Hopes invested in the next generation.

Bill Flint: Head of Editing Department, LOCCA. Amiable soul and craft technician. Always ready for a pint, or just another, ta very much, for the road. Ealing Studios. Hammer Productions. A touch of Hollywood, in the late Sixties, but pined for England, home and hearth. Returned and retired in Borehamwood. Tutor at LOCCA from 1975. And I won't say no to another, thanking you, my good man. Here's mud in your eye, squire.

Frank Gaines: Head of Sound Department. Coalboard Unit. Worked with Grierson and Flaherty. Nuts and bolts, cricket and family man. Pipe smoker. Domiciled in Pinner. Reticent, soft speech, trails off into silence. Appears, in his autumnal years, to be ever listening for aural phenomena unregistered upon the normal human eardrum. Has spent entire life in search of the perfect demagnetising gizmo.

Henry Gibson: College Director, LOCCA, from 1976. His was a life of unrelieved frustration. By day, he sat behind his desk, reeling in the flotsam of recycled, never-ending demands of students and staff, venturing down, now and again, to the coffee bar on the ground floor to commiserate with the Polish girl, Anka, who ran the concession, over a ham sandwich and paper cup of coffee, or to the various corners of the building's labyrinth, eavesdropping on the whirr and creak of tuition, the rapt faces over a zoom lens, or the thumbsmashing labours of young set builders in the fourth-floor studio. The fantasy arena. But at night he waddled off to the number 24 bus, to ooze out the rest of the evening and night alone in a six-roomed house in Belsize Park, prime real estate, but a mere shell of a dead career and a wife who had remarried a diplomat currently stationed in Abu Dhabi. They had a son, who had travelled the length and breadth of Wales but had settled in Surrey, south of London, at the 'ashram' of a religious charlatan, Adonai the Avatar, alias Nathan Bloom, a self-styled vicar of the Sun God Ra. The rooms of Gibson's house were filled with the debris of his professional life as a documentary cameraman and jack-of-all-film-trades: film cans of tens of thousands of feet of trims, negative outs, magnetic sound tracks, of a hundred old projects. An ancient ramshackle moviola, in the top-floor bedroom, was his frequent retreat, as he ran the old pictures and sometimes just the sounds of his cinematographic travels round the globe for advertisers and television features: elephants in Ceylon, juggernauts in India, riots in Accra, bizarre ceremonies in Sarawak, cultists piercing themselves with wooden staves in Manila, a delegation of Marxist pigmies meeting Mao Tse Tung, plagues of frogs in Australia, hurricanes in Samoa, all flickering on an illuminated square five inches by four in Belsize Park, reflected even smaller on his spectacles and as pin-size dots on his cones . . .

Asher would sometimes inveigle him out, around midnight, for late walks around Belsize Park, toiling up the hill towards the privileged ghetto of Hampstead, and Blok took to joining them on these witching hour wanderings, poking their heads into the dinkyland mews and alleyways, shouting abuse at the successful bohemians hunkered behind their Habitat blinds. Or they would venture on to the pitch black Heath and cock their ears, like Frank Gaines, for sounds that no one else had ever heard . . .

'Listen,' said Henry, raising his head, 'wolves!'

But it was merely a drunkard, calling alone, or perhaps two gentlemen engaged in a penetration of strictly minority interest.

'The stars!' Asher said.

'You can't see them,' said Blok.

'Exactly,' Asher moaned. 'The stars! The stars!'

Jacqueline Happenstance (Moore): The Unattainable . . . After her hiatus with Blok at *The Meaning Of Life* and the Pâtisserie Valerie in Old Compton Street, she spent her remaining evenings 'cruising' at congenial bars with names such as The Rose and Thorn, The Fallen Angel, The Alien's Club and The Tight Drum, once returning with a spiked and red-haired friend with green eyebrows, dressed in leather and studs, who regaled Annie and Walter with tales of gross sexual bigotry in Stockton-on-Tees. The next morning Jacqueline was gone, having risen early, grabbed her knapsack and departed for Paddington, leaving Blok a note with a photocopy ordnance survey map of the Cheetham Common area. An arrow pointed to a blank spot on the map upon which she had drawn an Uncle Sam top hat on a firmly etched skull and on the flip side she had written: 'Come up'n'see us some time!' Blok folded the paper into his address book.

'You're asking for trouble,' Asher told him.

'Just in case . . .' Blok averred. But a mere three days later he commenced his trial work period at the London College of the Cinematographic Arts.

Melancholy Jove: Nickname of Murray Duguid, Bursar and Head of Administration at LOCCA. He kept the books and knew the full depth of the financial quicksands lying in wait for them all: the wages of original sin, the preordained failure of man's highest endeavours unless harnessed to the utmost rigour and prudence, the awareness of the interpenetration of misjudgement and debit, debt and sin, bankruptcy and sloth, was writ in the wrinkles of his face. But would anyone listen? No – life continued, the senseless folly, frivolity, impudence, reckless abandonment and careless presumption of the lay masses just rolled on and on and on . . .

Asher Katzman: Third term course tutor. Born Tel Aviv, Israel, 1948. Education: Yes. Army Service: Yes. Film Student at LOCCA: 1969–71. Director/Cameraman independent documentary productions: *Inside South Africa*, 1972. *Greece of Christian Greeks*, 1972. *A Land Called Palestine*, 1973. *Voices of Torino*, 1975. Freelance editor, 1975–9. Prolific author of unfilmed scripts, documentary & fiction. Rejected titles: *A World at War. The Two Israels. A Revolution in Portugal. The Labyrinth. Arms for the Love of Allah. The Magic Potato. My Name Is Papadopoulos. Four Minute Warning, Oh Shit I've Left The Gas On Matilda* (a comedy series for the BBC). And so on. Married, separated, divorced. No offspring. Lives with Australian negative cutter (see further). Drinks occasionally to excess. Fond of generalised profanity. Chip on shoulder regarding the State of the World (*ibid, ibid, ibid*).

Belinda Kenneth: Diminutive College receptionist with clout. Quietly zealous in her protection of director Henry Gibson. She kept the worst wolves from his door and typed his letters and informed everyone of their wickedness in pressuring him towards an early grave. He was in love with her, despite her spiky hairdo, but said nothing, except to Asher, in his cups, and on the long night Hampstead walks. She had a boy friend named Brian, whom she kept on a stern diet, allowing him weekly visits to her flat, in Shepherd's Bush, on alternating Tuesdays and Thursdays. Brian was a police constable, and shared with Belinda a strong belief in the inherent decency and goodness of the common run of Humanity, although neither could produce overwhelming evidence of this. The previous year he had become a candidate for the Masonic Order, and was due to be initiated imminently as an Entered Apprentice of the First Degree in the influential North Wessex Lodge.

Klaus Lager: Second year tutor. Deutsche Rundfunk. Eurofilms GMBH. Producer of *Idi Amin, Man or Monster?* and *Was Adolf*

Hitler an Alien? Prods interlocutors with finger. Smokes cigars. Raucous, high-pitched laugh. Mounds of unattended white hair.

Nobbie Marx: Septuagenarian Head of Art Direction, LOCCA. Worked with Eugen Schufftan, Van Nest Polglase, William Cameron Menzies and Vetchinsky. 'I remember when Bill Menzies asked me to light the fuse that would burn down Atlanta. I cried real tears. A magnificent set. Of course Clark Gable hadn't been cast yet. We did that whole scene with stand ins. Later Bill asked me to build him a Martian spaceship for the film he was directin' . . . ah, but Ginger and Fred, now they was a real joy to work with . . . hard work, but it was worth every minute . . . We did fifty-three takes in *Royal Weddin'* . . . wait a minute, Ginger wasn't in that one . . . was it Jane Powell, or . . . ? It was a long time ago, mind you . . . is the toilet still busy . . . ?'

Sonia Prang: Script Consultant and tutor of first and second terms. A petite blonde of forty-five, ever clad in a tracksuit, clocked in on the dot of nine thirty each morning, having run with her Alsatian dog, Robert, all the way from Camden Town. Robert spent much of his time at the College's fourth-floor studio, kibitzing at the shooting of the student films, barking only at fluffed lines. Ms Prang had specialised in productions of the Children's Film Foundation and BBC Junior Programmes, such as *Bonzo Broom*, *Reggie the Rabbit*, *Pobble Mill* and *Rajendra and Buchi's Cabin*.

'Exposition! Exposition!' she would cry, striking her left palm with her right fist. 'That's the secret you have to find!' Robert sagely nods his head, dripping saliva on the floor. Students from twenty-five countries, spread across the five continents, write down her words, cough, creak, snore. This is the gateway to fame and fortune. Names in lights. Creation's joy. Fluff falls intermittently from the unrepaired soundproofing on the ceiling as the pre-production students, above, hammer away at their illusions . . .

Sheila Ratchett: In charge of scheduling classes, tutors' hours, outside lecturers, etc. Large and brassy. Braless outsize bosoms.

Member of the People's Proletarian Party of Great Britain (Marxist-Leninist) (otherwise known as the PPP, or Threepees to its many rivals and detractors). Diligently attends demonstrations, pickets and summer school seminars under the heading 'Preparations for Proletarian Praxis'. Strained relations with Asher since his proposal to her of a private seminar on 'cravat advocat'.

'A semenar, Avram, that's what we're all fighting for. There are age old urges that do not die!' Asher was mainly engaged however, in a free tag contest with a statuesque Australian negative cutter, 'Calamity' Jane Springs. She was sharing his flat, for a trial period, although she maintained a pied-à-terre shared with three other antipodeans a little way off in Brondesbury Park, 'She lifts weights in the Queen's Park Fitness Centre and eats yoghourt at six in the morning, how do you expect me to survive?' Asher moaned. 'The New Woman, Avram, is this what you really want? Go back to the Dark Ages while your return ticket's still valid.' But Blok said, 'Well, let's see how things turn out . . .'

Delmer (Del) Rushforth: Tutor of Acting/Directing. A robust sixty-year-old Hollywood B-picture artisan. His directing credits: *Mugs and Angels*, 1953; *Killer McGuire*, 1954; *Bugles at Dawn*, 1955; *The Stacked Deck*, 1956; *Do Not Go to Cocatlan, Señor*, 1957; *The Banana Trail*, 1957; *Hell's Not For Cissies*, 1958; *The Big Bust*, 1958; *I Dug My Grave Deep*, 1959; *The Lady From Acapulco*, 1960; *Banjo Jim*, 1961; *Mad Dog Feigenbaum*, 1962. *The Return of Santa Claus*, 1963; *Chocolo Molto*, 1964. TV credits: *The Wyoming Trail*, 1964; *Perry Mason's Younger Brother*, 1965–7; *The Lullabelle Beau Show*, 1967–70; *Attacked!*, 1969; *Sozzled!*, 1971; *Rubber Legs Malone*, 1972; *Bankrupt!*, 1973; *I Owe My Soul to the Company Store*, 1975.

Douglas Swope: Assistant, Camera Department. Quiet ex-student. Efficient. Pedantic. Hoards words, thoughts, expectations. Lives in a private world of his own.

Christos Trikeratopoulos: Assistant, Sound. Ex-student. Said to have the smallest ears in London.

'Blind Lech' Wojciechovski: Projectionist. Ex-student. Focus! Focus! for the Love and Glory of the Father, the Son, the Virgin Mary and the Holy Ghost, cholera!

. . . And a cast of transient lecturers and numerous, transnational students who have bussed themselves in from the four corners of the globe; from Andorra, Australia, Austria, Belgium, Benin, Bhutan, Brazil, Canada, Cyprus, Denmark, Egypt, Eire, Fiji, Finland, France, Germany (West), Greece, Iceland, India, Iran, Iraq, Israel, Italia, Jamaica, Japan, Jordan (Hashemite Kingdom of), Netherlands (The), Norway, Oman, Pakistan, Philippines, Poland, Portugal, South Africa, Sweden, Switzerland, Turkey, Zambia and Zimbabwe . . . blurs across the wiped tracks of time, they swarmed up and down the narrow staircases, bearing the thermos flasks of their ambitions, their secret passions, cravings, hallucinations, desires, aspirations, delusions of grandeur and terrors of insignificance, cargoes to be downloaded to long-suffering staff members, among them, now: Avram Blok –
Hey man! As if I don't have enough problems!

★

The Problem of Sex. This never abated, 'the age old urges that do not die'. Not, necessarily, the remembrance of stings past or the sporadic balm of earlier incarnations: Nurse Nili-Honey, Georgina of ancient days or Shuli the Policewoman who suddenly cared, but the desperateness of a libido crawling about the floor in search of fallen crumbs or climbing up the walls, hanging like a spider from a thread off the ceiling in wait for passing flies. LOVE, one-to-one carnal interface, the Big Bust, the peels of thrown out of the window of 1960s Jerusalem, the hurricane dreams and cradling seas, the dialectic of the divine and the gross. Once, upon his previous English sojourn (the era of Edward Heath and cheap oil), he recalled climbing up a dilapidated stairway in an alleyway of Soho adorned by those enticing scrawled notes of Mitzi, French Model, Fourth Floor: knocking timorously on the door, then to be confronted by a massive blob of female jelly vibrating below his nose like the rotting carcase of a Fellini film.

44

'I'm looking for the – uh – French Model,' said he.

'I am she,' the wobbling mound declared. He turned and fled. But those were golden days. Now the professionals of the alleys seemed mostly to be under-age junkie tots, blank spaces living down the caricature of individual oomph and free trade. And the age-old Pox, a very English accompaniment to the *symphonie d'amour* . . .

Nor could self-abuse salve all ills. He sat, perusing in Walter's flat an old *Newsweek* cover story entitled 'The New Celibacy'. Women in particular, it seemed, eschewed sex in order to pursue their careers. Men took cold showers and jogged in desperate solidarity or found their solace with each other. New heights of spiritual sublimation, self-knowledge and enlightenment were forecast. But of this dawn, in practice, no sign . . .

The Problem of Food. This was, at this point, technical. An abundance, of sorts, was handy. Walter was a dab hand at obscure Boer stews which contained enough seasoning to fell a buffalo. Annie made dips and salads. There was a Kentucky Fried Chicken nearby, staffed by a Lebanese youth who often stripped to the waist, and a young Korean girl, who did not. Nevertheless her breasts heaved against a tight red T-shirt, her face sweatshining in the ambience of flour, grease and Colonel Sanders' secret recipes. Down the road, towards the underground station, there was an old-style workers' restaurant with chips, beans, fried eggs, bacon, sausages, and spam. Guest arbeiters from council flat estates, renovating the semi-detached houses, ate there, in paint-spattered overalls. Older men sat there for hours, struggling to glean comfort from *The Sun* and *The Star*. There was also a Wimpy Bar and a Doner Kebab takeaway in the adjacent neighbourhood. Meals in colourfully designed packs were available besides from the supermarket chains. Cobblethwaites Exotic Oriental Dishes could be warmed up in twenty-five minutes in the oven to provide a survivable repast. Sparrow Eye fishfingers and peas became for a while his staple diet, especially after he moved from Walter's flat to the basement beneath Asher's own abode, setting himself up in true independence while Asher, on the floor above, fought his endless bouts with Calamity Jane. 'That stuff will line your intestines with zinc,' Asher warned him, in between rounds. 'You will rattle and clink at every shit.' But Blok was fond of the portrait of the jolly sea captain on the packet, which put him in mind of old pirate movies, *Treasure Island*, enchanted nowheres with palm trees, Hawaiian maidens, coconut milk and chocolate bars. He fried them in butter, in an encrusted frying pan borrowed from Annie Dhlamini, who had brought it naively in her suitcase from Cape Town, in 1966.

The Problem of Shelter, resolved not long after Blok began his duties at Henry Gibson's London College. Gibson offered to rent him out a guest room which he occasionally made available to students for short periods. But Asher assured him this was a gesture of self-denying kindness, for Gibson actually preferred living alone apart from those brief bursts. Living at Walter's would mean depriving the various waifs of Southern Africa who came in search of asylum. But Asher's own landlord, it appeared, having become rid, unexpectedly, of a troublesome Greek tenant in the basement underneath Asher's flat, a croupier who came home in the small hours of the morning, played the bouzouki execrably and banged his head on the walls in fits of despair, and had finally decided, to both Asher and the landlord's delight, to emigrate to Newcastle-Upon-Tyne, was quite willing to rent the basement, a one-bedroom flatlet, to a recommended body who would keep normal hours. The previous tenant, pre-bouzouki, had been a wraithlike Japanese girl who worked in some mysterious capacity in the City and was often absent on long trips abroad. However, one night she arrived home at midnight with a band of fifty giant Hell's Angels, who rode up and down the street on their motorcycles and held a tomahawk contest on the patio. Three days later she was arrested and charged with industrial and financial espionage on behalf of the East German government.

'We have a long history in our street,' Asher told Blok, 'of infectious mania. Don't let it get you down. If you see and hear fire engines, it's just routine. The people across the way set their mattresses on fire at night and throw them out of the window. Here in England we hate our neighbours in silence. That low rasping sound you will hear in the night is all of us grinding our teeth.'

The rest of the residents of 24 Inglenook Road were now a

reasonably placid lot, in a blend of leased and rented accommo-
dations: Asher's flat having been bought with the half proceeds
from the sale of the house he had owned with his ex-wife (of
whom, more later) in Walthamstow, the flat above leased to an
extremely quiet couple who wrote computer programmes, and
who emitted nothing more alarming than muted trills, beeps and
squeaks from the guts of their machines, and the top floor attic
rented to a German gentleman who came and went at regular
office hours, but no one knew where. 'He is vaiting for ze next
round,' said Asher gleefully, though the landlord, Hayim Lubovici, commented only: 'He pays the rent like clockwork and lives
like a mouse. I don't participate in ancient blood feuds.' Mister
Lubovici was an elderly but unorthodox Golders Green Jew who
hated the State of Israel, West Indians, Turks, old-style Conserva-
tives, dog owners, the Royal Family, hippies, squatters, Libyans,
Saudis and social security scroungers, and welcomed Blok as
another escapee from what he called: 'The land of bilk and money.
They want to squeeze the Diaspora dry so they can oppress the
Arabs. I don't like the Arabs, but they have a right to their own. I
always knew Zionism was a nonsense. Jews are not a Nation, we
shouldn't all be in one place. One place is Auschwitz, do you get
what I'm saying? All that desert, it's got into their brains. Once I
believed in the proletarian revolution. And what did we get? The
Soviet Union. Mrs Thatcher, she is the revolutionary of today.' A
thought leading to –

The Problem of Spiritual and Intellectual Succour. At Blok's
first station, Walter's flat, he had found a cornucopia of books and
magazines which had caught Walter's eye at the library where he
spent his day sitting guard over the catalogued words: a new
collection of speeches by Robert Mugabe, a recently translated
Danish spy novel, an encyclopedia of interior decorating, Kwame
Nkrumah's *Consciencism, The Day Khrushchev Panicked, The Illustrated World of Moths*, Marx and Engels' *The German Ideology,
Secrets of the Lost Races, Oregami for Beginners, Berlitz Polish for
Travellers, The Encyclopedia of Prophecy, How Things Work, Revolutionary Islam in Iran, Which Catalogue of Mopeds and Tricycles,
Teach Yourself Esperanto, 101 Things for the Housewife to Do, Crisis
and Conflict in Nigeria, Teach Yourself Banking, Why Not Eat Insects,*

47

Beyond the Nation-State, The Miracles of Chairman Mao. Most were marked 'Property of East Willesden Library: Reference Only: Do Not Remove From Premises'. Blok read:

AIRBORNE WITH CHAIRMAN MAO

Air hostess Tsao Chun-Ling has overcome selfish ideas and now propagates Mao's thoughts in an exemplary manner. During a flight from Lanchow to Peking, she led the passengers in cheering 'A long, long life to Chairman Mao', and then held a combat-self-interest-and-repudiate-revisionism session which lasted most of the flight. When she was called upon to turn the aircraft into a position for the dissemination of Mao's thought, she worried that her educational, theoretical and political level was not high enough. However, aided by a study of the relevant quotations from Chairman Mao, she learned to dance, recite poems and ballads and sing Peking and Yuehchu Opera and to use them as instruments for the propagation of Chairman Mao's thought.

New China News Agency, 17 November 1967

'Those were the days!' said Walter. 'Have you read *The Old Man Who Moved the Mountain*?' But Blok skimmed the rest, passing on to *Why Not Eat Insects* (Vincent M. Holt, 1885), a special reprint, which Walter gave him as a gift ('Fuck the library! The fucking council is going to close it anyway. This little book will come in useful one day, you mark my words, Aybraham'). Burrowing even further in nostalgia:

Of course the rich can afford to please themselves and reject so pleasant and wholesome a food if they choose; but it seems a sin that our starving poor should continue to neglect this abundant food supply. Something could be done by force for example. Masters might prepare savoury dishes, according to the recipes used in all parts of the continent, and in due course the servants would follow suit, preparing perhaps the following menu:

48

Slug Soup
Boiled Cod with Snail Sauce
Wasp Grubs Fried in the Comb
Moths Sautés in Butter
Braised Beef with Caterpillars
Gooseberry Cream with Sawflies
Devilled Chafer Grubs
Stag Beetle Larvae on Toast

'Maggie's Own Cookbook,' Walter said approvingly. But Blok remained with Sparrow Eye fishfingers, and later, the more varied cuisine of Asher and 'Calamity' Jane Springs, who cooked him occasional meals in Asher's flat, while he browsed about his compatriot's own extensive bookshelves of fiction, film, philosophy and politics: Kafka, Quixote, Musil, Mann, Joyce, Camus, Cortazar, Conrad, Beckett. Graham Greene and Gunter Grass. Dostoyevsky, Bely and Bulgakov. Twain, Heller, Pynchon, Proust. Bashevis Singer and Asturias. Orwell, Brautigan and Durrell. Avram alighting, with familiarity, on his old friend Nietzsche, telling Asher and Jane of his encounters with the madman in Jerusalem who was the great man's reincarnation. 'MORE DANGER! MORE EARTHQUAKING! GOD DIED OF HIS PITY FOR MAN! TRUTH IS CROOKED! TIME IS A CIRCLE! EVERYTHING CACKLES, BUT WHO WANTS TO SIT QUIETLY AND HATCH EGGS?'

'Who indeed?' Asher asked. 'You should meet my American friend, the One and Only Professor Art Mattock, selah. He should be here in a couple of weeks, if you can believe his postcards, chasing his convoluted causes. Art Mattock, Jacqueline and The Jesuit, the infamous Massachusetts Pacifist, used to hammer nuclear nose cones in Arkansas together. You should meet them all, Avram, a formidable team. The nook-kooks, as they're known to the Enemy in the United States of God Bless America. The Professor has a big house in Brooklyn with an all-points burglar alarm which is used as a sanctuary by all the wretched of the earth. I've stayed there often. It's one of those experiences, Avram, without which you cannot say, et cetera. Nietzsche, pshaw! A mere theoriser – there are tougher hatchers of eggs nowadays . . . Jane, honeybunch, you hid the whisky again.' He groaned at Blok, 'She thinks I'm Ray Milland in *The Lost Weekend*. But when I see roaches coming out of the walls, they're real. I keep the evidence, in Nescafé jars.

'Michel Foucault,' he added, 'that's the new mother hen.' Tossing Blok two volumes off a mid shelf. '*Histoire de la Folie. Surveiller et Punir.* I am now reading *Les Mots et les Choses.* This is the man who turns everything on its head in our time. Janina, amore, my little wombat, where did you put *The History of Sexuality*?'

'I didn't touch it, sunshine.' She was attempting to watch a television programme on Channel Four which featured a man who was crossing the Arctic Circle with nothing but a Hercules Transport plane full of supplies above and three union approved TV teams in tow. Blok opened the paperback of *Madness and Civilisation* at random and read an underlined passage:

> *The classical mind condemned in madness a certain blindness to the truth; from Pinel on, madness would be regarded rather as an impulse from the depths which exceeds the juridical limits of the individual, ignores the moral limits fixed for him, and tends to an apotheosis of the self.*

'Who is this man and what does he want from me?' he asked.

'A bald Frog egghead,' said Asher, finding his bottle behind a pile of magazines, 'who crawled out of the Sixties. The gist is, everything we thought was true is false. And vice versa. Including what I just said.'

'You're right, I did take *The History of Sexuality*, now I remember. It's probably in the Brondesbury Park flat . . .' Jane gave up on the Arctic Explorer, who was just giving a press conference on the Lomonosov Ridge on the hardships of his solo voyage. 'But you're oversimplifying, as usual. The whole idea is that the way we think and what we take for granted are part of a process of which we're ignorant because we can only define it with those same premises. We're constantly chasing our own tails because we're not bothering to see how our Knowledge came into being, how previous societies organised Knowledge and how different their ways of thought were from our own.'

'It's the cold that gets to you,' said the Arctic Explorer, 'the cold and the loneliness, I expect.' The interviewers nodded their frost-bitten parkas in sympathy.

'You have got it ass forward,' said Asher, 'epistemologically and phenomenologically . . .'

But Blok had realised by now how Asher and Jane's arguments only sublimated their peculiar sexual stasis. He read on:

> *'Madness is no more than the derangement of the imagination.' In other words, beginning with passion, madness is still only an intense movement in the rational unity of soul and body; this is the level of unreason; but this intense movement quickly escapes the reason of the mechanism and becomes, in its violences, its stupors, its senseless propagations, an irrational movement; and it is then that, escaping truth and its constraints, the Unreal appears.*
>
> *'And thereby we find the suggestion of the third cycle we must now trace: that of chimeras, of hallucinations, and of error – the cycle of non-being.'*

'What has this got to do with the price of fishfingers?' Blok asked. But there was no immediate answer.

The Arctic Explorer plunged onwards, into the depths of the cathode ray tube . . .

★

Scene: The Coffee Bar of the London College of the Cinematographic Arts. Nine wooden four-foot tables in booths with benches on either side. Tubular hanging lightshades above each table allow a dim pool of light to fall on hands, film-can lids used as ashtrays and foodgunged paper plates. On the walls, in perfect shadow, notice boards relaying the schedules of the week, special events ('LOCCA RAMBLING ASSOCIATION: Walk from Epping Forest [Ongar] to Bishop Stortford. Bring rucksack, wellies or strong boots, waterproofs. Get off your backsides, loafers! Raus with Klaus, schnell, achtung!' 'Visit Humphries Laboratories.

Thrill to the Underground Darkroom! See thousands of pounds-worth of rushes dropped in the bath by experts. Lunch for survivors, 1.00 p.m.'), and two film posters, one of Marlon Brando in *The Wild One* and one of *For A Few Dollars More*. Around the furthest table from the entrance, five students crowd about Asher, who is trying to engage a student's typescript. Avram Blok, sipping a cup of lukewarm tea neutrally, sits on the edge of the bench and listens as Mahmud R., diminutive exile of the Iranian Islamic Republic, exegises:

MAHMUD: In the first shot we see the man. He is tied to the chair. It is a very dark room but there is one light which is shining on the man and the chair. In the second shot we see the door. It is a big iron door with a hole in it. There is an eye looking through the hole. Then we go to a medium shot. The door is opened, and the Interrogator comes into the room. Behind him we see, in another room, in the background, there is a woman and a child. The Interrogator closes the door on them. Then he goes to the Prisoner and takes the hood from his head. It is the first time we see his face.

ASHER: So we're talking about a set with two rooms.

MAHMUD: But in studio upstairs we can use the brick walls, it will be all right . . . (Asher gestures for him to continue. Student compadres pick noses, gaze at ceiling. Blok sips tea noisily.) The Interrogator looks at the Prisoner. The Prisoner does not speak. Two guards come now from the darkness. They take the Prisoner from the chair. There is another light switched on. In the corner of the room there is a table, with a piece of paper and a pencil. The guards push the Prisoner to the table. The Interrogator points to the paper. The Prisoner shakes his head. The guards begin to beat him with sticks. Then they hang him with his feet to a hook that is in the ceiling. They continue to beat him. Then we cut to the woman and the child. They hear the screams from the other room. There is another Interrogator there. He puts a piece of paper and a pen in her hand. She signs the paper.

(We have now pulled out to encompass the whole group, from a

52

high angle, showing the circle of light on the agitated papers and Mahmud's gesticulating hands.)

ASHER: Yes?

MAHMUD: Then we go to the location shots. The Pasdaran are arresting people in the street, and in their homes. There are four people who are brought back to the prison. Now we see them in the interior, they are in the cell with the first prisoner.

HARALD (tall Swede with crew cut): But would they put them all in one cell if they want to get information?

MAHMUD: This is the psychological warfare. Because it is important that they should not know who betrayed them.

ROBERT (naïve Englishman with ring in ear): But we don't know of any betrayal yet, all we know is the woman signed something under pressure . . .

MAHMUD: Yes, that is the betrayal, because the man, he is ready to die and not sign . . .

ANNA (ice cool icelandic blonde): You mean for you the woman signing is an unacceptable weakness. That is the betrayal?

MAHMUD: Exactly.

HARALD: But if you set it up the other way, and the woman was being beaten and the man asked to sign, should he not sign to save her?

MAHMUD: No, but this will happen in the next scene. The man will be asked to sign and he will refuse.

ANNA: And what will happen then?

MAHMUD: Of course, they will shoot her, and the child also.

ANNA: I don't like this script at all.

ASHER (turning to the fifth student, who has been silent so far): Farid, you haven't said anything. What do you think?

FARID: I liked the other script, that Robert had, about the footballer . . .

Blok rises and leaves the group, exiting for a breath of dank air into the alleyway off Drury Lane, past the newsagent and the sandwich shop and the Albanian Bookshop, with its piles of yellowing tourist brochures and pamphlets of speeches by Comrade Enver Hoxha and London's most exhaustive collection of 45 r.p.m. jazz records and post-war US war comics, up past the art galleries and nutmeg vendors, to be waylaid at the corner of Long Acre by Bill Flint who invites him to join him for his snack lunch at the local Community Centre, booking him in, handing him his visitor's chit containing the printed warning:

> **CAUTION:** Visitors are strictly prohibited from obtaining or attempting to obtain, by payment, directly or indirectly, any excisable articles whilst visiting this Club, and should any visitor be detected in doing so, he will be immediately removed from the premises. The Member who introduced him will be expelled on the fact being proved.

They sat down to exercise their rights and gossip about the latest altercation between Asher and Del Rushforth, Asher being fond of needling the veteran American helmer of B-movies by comments such as 'Nicholas Ray couldn't direct ants out of a paper bag', whereupon three beefy Turkish students had to restrain the mercurial old master from taking physical action.

'It's always who's punchin' who in the nose,' Bill said, sadly, 'who's stabbin' who in the back. I don't hold with it. When I was young, we worked as a team.'

Aye, Ealing, home and glory. But Blok felt no need to worry too much as yet, as he settled down to his daily chores, helping the gilded youths find their way round the old technology of pic-synchs, split spools, splicers and ancient movieolas which sounded like damaged Spitfires coming in for a crash landing, moving happily up and down the stone stairs of LOCCA's old warehouse in the interstices of other people's dreams. The dull days of winter giving way to the first cuckoo and the siren songs of spring, encapsulated by *The Times'* Nature Notes, which he diligently cut out and kept for their rustic fairy-tale charm:

> Though some summer visitors have not yet arrived, thrushes and starlings are already nesting, waking at dawn with much chirring and clucking in the trees or thick hedge. On a sunny morning, blackbirds sing a soft, whispering song to themselves in the middle of a bush. Swallows and house martins

trill and twitter, and the hedge sparrow's eggs will soon hatch. The new leaves of old oaks in South England burst forth in golden green. Red campions and wild hyacinths blossom and fields thick with daisies and cowslips entice the rambler with the sweet smell of new life . . .

The Venus Flytrap of Maggie's Spring Snap Election, no doubt: Conservative gains – 186. Labour losses – 123. Social Democrats and Liberals also ran, lopsidedly, bound together by expedience. The swimming crocodile of properliberty, severing limbs, masks, ganglia. The tick-tock clock of history firmly caught in its gut. Avast, the Arctic Explorer, plunging on towards the Pole! His television crews already left far behind, fallen into jagged crevasses, eaten by mysterious beasts of the ice, or spontaneously combusted. ('Who loves ya, baby?' 'And let's be specially careful out there . . .') The radical old man continues to walk his mutt on the Heath, while the ship of state sails on without him, coursing across the 605 lines (PAL SECAM, European Standard). Never-never-land, me hearties! Changing channels is no help. The dots merge, coalesce, amalgamate. It's every man for herself! As we settle down to our daily diet of ashes, downtrickled offscourings garnished with cockchafers, wireworm sauce, and moths on toast . . .

Blok too, chewing the cud of his free market clover, still with Jacqueline's open invitation nesting in his shirt pocket, sampling the New Dispensation on a rare sunny weekend that tempts even director Henry Gibson out of his Dracula's mansion, to amble with Blok and Asher on a bright if hazy Saturday noon up Haverstock and Rosslyn Hill and the High Street to the crowded gambolling grounds of the Heath, essaying a brief nod to the old man and his mutt, turning off at the corner of the North End Way and Spaniard's Road into the whirligig world of the Bank Holiday funfair: hot dogs and hamburgers and candy floss and Real English Fudge and Traditional Boiled Sweets and liquorice and roast chestnuts and jellied eels and pies and doughnuts and the charity stalls of the Guide Dogs for the Blind, the Hearing Aids for the Deaf, Appeals for the Mentally Handicapped, old clothes and second-hand books for Oxfam and War on Want, Christian Aid, the Jewish Appeal for the Crestfallen, Hampstead Friends of the Earth, Adult Education, Save the Whales, Age Concern, the Royal British Legion's Women's Section, the Army Information Centre, Hampstead Epilepsy, Rotary Clubs, Cancer Research, Belsize Park Arts and Crafts, Do-It-Yourself Polish Country Dancing, which they passed swiftly by. The thudding music, the coconut shies and kiddierides, the Giant Twister, Savage Swings, Wheel of Death, the Monster Mangler, Stick Three Cards and win a Goldfish, Reg the Dancing Bear, the Water Torture, Fred Bloggis the Thinnest Fire Eater in the World and D. Fletcher's Peppermint Hoola-Hoops. Gibson, gob full of old-fashioned candy floss, halting them before the Fabulous Snake Girl's cara-van, illustrated with spectacular jungle creepers and a nude Amazon encased in pythons. A middle-aged lady, probably the Snake Girl's mother, presiding over a reluctant queue from a rickety chair behind a folding table: 'Roll up! Roll up! She lives with snakes! Live snakes! Fifteen pee! Keep moving!'

They filed past her into the dark interior, winding past hanging tarpaulins to emerge into the dim light cast by a large glass tank, in which a blonde teenage girl in a leotard sat on a folding chair on a bed of straw, tickling two sluggish twelve-foot pythons while a third slept rolled up in a corner, emitting its intangible Zs. The awed punters shuffled past, sniggering. Gibson laid his flossed mouth on the pane.

'Aaaaaahhhhh! If only life were really like this!'

They marched off into the Heathy foliage, leaving the razz-matazz behind. 'I made a film about the Cirque Medrano once,' Gibson recalled. 'They had a troupe of acrobat chimpanzees who liked to shit from the high wire. The low angle shot was putrid.'

'So are they all,' said Asher. 'You have to float above the crowd, like a Zeppelin, and make the Law of Gravity work for you.'

'No problems!' responded Gibson, spreading his pudgy arms.

They floated, in effortless appearance, above the trees, the glades, the vales, the kite flyers, the dogs leaping into the bathing pond to retrieve sticks, Kenwood and its ennobled old mansion and the summer concerts yet to be, brass bands and copper culture, oak, ash and thorn, and beyond, the vast swathe of

London roofs, hiding whatever joys and miseries, disappearing into haze behind the mounds of Parliament Hill.

'Ah, women!' breathed Gibson. 'You love 'em, but they always break your heart!'

'The best thing is to get a plastic replica,' said Asher, 'and then you just don't give a damn. We should all just be machines, programmed by logic.'

'What an old-fashioned view,' Blok observed. A few days before he had met Asher's ex-wife, the red-headed and taciturn Janet, not to be confused with the present not-quite incumbent, Jane ('That was how my Australian phase started,' Asher explained. 'Janet – Jane, I am plagued by Jays. Ja, Jawohl, Jahweh, et cetera. I said to this big girl in the cutting room: "Jane, ah? My ex-wife is Janet." "Good luck to the poor sheila," she said. Then we met again at the National Film Theatre, having suffered a goalkeeper's angst . . .'). Janet had come in to the flat in Inglenook Road to iron out remaining financial differences over their joint ex-house sale. Knives, axes, potato peelers, lobster pickers, remained safely hidden in the kitchen cabinets, while negotiations were conducted in a business-like atmosphere of mutual ongoing cordiality. Blok warmed to the quiet, serious but not solemn air of the Scottish girl with the Lothian twang, a television researcher from Edinburgh who worked in the children's department of the British Broadcasting Corporation.

'You should ask Sonia Prang about her,' Asher had told him, after she had left, in a Citroen 2-CV. 'They are both in the Kiddiekorner mafia. Jolly Japes and Trish the Feminist Tractor and Billy Bugger the Singing Baboon. I had it coming and going, I can tell you. There are things I know about the Wombles that would make your hair stand on end.'

'I thought she was a peach,' said Blok. 'How could you ever have divorced her?'

'She divorced me,' said Asher. 'But listen to Papa, do not succumb. Forget the whole idea, unless you want to find out things about the outer reaches of dental flossing that man is not meant to know. You are quite safe, though,' he added. 'She has one motto in life: Never another Israeli.'

'Who can blame her?' said Blok.

'We stalk the earth,' agreed Asher, 'leaving empty larders and unclosed loo doors in our wake.'

They floated on, swooping down on startled passers-by, Sabbath shit kickers and Pâtisserie freaks, devotees of the High Hill Bookshop and Fagin's Kitchen and Haute Couture and the Antiques Trade, marvelling at the scrawled signs for lost pets on trees ('Brown tabby, answers to the name of Fritz'), and the jejune headlines of the local newspapers: PINING CAT DIES IN QUARANTINE, VICIOUS SQUIRREL ON THE LOOSE, the religious bookstore advertising MEETINGS WITH GOD, yellow posters of the coming World Gnatweight Championships and Convocations of the General Synod, LONDON VICTIM OF KILLER BUG CHEESE, HEAD WAITER STOLE STEAK, the highbrow second-hand bookstores in passages, *Documents of the First International*, *The Memoirs of H. Bulwer Lytton*, *The Complete Letters of Ida B. Fitzherbert*, *Winemaking in a Closet*. Extending their telescope eyes to read the small print of the microcosmically melancholy *Evening Standard* tales:

> Three fieldmice are alive and well today, thanks to prompt action by firemen. Six baby mice were found in a nest when the Brigade tackled a grass fire at Highgate. Three were already dead. A spokesman said: 'The other three were in a poor state so we decided to revive them with resuscitation equipment. We put it over the top of the nest and gave them four or five minutes of oxygen until all three revived.'

'There'll always be an England,' Henry Gibson said, proudly. But out of the east, a chill wind came . . .

★

The Vortex, II (Blok's second dream):
And looking behind him he could see the last rays of sunlight glinting on the high walls of the parapet, but ahead the mouth of the tunnel shimmered with the dim rows of torches, fading into the dark. Once in the shaft the darkness gave way gradually to the tiled walls of the underground chambers, the catacomb rooms

stretching into infinity in every direction. Squads of tourists and other condemned souls passed clippety-clip through one room or another, looking neither right nor left. The low murmur of official guides rose and died on the dank air. Blok chose a paved path at random, following a dim row of lights. The pitter-patter of feet died behind him, and he realised he had entered the antechamber leading to the pitchest black passageway. Once there he had only his wits to guide him through, for how long he could not guess, back to the mouth of the system. It was at this point that he often faltered, choosing to retrace his steps and meander through the minor exhibits of the frontal chambers, the mundane hats, jewels and old weapons and bespoke over- and undergarments rusting or moulting within glass cages. But this time he stepped firmly forward, groping his way in, seemingly for ever. Small squares of light opened on either side to chambers impossible to enter. In one of them he saw his dead ancestors roasting on spits, passing the time of day as their faces rolled towards each other. In another he saw a long row of wigged judges, bent over scrolls of the Law. In yet another the Founder of the Jewish State, Theodor Herzl, was lecturing to his mirror image. In tiny, cramped cells the Great Philosophers curled up inside vintage wine bottles. Friedrich Nietzsche threw him a wink. Karl Marx, chained to a dying parrot, was asleep. In another cell the re-elected Margaret Thatcher harangued her reshuffled cabinet of cards. Distracted, he felt himself pulled upwards in the dark by a conveyor belt, enveloped by the whispering sounds in unidentified oriental languages. He could sense the drawing of ancient implements of torture from faded and neglected scabbards. A figure in a tutor's gown and mortarboard stood poised with a long needle. A barred prison door closed behind him as robed figures closed in, undressed him with flabby hands and laid him on a slab. The needle approached, penetrating his leg. He felt the prickle of embalming fluid. Priests with masked faces stood by with swaddling rags. His father, Baruch, sat strapped in a chair. Unidentified homunculi writhed in jars. Several students and staff of the London College of the Cinematographic Arts hung suspended over pails of slimy water. Henry Gibson twisted slowly in the wind. 'I filmed in the third circle of hell once,' he said, 'for the Post Office unit. We couldn't

59

get in our crab dolly. We had to use our thingumajig.' He held out a totally blackened thumb. A demon twirled him with a pitchfork. A smell of overburnt roast came from iron grilles in the floor.

'We'll be here for thirty-five million years,' said Gibson. 'We'd better get used to it.'

A man in a white coat laughed, extracting, with dripping yellow gloves, a wriggling foetus from a jar. Musical notes dribbled out of the foetus's half formed mouth and floated languidly through the room, which began to pulsate like a drum. The High Priest stretched his ten-fingered hand to Blok's face, extending them into his mouth, down his throat, seizing his larynx.

He could not cry out.

There was no option but to return.

THE FALL

THE BIG BANG, REMEMBER?!

After the first millisecond, several hundred thousand million stars were created in the Galaxy, which was itself a mere speck of a fleck of the billion clusters in the cosmos . . . the Earth, eventually being formed out of various pieces of rubbish orbiting a minor star . . . the continents, several billion years later, separated from the seas by means still shrouded in theological controversy . . . In the Beginning (quoth the Times Atlas*), there was one continent, Pangaea, surrounded by a single ocean, Panthalassa. A mere two hundred million years ago, this continent separated into two, Laurasia and Gondwanaland, separated by the Tethys Sea. Subsequent break-ups and collisions separated Australia and India separated from Antarctica: India drifted north to impinge on Eurasia and caused the buckling which is the Himalayas. But drifting did not just begin two hundred million years ago. It has probably been going on for 2,500 million years . . .*

★

TWO FEMINISTS FALL FROM AIR BASE TOWER

Ministry of Defence sources have vigorously denied that two women protestors who fell from a radar tower inside the perimeter of the US Nuclear Base at Cheetham Common were assaulted by US Security men. The two women managed to cut through the outer fence of the base early on Monday morning and were attempting to climb up one of the early warning system towers when they slipped, half way

63

up, and fell, according to the M.o.D., Accusations by supporters of the women from the CND camp outside the base
that US Air Force police threw the two infiltrators off
the tower after they had already climbed to its top were
dismissed as 'absurd'. The two women were named as
Jacqueline Moore, who holds double US and British
nationality and Frida Weisdacker [sic] a West German
national. Both are being treated for broken limbs and minor
contusions at Cheetham General Hospital. Investigations are
proceeding into the security lapse at the base. A local Conservative Councillor, Frederick Ashton-Beade, has called for
a Home Office inquiry into the implications of foreign
passport holders being allowed in such close proximity to
'the most sensitive military facilities vital to the Defence of
the Realm . . .'

(The London Standard, June . . . 1983)

★

*See Jacqueline Moore (Happenstance) and Frida von Weiszacker (non
sic) crawl on their bellies towards the American nuclear base. See the June
sky, grey and drizzly in the dawn. See their padded anoraks, caked with
mud, and their faces, daubed with boot polish. See them pull themselves,
arm after arm, up to the wire fence. See the two pairs of wirecutters in their
mitts. See, in the middle distance, a great white radar dish revolve silently
on a concrete tower, watching for Soviet ballistic missiles. See the dull,
grey hangars and concrete buildings where the American Air Force boys
and girls, far from home, toss and turn towards reveille . . .*

★

'When I was young and bouncy and believed in things,' Asher
daydreamed, 'the entire episteme appeared different! The possi-
bilities and potentialities were endless. History was progressive
and linear. We began with the caveman and had already reached
Einstein. We began with Isaiah and were surpassing Marx. 1968
had become the year zero. The ancien régime was incipient ashes.
We could escape our bodies and rebuild the world at one and the

same time! We could achieve something! We were not doomed to failure like our predecessors, our betters, our bosses and boobs. Our zeitgeist was charmed. We were right – They were wrong. That was all there was to it. We burnt effigies of our fathers and mothers. We threw our genes on the pyre. We cheered and jeered the society of the spectacle. We had bifocals on our retinas. We were practical and dreamed the impossible. History ended with us and Fun began. Man! We would laugh oppression into the grave!

'But the other day I met Che Guevara in the Deux Magots. Looking a bit downcast, as well he might, given the way things turned out. He was on his fifth creme de menthe. The pretty girls had already deserted him for a rising deconstructionist of the Derrida school. There were bags under his eyes, but they were empty. He was smoking Gauloises. "Hello cousin, what's buzzin?" I asked him, clapping him merrily on the shoulder. He blew filthy smoke rings in the air. You're travelling light today, I said, didn't you write: "The guerrilla fighter must have a full set of instruments, good saws, large quantities of dynamite, picks and shovels, apparatus for lifting rails, and in general adequate equipment for the work to be carried out." A fat lot of use you were to us, he said, what we needed was porters and not dilettantes. Soldiers not slobs. Daredevils not dopeheads. I offered him my last joint. I am going straight after this, I told him. No more coffee, tea, just neat Bells. As you yourself wrote: "The revolutionary in a clandestine situation preparing for war should be a complete ascetic." Aren't you happy that Regis Debray is now the advisor to the Président de la Republique? The stone rejected by the masons has become the foundation! After all, we made it. Si, he said, but the peasants still die. I left him like that, drowning his sorrows in rotgut. Some people will never learn.'

'That's very true,' said Walter/Selope, 'but you meet such people all the time. Mao Tse Tung in the laundromat, Bukharin in the tube, Karl Marx at the fish and chip shop, Jomo Kenyatta in the cinema queue. We can never tell how we will all end up. The whole story is touch and go.'

'Guilt,' said Asher, pouring himself another tot of Bells, 'guilt at not being ourselves of the Vanguard of History. Not being the true sons of soil and toil. Not being a born exemplary worker, or prodigy, or concert pianist, or Isaac Newton. Revolt against the petite-bourgeoisie, which alone sustained us. Lucky you, Walter, you were born a victim.'

'Ah, but you yidlas had a good run of that!'

'No smoke without fire,' said Asher. 'Is oppression a self-fulfilling prophecy? Are the tyrants our own tools after all? These are weighty matters, which cannot be pondered until at least half a bottle is gone.'

'Bastards are bastards,' said Walter firmly. 'They should not be let off the hook.'

★

'Let's go,' Jacqueline whispered. The two women rose into a crouch and ran forward, into the dip of a concrete trench. The barrack huts of the US airmen loomed ahead in the drizzle, but the women veered left, heading for a bare concrete igloo. Jacqueline took an aerosol can from her pocket and began spraying upon the curved wall:

'WARNING! NUCLEAR BOMBS CAN SERIOUSLY DAMAGE YOUR HEALTH AND CAUSE DEATH, GENOCIDE AND UNWANTED MUTATIONS!'

Nothing happens. The radar dish slowly revolves. The sky's too overcast for the dim of dawn to give way to morning light. No guards in sight. The two women edge along the igloo walls, past the notices: 'PROPERTY OF THE UNITED STATES AIR FORCE. NO UNAUTHORIZED ACCESS.' They find a bare steel ladder leading up the side of the tower, climb up it and sit on the flat top, dangling their legs over the edge, while the dish above their heads still revolves, searching for World War Three. Beneath them the dull swathe of the hangars hiding the long-range bombers and fighter aircraft, the grey runways stretching far into the damp English heathland, parallel lines lost in the haze.

'Did you bring any breakfast?' Jacqueline asks Frida.

They sit munching cucumber and cress sandwiches, as the rain continues to fall.

★

'When I was a hot shot Marxist . . .' said Asher, still reminiscing in Willesden Green, 'I had already left the Homeland, *après* the glories of the Victorious Six Day War (Hallelujah!), in which we all cut our milk teeth, Avram, did we not? How about you?'

'I was a sound recordist for the Army magazine,' Blok replied, unwillingly dredging the past.

'Synchronicity!' said Asher. 'I was an Army cameraman, but it's no surprise our paths never crossed. I worked for an Intelligence Corps hush-hush unit. Research and Underdevelopment. Our unit had telephoto lenses that could pick out the nuts and bolts on a T-70 tank, from fifteen miles. Where others saw the broad picture of the Middle East War I photographed its bacteria. Everything was a purely technical problem. I shared quarters with an engineer who had found the optical solution to the Arab-Israel War. Next bed was a mathematician who had won total victory already by means of Boolean Algebra. The next was working on the chemistry of synthetic kebab. One of our senior officers had been addled for years, isolating the antisemitic gene. He had plans for a giant ray machine which would bombard the globe from outer space with pulses targeting this gene alone. Ah! but one could masturbate, alone on night duty. There is nothing that can't be survived. In 1968, I skedaddled immediately towards the outside world.'

'Paris?' said Blok, with a tinge of interest, a spark of fondness nevertheless.

'No,' said Asher. 'I met some exiles here, in London. People I always believed were Enemies of the Nation. Monstrous traitors who had chosen the Arabs over the Jews, who thought the Arabs were right and the Jews were wrong. Can you beat that? Can you believe such outrage? I must take you to meet them, our Kilburn Park Dinosaurs, if you can bear the humus and nostalgia. Stegosaurus. Brontosaurus. Tyrannosaurus Rex. Not forgetting the amazing Pterodactyls with their prehistoric leathery wings. We huddle together, against the sharp claws of the mammals. We don't wish to be sealed in ice, like mammoths. We still like to gnash our teeth and thump our tails, on occasion, when the state of the world gets too much for us. The last time was against the Lebanon War, last year. Everybody but everybody was there, by the Antique Hypermarket, our annual perch for anti-Embassy demos. Standing vigil boldly with our Palestinian Arab comrades, waving our banners at the red double-deckers and the trippers rushing from British Home Stores to Marks and Spencer:

"INVADERS OUT OF LEBANON!
STOP THE SLAUGHTER OF THE INNOCENTS!
DOWN WITH THE OCCUPATION!
A PEOPLE WHICH OPPRESSES ANOTHER
CANNOT ITSELF BE FREE!"

The Palestinian comrades used to have a song, which went like this: "Red is the colour / Kalashnikov the gun / we all together / viva Palestine!" It did lack a certain *je ne sais quoi*. Still, it was our powerlessness we were in love with! The idea of being the little boy who points out that the emperor has no clothes. But what we did not quite realise then is that the emperor does not need clothes if he has an efficient police force.'

'And central heating,' Walter added.

'Well, at least you did something,' Blok said. 'and you made a few films, which I haven't seen, but I'm sure they made an impact somewhere.'

'Prix de Futilité, Nyon Festival,' said Asher. 'Palme de Merde, Grenoble. Most Starving Director (Documentary Section), Oberhausen Festschlugel. Least Seen Motion Picture Nomination, Toronto Small Fry Festival. Special Catholic Necrophile Midgets Award, Colombey-les-Deux-Églises.'

'This man always puts himself down,' Walter protested.

'I just like to be at the top of the queue.' Asher poured the dregs of the bottle of Bells into his glass. 'Uncoupling history from the myths is all very well, but we all have to face Reality in the end, do we not, Avram? Even Rip Van Winkle! Even King Kong, Godzilla, Gamera, Barugon, the Hydra, Gorgon, Superman and the Hulk. The world slags on, but we are preserved, in vinegar, reading Derrida and Deleuse. Althusser and Mandel, too, can you believe it? And when did you last read a line of Rosa, pascudniak? So what else can we do? We wave our arms in protest. We march, on gala occasions. We indulge in art which articulates the truths we can at least repeat to ourselves. Anything not to register as the silent majority and fall into total disrepute. It's the era of total democracy, Avram – everyone speaks, no one is heard!

'And nevertheless, Avram, what the fuck! I still piss on the bastards – how about you?'

★

The first bomber edges its way on to the runway, swivelling to face the Cheethamshire fields. A squad of four somewhat heavy US servicemen in flak jackets look up from the foot of the tower. Their amiable Sergeant calls: 'Now y'all have to come dauwn, ladies. This show is owver fer the daiy.'

'Ve vill come down,' Frida calls back to him, 'if you take your nooklir vepons avay und go back to Arkansaw.'

'Nauw, you know ah cain't do that, mam,' the amiable Sergeant demurs. 'Nauw be reasnable an do yoreselves a favor.'

The F-111 squats rumbling on the runway, in the throes of a mighty mechanical morning constipation. Several more squads of armed men have taken up positions by the nearby buildings. A siren blasts through the dull grey summer. From the encampment just outside the breached fence, the sound of women singing drifts.

'Where are you from, Sergeant?' Jacqueline calls out, but the siren drowns her words. She senses a movement behind her, too late. Uniformed hands clamp opaque tarpaulin hoods over her head, pinioning her wrists together with wire.

'Move 'em out! Move 'em out!' The siren stops abruptly. The waiting aircraft, with a roar, springs forward, climbing swiftly to a height of 42,000 feet, then swinging east towards the Soviet Union, able to bear if required, several thermonuclear devices capable of kinetic processes akin to the following:

$$D + D \rightarrow {}^{3}He + n + 3.25\,MeV \qquad {}^{3}He + D \rightarrow {}^{4}He + p + 18.3\,MeV$$
$$D + D \rightarrow T + p + 4\,MeV \qquad T + D \rightarrow {}^{4}He + n + 17.6\,MeV$$

(D denoting a deuterium nucleus or deuteron, T a tritium nucleus or triton, p a proton and n a neutron, with He as helium nuclei. The resulting energy released being expressed in mega-electron volts [1 MeV = 4.45 × 10^{-20} kWh], which, if released as a detonated explosion, would represent

69

familiar clichés: nuclear winter, megadeaths, genocide, the death of History, graveyard cities etcetera etcetera [notwithstanding the usual government assurances that appropriate defensive measures would enable the prudent to survive]. But the two crewmen of Mission 345/b/768 nevertheless intended to return, a few hours later, to a late breakfast of old style hominy grits'n'hash browns, washed down by strong coffee and topped up by a Hershey Bar and leisure activity of a sexual nature in Little Cheetham, if they could run the gauntlet of the screaming women waving banners and clashing cymbals at their cars.)

'Goddamn these mother fuckin' dykes, Jake!'

'They're only doin' their job, Zachariah.'

'Aw! Sheeit!' Crash, bang, flip, the well-trained hands slip open (by mistake? by design? who can tell? who cares?) as the hooded women are dragged down the ladder, slithering, falling, tumbling, rung after rung, crack on to the concrete ground . . .

★

I? thought Blok, I, no. I shall just continue to keep on out of harm's way. The established Blok tradition. As he continued to ride the tightrope of his routes of escape, travelling about the streets of London in red double–deckers, eavesdropping on the metropolis from the top deck, front seat: south, via Camden Town, to Victoria, on the Number 24, proceeding thence on the Number 2b to Brixton, returning on the Number 45 to Kings Cross, from which he took the Number 14 to Turnpike Lane, continuing on the 221 to Edgware, turning back, on the 254, to Golders Green, then taking the Number 28 to Wandsworth, returning, via the 295 and 45, to the Elephant and Castle, then taking the 141 through Blackfriars, Farringdon, Saint Paul's, Moorgate, Manor House and all the way to Wood Green, where he caught the 67 back to Aldgate . . .

Hide, man, hide in the labyrinth, and reel that thread in with you! There is at least some comfort in numbers, in the fraternity of the herd. Moo! Moo! Just show me that lush, verdant field . . . The grimy edifices of a defunct empire, Big Bong, Vastminister Abbey, Thames River Tours, Take a Day Trip Out, Be Transported To a Bygone Era, The Skyline of Windsor, Cheap Day

Return, the Elgin Marbles, the Egyptian Pharaohs, the original handwritten *Alice in Wonderland*, preserved inside a glass case. The Museum's Stamp Collection (ah, Papa Baruch Blok, how he would love to browse here!) . . . In a word: Civilisation. The secure balm of banished fear . . .

But, nevertheless, mundane worries, night alerts of Inglenook Road, the youthful traumas of the London College of the Cinematographic Arts, massaging the egos of would-be Spielbergs, pursuing panicked demands for extra cutting room hours and additional rolls of splicing tape, and the dull gossip of Christos Trikeratopoulos, the sound assistant, who seemed to have adopted him as a fellow Mediterranean, asking him such questions as: 'Have you ever fucked an English woman in the ass? You would be surprised how many of them want it. Do you know how many English women fuck dogs? I did not believe it myself until I saw it with my own eyes.'

'You don't say,' said Blok. 'You don't say.'

Proliferating words and images. Outpourings of the soul, semaphores and distress calls, celluloid angst in the psychodramas of the termly film screenings, in the ground floor theatre, where the students' eager efforts are torn limb from limb by the staff onslaught of critical comment and abuse, flowing across the warring factions of Asher, Del Rushforth, Klaus Lager and Sonia Prang, taking no prisoners:

  – 'Thish film ish a dishgrashe to the College . . . We should be paid danger money to watch thish . . .'

  – 'This is not a case for film criticism, but for psychiatric care . . .'

  – 'Where's the passion? Where's the feeling? Where's the intelligence? Where's the craft? Where's the first glimmer of art?'

  – 'It is possible there is some value here, from a strictly entertainment point of view . . .'

  – 'Asher's comment is, as usual, one of the most asinine and ignorant remarks ever made here by a member of staff . . .'

  – 'The way Howard Hawks would have done this . . .'

Red entrails oozing on the floor, while Henry Gibson sits curled up in a silent ball at the far end of the back row, blinking owlishly at his own trouser fly and shuddering visibly as each crossbow bolt

71

strikes home into the lacerated flesh of a supine student, groaning loudly or muttering under his breath imprecations such as 'beam me up, Scottie . . .' or 'it is a far far better thing that I do . . .' as the mangled dreams shine forth in the hazy glimmer of 'Blind' Lech's fumbling in the projection booth, lamenting after the post-mortems to Blok and Asher, in private:

'Why oh why do the little darlings have to express themselves, when they can go by surface mail?' Giving way to the pressures of irresponsibility by swinging a few times on the lead piping running just below the ceiling of his office, which conveyed the plumbing of the toilet overhead. The sounds of vigorous flushing often disconcerting distinguished diplomatic visitors come to query the wisdom of investing their strapped nation's cash in the education of their budding cineastes here. Flokkhhh-Schhhwoong, as the Congolese Under-Consul tries to explain the needs of Brazzaville Broadcasting. Dropping from the pipe, out of breath, into a hunchback crouch, Gibson confronts Course Tutor Klaus Lager entering to stack his own woes. 'I am Ugly, Ugly!' cries Gibson, clutching his subordinate's knees. 'Tell them I'm too young to die!' Pretending to pick fluff off the floor as Sheila Ratchett enters with a new query about the morrow's schedules.

Trapped in a bubble, they swirl, they swirl. When one's business is dreams, the mental arteries harden, imagination splits into categories, memories warp, loyalties and prejudices bristle, hackles rise in the steambath of aesthetic blood feuds, the cauldron of clashing metaphors. And nevertheless, the students' phantasms, imperfectly fixed as they are: a man who loves himself locks himself in his bedroom, for fear of betraying himself with another person. A little girl who cannot speak or see is kidnapped by a madman who cannot hear. A woman alone at night is attacked by her shadow. A man in a bedsitting room thinks he is God. A five-year-old boy wins the heavyweight championship of the world. The Crisco Kid terrorises Studio Two. Keats and Tarzan meet on a riverboat and fall in love. A symbolic orange takes over the world. Two Chinese dead men play chess for their souls. A young boxer fails to be like his father. A prisoner recalls his youth in an Iranian jail, then dies. The tender tale of a blind man and his dog. After the nuclear holocaust, a maker of toupees becomes the world's most powerful tycoon. Two lovers arrange to meet by British Rail, miss each other and commit suicide. Jesus Christ is mugged at Stockwell underground station. A strange woman, on the beach, lives on worms.

The ebb and flow, and solace of a new routine, a new, mundane security, until that June afternoon, a few hours after word from Asher that Art Mattock, the nook-kook from Brooklyn, was due in on Pan American Airways, when Asher sought him out again, in the College corridor, shoving a London *Standard* news item under his nose:

'Hey, Avram! Have you seen this about Jacqueline? The first casualties of World War Three – there's been an Incident at Cheetham . . .'

'Avram, this is Professor Art Mattock. Art, meet the one and only Avram Blok.'

'Good to know you, Avram.'

The Professor was a small, roly-poly man with two tufts of jet black hair rising from a central bald patch, and an infectious laugh which sounded like a hyena through a megaphone. Arriving at the dead of night at Asher's flat in Inglenook Road, Blok and Jane Springs watched him and Asher pummelling each other on the back like long lost bears.

'Hey, Art, you fucking bastard!'

'Asher! *Allahu akbar!*' He immediately asked: 'And how is Jacqueline?'

Asher reported: 'One broken leg and a dislocated shoulder for our comrade. Two broken legs for Frida von Weiscracker. Rather a damper on clit sucking.'

'Glad to see you haven't lost your bile, Asher. Do you have a map? I hired a car so we can drive up there. Hey, man – it's been a long time . . . !'

★

TIME, AYE! . . . From the separation of Adam and Eve, through the Neolithic and the Ritual Love-Death, the shamans and graffiti artists of the deep caves, the Ancient Tuna and the Toltec/Mixtec, the secret

73

ceremonials of Paleolithic tribes and planters, and the earth Mother, and the moon turning into a pig, and the Great Serpent and the Bull, and Abraham, Osiris and Seth, and Tefnut and Shu created by wanking Atum, and the Sphinx, and John the Baptist and Salome, and the Dialogue of the Misanthrope With His Soul, through the Vedic-Aryan gods, and the Rose-Apple tree of Delights, the Road of Flame, the Buddha, and the Tao, and Orpheus, and the Alchemical nebish, up past the vendor of used Holy Grails, the Paraclete's stall, the Maimed Fisher King, wielding his tin can, the Moneylenders at the Temple, Sir Launcelot stupping Guinevere, male and female created he them, masculine feminine, two by two into the Ark . . . Haroun el-Rashid and Martin Luther and Michelangelo . . . No! No! No! Sheer confusion! There must be clearer routes through the stem! . . .

'Old times, Mattock! Old times!'

'New York . . . San Francisco . . . Tangier . . . no, you were never with me in Tangier, were you, Asher . . . Have I ever told you the story of the Algerian Arse . . . ?'

'Is that the same as the tale of the Moroccan Egg?'

'No, its not the Hunza Water story either . . .'

Speeding up the A203 to Cheethamshire, the Professor propelling his Hertz Rent-a-Crock like a spastic dwarf, elbows akimbo over the wheel, his eyes darting between the road ahead and the rearview mirror as if enemy attack were imminent.

'Art is used to driving in the Orient,' Asher explained to Blok.

'And on the Queens Expressway,' said Mattock.

Blok had been represented to him by Asher as 'my compatriot who has escaped from Sparta. We must rebuild his shattered psyche.' Art Mattock sympathised. 'I met Golda Meir in 1971,' he said. 'I told her Israel was a disgrace.'

'What did she say?'

'She said I should go to a kibbutz.'

'And did you?'

'No, I went to the Old City and had a good cry with some of my Arab friends.'

'That's all you can do there,' said Asher, 'cry, and bang your head against the wall.'

Sighing, beeping and groaning in empathy, turning off the arterial motorway on to the bright sunny country roads. Cows lolling in fields, birds trilling in hedges, snoozing cats, hand-written notices for '50 POUNDS KING EDWARD – ½ MILE' and 'PET HOTEL – BEST RATES'. Birdwatchers glued to tripodal binoculars. Picnickers, in designated areas. Three men in a boot drifting on – Asher's girl friend, 'Calamity' Jane Springs, having cried off the venture, pleading work on a twelve part TV series on life in Prehistoric Britain . . .

'Ah, the time we first met, eh, Art? Italia, 1975! Perosa-Perrero . . . those freezing Alpine nights, the Ecumenical Conference, Goddammit! What on earth were we doing there?'

'The International Youth Village,' Mattock remembered, 'the Trans-Africa Year. I'd just come from Angola, the Independence ceremonies . . . I was delivering a paper on the National Liberation Movements and their differences. It was a long paper . . .'

'Ah, yes, I went with Walter, as a black-and-white minstrel,' recalled Asher, 'showing them my two documentaries on Suid Afrika and on the Zionist Imperialist Entity. Remember those German Maoists who foamed at the mouth and denounced us both as CIA agents . . .'

'It was that flathead Emil, who looked like Nosferatu. But you took his girl friend away from him . . .'

'Mmmmm, Adela, from Lotta Continua . . .'

'God, that was an adroit manoeuvre . . .'

'The cold snap of them mountain bushes . . . that was the night we stole ZANU's whisky, wasn't it . . . ?'

'Ah yes . . .'

'Arise, ye wretched of the earth . . . ! Chiringora, that was his name, the ZANU delegate . . . he was having it off with that East German fatty, Christa . . . we told him she was waiting in the bushes, as Abdel, from Dar Es Salaam, snuck up to expropriate the booze . . .'

'While you were peeling the dark princess off the tedesco comrade . . .'

'The *pied rouge*, ah! A long long life to Chairman Mao . . .'

'I gave up on the Chinese, when they rehabilitated Lin Piao . . .'

'Not to speak of Liu Shao Chi! But at least we got away with a good spaghetti recipe . . . I still make it – Father Zavattini's spag!'

'And at least you got laid . . . what happened to the girl, Asher?'

'I came back to London and never saw her again. She sent me a letter saying she was going to Vietnam as a penance . . . It was about that time I met Janet, and got married. It's for sure an odd world . . .'

'But at least we kept the recipe . . .'

'The Bolognese, aye, that we have . . . !'

Old menus resuscitated . . . Iron faiths grown rusty, brushed memorials and cenotaphs . . . 'LITTLE CHEETHAM AHOY!' The sleepy provincial town rises like a scarred dimple in the calm English landscape. Pretty little streets with pretty little shops of antiques and knitwear and local arts and crafts and a shopping High Street with Boots and Marks and Spencers and all mod cons with added charm. New housing developments up the hill leading to the concrete box of the new General Hospital. The soft burr of regional tones. A ruddy policeman sitting at the entrance to Ward 3 stood up to look them over as they were led in by a disapproving head nurse. 'You can only have fifteen minutes.' Art Mattock rolled his eyes up at her like an infected rabbit carrying phials of plague, driving her back in alarm. Jacqueline, in traction, faintly waved. Three close-cropped sisters in the struggle surrounded her bed in a protective brood, the second injured party likewise covered in a more supine mode beyond, all gauze and plaster. But Jacqueline was cheerful.

'We're under arrest, as soon as we get our wheelchairs. Wot, no bowls of fruit, you bastards?'

'Jackie, goddammit! How did it happen?'

'We slipped on a bar of soap, didn't we, Frida?'

'You should sue the bastards, for violating your civil rights.'

'This is England, Art. We don't have those heah.'

'Well, at least you didn't land on your head.' This from Asher, who had uncorked his small flask. Two of the bedside sisters took swigs. Blok looked on silently at the short-haired girl in the bed, bearing her plaster in sharp defiance, twisting to clap the Professor on the back. 'Gee, it's good to see you, you maniac.' 'It's a treat to see you, Jackie, even like this . . . Anything I can do . . .' Opaque queries after the health of persons Blok knew absolutely nada of. Once again a locus of comrades up in arms for causes he would not want to assume. Count Me Out. I Do Not Wish To Enrol. I Doan'

76

Wanna Be a Member. Remember my vow to be faceless in the crowd. But nevertheless, the faces crowd, emerge: The manic apathy of Asher. The Professor's hyena laugh. The irrepressibility of Jacqueline. The eccentricity of these close-cropped girls in strange tatters of T-shirts strung with garish trinkets, crucifixes, occult symbols, odd triangles of tin twisting and tinkling from ears. Tales and reminiscences of people and events wrapped in the glow of instant nostalgia –

(. . . October, 1981:

(See Jacqueline and the Professor loping across the desert brush, a couple of clicks north-east of Amarillo, not far from the Texas Panhandle Pueblo Culture National Monument . . . By their side, the undaunted trick-or-treaters of the Movement for A Nuke-free America [ANFRAM] – The Jesuit and his Non-Violent cohorts: Matilda Pugh, of the Grand Rapids Methodist Caucus, Mike Shields of the North Dakota Peace Pledge Project, Jemima Urquhart of the Nashville New Agenda For Peace, Lawrence Montgomery of the Harrisburg North-South Alternative, Calvinette Coolidge of the Episcopalian Radical Perspective of Georgia and Tim Beiderbecke of LITSASAW, Liberation Theologists for a Sane and Safe World. The Jesuit himself carries the mallet and chisel for the assault on the nose cones, while the Professor and Jacqueline haul rucksacks full of leaflets to be left in the Facility. Jemima Urquhart wields the wire cutters, while burly Lawrence Montgomery pries the gap in the fence open to allow the other eight to pass through . . . The Jesuit was taking the greatest risk, as he was inter alia on the run from a parole violation commitment incurred due to a charge of Criminal Trespass on the Burr-Mackee Nuclear Reprocessing Plant in Bushwah, Indiana. For several weeks he had been staying in the attic of Art Mattock's house in Brooklyn, sallying forth to conferences, movies and art galleries disguised by a massive black beard and thick bifocals which totally covered his well known ascetic features. 'Better be hung for a goat as for a sheep,' he said. In the end he got seven years. The rest of the group received suspended sentences . . . And now, two years later, The Jesuit was hiding once more in the Professor's attic, reading Finnegans Wake *and* William Gaddis, *while Art Mattock sallied forth, having set the burglar alarms diligently, on his peripatetic world tour . . .)*

Save the world!!

. . . Crowds gathering at the gates of the Cheetham Common

Air Base, protesting the assault on the women: male, female, clergymen, radical lawyers, Labour councillors, Hare Krishnas, Zen pacifists, nuns. Candles and singsongs and prayer meetings in the sight of God, Man, NATO and Ministry of Defence surveillance, photographing every move from afar. Dossiers building up in graphic databanks. Fresh faces added every day. Saved and filed. A modern love story. Men in bunkers and their bytes. A group of polytechnic staff sing 'We Shall Overcome'. Women lie down in the way of army vehicles. Thirty-five arrests by the end of the first day, and mounting, as the wheels of justice grind on . . .

Blok took a swig from Asher's flask. Suddenly, he has been surrounded again. The cackle of Art and Asher, the booming laughter of the prostrate Jacqueline, and anon, the tremolo despair of Henry Gibson, the fraternal pipe smoke calm of Walter, and Annie, and even Janet, the cast-out Scot who's not there, not to speak of the body-building Jane Springs, chequerboarding on her bench . . . A new matrix, a new sunrise, for Blok a new whirlpool, in which he has to revolve . . .

(Nights and days of steamy dreams . . . How should a man live? How should a man die? Paris, springtime: Che Guevara, after his depressing encounter with the sardonic student, rises and leaves the Deux Magots Café. Making his way, sunk in thought, down the Boulevard Saint Germain, turning by Mabillon down Gregoire-de-Tours and right into Saint André des Arts. The population of has beens, cocaine dealers and tourists depressing his spirits still further, he ducks into a small Moroccan Pâtisserie, closing the glass door behind him and, ordering a borekas and black coffee, sits gazing into the shining bubbles swirling in the thick and pungent brew.

Outside, the police sirens ebb and flow . . .

The Great Revolutionary gazes into the little bubbles of kahve, pricking them out with his spoon. Images and catalogues of youthful wars, struggles against the most amazing odds, victories beyond belief: eighty men, set sail in a leaky tub, reduced to twelve by instant ambush. True legends, heroism, glory. And the decline, and the recurrence, and betrayal, and death. But a legend cannot die, it has to wander the back streets, alone. He remembers a poem by Neruda:

Do not call me; that is my occupation.
Do not ask my name or my condition.
Leave me in the middle of my own moon
In my wounded ground . . .

He swirls, destroying the bubbles with his spoon . . .)

. . . The head nurse moves forward, blazing at the bursts of merriment from the ward of broken limbs. 'Out! Out! Out!' The policeman watching them wearily as they back away, a phalanx of ne'erdowells . . .

'Well, at least we still have the Bolognese recipe!'
Some messages endure from the past.

★

Father Theo Zavattini's Special Recipe for Spaghetti Bolognese:

1 pound lean minced or ground beef
1 finely chopped onion
2 small cloves very finely chopped garlic
½ finely chopped red pepper (optional)
2 rashers unsmoked bacon, finely chopped, separated from fat
1 pound best spaghetti
Salt, pepper, oregano, basil, paprika, nutmeg, rosemary, a dash of mustard, Worcester sauce, a dash of tabasco
1 small tin concentrated tomato purée
1 beef stock cube, dissolved in a cup of hot water
½ lb small mushrooms.

Heat olive or corn oil in pot, add onions and garlic, sauté over medium heat, then add minced or ground beef, stirring till meat browns. Add chopped bacon, continue stirring for 15–20 minutes, lowering heat as required. Add purée and stir a few minutes. Then add mushrooms and ditto. Pour in stock cube dissolved in a cup of heated water, then add seasonings to specifications derived by instinct and experience, preferably under the influence of intoxicants. Reduce heat, simmer with lid for 25–30 minutes. Then remove lid and simmer for approx. 30 minutes. Meanwhile cook spaghetti in boiling salted water to specifications on packet. Dot with butter. Serve. Yum, yum, yum.

★

'It's so difficult to tell the truth,' said Asher, 'nobody gives a damn, yourself included. Why believe the evidence of your own senses and intellect when everyone else knows you're wrong? Your elders, your betters, your worses, your contemporaries, the government, the press, the pull, the stretch. Wot, me worry? Wot, me wonder, gape, scream and yell at abuse? Be like Candide and tend your own garden. Leaflets How to Do this cascade through my door. Care of Your Lawn. Proper Watering. Weed Control. Moss Control. What to Use on Pests and Insects. How to Put Down Ants, Aphids, Cabbage Root Fly, Leatherjackets, Cutworms, Wireworms. Caterpillars, Rats, Mice, Slugs and Snails. Get Your Slugit Pellets here. Tumblebug SprayKill. How to Prune, Band, Grease, Sterilise, Which Insecticide and Fungicide. I can do a total Auschwitz in my back yard, who cares about the world outside? And if anyone comes to my door claiming to be the Postman, the Gasman, the Meter Reader, the Window Cleaner, the Taxman, I can ask to see their badge and if unsatisfied spray them with my little can of mace. I have a leaflet from the Local Council which explains my right to do so. My home's my castle. Drawbridge, up! Why run away if you take the world with you? Leave it at the doorstep, Goddammit! We have a collection of waste here by environmentalists every Thursday afternoon . . .

'The waste! the fucking waste of tyrannies, that's what drives me to my burrow – so many lives blighted, snuffed out, crushed, in the name of some grotesque outrage that future generations gape at: *Slegs vir blankes*, back of the bus, *juden raus*, arabs are dirty and wear schmutters, catholics smell, blacks take our jobs, chinks are evil, homosexuals are a pain in the ass, all tsigoiners are thieves. The International Cartel of Delusion, the World Bank of Pork Pies. Why did we have to grow up? We could all have stayed wallowing in our bunkers, shooting the whites of strangers' eyes. Rooting in the dustbins of our tribal dilemmas: can the Messiah

80

make a phone call on the Sabbath? Was Jesus Christ guilty? I would rather they had crucified the man because they believed he was God, not because they thought he wasn't. Humility, comrades, a little humility! Why can't anybody just be a mensch, and take up a good hobby, like interior decorating, and mind their own business? Why are we always required to ride out like the knight on his white horse, to rape the goddamn fucking Princess?'

Why, indeed? Nevertheless, to draw Blok out of his own shell, Asher took him to visit his fraternal 'Dinosaurs', the Israeli dissidents living in West Hampstead and environs. (Jacqueline recuperating in her Cheetham Common tent, surrounded by the gathering peace women, preparing her court case on the charge of trespass, the Professor professing his solidarity from a Bed and Breakfast in the nearby town of Little Cheetham, walking the fields and artillery ranges with a runcible hat and a perpetual leer.) A leisurely summer Saturday in London, a good picturesque British July, birds trilling in the back garden tree out of reach of the Laurel and Hardy cats, the lawn bright green and untidy, the folding chairs out and mine host, Dudik 'Big Daddy' Birenbaum, lolling on a deckchair in an immense floppy straw hat, digging Kalamata olives out of a can. His ebullient wife Hannah greeting the assorted visitors from the Holy Land, self exiled members of marginal political parties, Arab and other, and their sympathisers, living in the neighbourhood or just passing through, who meandered in and out, sampling bowls of humus, reheated garlic bread, cooking chocolate and sipping mint tea. Dudik was discussing with a nervous bald youth called Elchanan the up-to-date situation in Ramleh prison, south-east of Tel Aviv, from which the youth had just been released.

'Have you heard, Hanchke? They're not growing the marijuana behind the politicals' latrine any more – the PLO cadres have objected.'

'Why? Is it an inferior strain?'

'No, it's still the best stuff. But they have other things on their mind.'

Asher introduced Blok to the amorphous assembly: 'Elik Boehm, the first journalist to interview Trotsky's ghost by seance. Yosske Blanco, who was disillusioned with the State of Israel ten years before its foundation. Amram Klein, who was the first Jew to be detained under the Emergency Defence Regulations. Didi Blum, who paints the flags of all nations as turds. Habib Hatib, who writes for *The Marxist Echo*. Salim, who is available for cheap loft conversion. Shaul Glik, who is now into mushrooms. Adina Stein, she is a shrink, take her telephone number. Rosamunda, she lives round the corner. Hannah our hostess you already met at the door. Avram Blok, comrades, another refugee.'

'On a day like this, it all seems worth it,' said Dudik, waving him to a chair. 'Have some Kalamata olives. Enjoy it while it lasts.'

'And how's Yoram? Still in the trenches?'

'I spoke to him on the phone the other day. Nothing much happening. It's a lull . . .'

'The Americans trying to muscle in . . .'

'This Lebanon troop withdrawal is just another ploy . . .'

'There is no way these are toadstools . . .'

'From Marks and Spencer. It's a new line . . .'

'But you can't expect Arafat to make a move at this stage . . .'

'I can't understand a man coming out of Israel and not bringing *s'hug* . . . it's that Yemeni hot sauce, Rosamund . . .'

'Discussed at the Palestine National Council . . .'

'You can get it at Grodzinski's . . .'

'It all depends on the height at the apex . . .'

'And Nitsa . . . ?'

'Divorced, like everyone else . . . speaking of which, I met your ex-wife, Asher . . . something on location with *Joe'll Fix It* . . .'

'You need planning permission for a back mansard . . .'

'My only lasting regret is that she took back her Cheech and Chong record . . .'

'The Popular Democratic Front . . .'

'Pure and simple schizophrenia . . .'

'Yes, I'm working with Asher at the Film College. We've just had our End of Term screenings. There are some plans to take a student film crew up in the summer recess, to Cheetham Common . . .'

'A very cheap deal with Ipale Tours . . .'

'Howard Hughes, with Kleenex boxes on his feet . . .'

'Spies For Peace, in the Fifties . . .'

'She used to write off for all those junk mail catalogues . . .'

'Saint Moritz, where Nietzsche wrote *The Wanderer and His Shadow* . . .'

'Remember Bertie Russell, Hanchke . . . ? Was it 1961 . . . ?'

'She said they came in useful, for swatting flies . . .'

'You could be rescued by a Saint Bernard . . .'

Indeed. Blok, laid out on the pure white *Schussenstiefel*, mouth agape to some moronic mutt loyally pouring Smirnoff vodka from a keg. Give us this day our daily dread. In the eye of the cyclone, something stirs. A diminutive and lissom Far Eastern girl, with jet black hair and a Gioconda smile, had suddenly materialised by the kitchen door, hovering, in a sleeveless black dress. She came up to Blok, as if drawn to his separateness, and said to him, in a softly accented lilt: 'Do you know these people? I am staying with Rosamunda, in Terrence Road. My name is Mipi.'

'I'm Avram Blok,' he said. 'I'm just visiting, with a friend. Can I get you anything?'

'Do they have some Jarlsberg cheese?'

They hunted together, in the Birenbaum frigidaire, coming upon an immense chunk on a plate. 'You don't think they'll mind if I take a little bit?'

'No, it seems a big free for all.'

She was, it appeared, a student of Business Studies at a college in the West End. Her uncle dabbled in the Far Eastern stock markets. She was from Singapore. Have you ever been there?

No, my furthest east was Jericho.

'I would like to go to the Victoria and Albert Museum,' she said. 'There is an exhibition of old costumes. Will you come?'

They abandoned the Sabbath gala without further comment. Riding the crowded underground tubes mutely, walking the short distance from South Kensington Station, joining the streams of tourists entering the grave old building to gawp at the gathered junkyard of ages: Islamic carpets, Jain pottery, Sumerian reliefs, medieval tapestries and paintings, Greek busts, old trinkets from ancient Iran. He wished to linger by the old chain mail and armour, swords, muskets, blunderbusses, *et al*, but she whisked him along to admire the fine needlework on the garments slung on faceless life-size dolls. He yawned, but tagged along obediently. They then went into in the green quadrangle with its Japanese trees and bushes, facing the immense bronze Buddha, by the tinkling fountain flow. She sat and closed her eyes, still silent. He sat. Eventually, she rose.

'Do you want to come home? I can make us something to eat. I think Rosamunda will be out.'

But the consummation occurred not that night, but the following weekend, when the initial shock of acceptance had mellowed, though Asher already barked at him, when they met emptying the rubbish, the day after the Birenbaum gathering: 'Avram! You fucking sly dog! You had us all fooled! The one available cookie, and you swiped her from under our noses! Goddammit, I'll never trust you again!' Slapping him on the back, shaking his head. 'It's just the way things happen,' said Blok. 'I'll expect a written report by Wednesday,' said Asher. But Blok just vaguely waved his arm, adjusting the bins outside his window for the Monday dawn clatter of the heavy-boot brigade. (Rattle, rattle, rattle. 'What they got in this one, garden junk?' Mutter, mutter, mutter, mate.) 'A real beauty, fuck your arse, Avram. Some people have all the luck.'

Is this, indeed, the changing wind? At the Film College, sexual opportunities were fraught with obvious problems. The staff environment was not conducive to options. The receptionist, Belinda, had clarified her devotion to the Police Constable, Brian, who had now become an Entered Masonic Apprentice of the First Degree. Sonia Prang ('that ball busting bitch': Del Rushforth), never appeared in public without the canine Robert by her side. Sheila Ratchett, still pursued by Asher, claimed she was prepared to commit her body only to those who shared her political position on the Proletarian Thrust for Power. Blok had found himself attracted to three female students: Aziza, a citizen of the Hashemite Kingdom of Jordan, who asked him to explain the racial myths of Zionism; Chrysula, from Greece, who worshipped Luis Buñuel and had big brown eyes which made him rush all over the building to dig out an unused pic-synch or an extra roll of magnetic film; and Isolde, a Venezuelan beauty who smoked Gauloises and carried a dog-eared copy of Simone de Beauvoir's *The Second Sex* peeking out of her satchel. But he looked at himself in the mirror and became grey with the collapse of his face, the bent gracelessness of his contours, the sagging of his eyes, the protruding waistline, the greasy hair, the idiocy of his spectacles, the stubble which never seemed to be excisable from his chin, and retreated into ethical rationalisations. Asher said: 'The Hellene likes you, Isolde yearns for your soul, the Hashemite wants to suck your cock till it aches. Go for it, you stupid piece of shit!' But he could never find the nerve. All the more astounding, then, that he lay cradling, in midsummer laze, the soft dark flesh of Malay Mipi . . .

'Abraham?'

'Yes, my honey?'

'Do all the Jews think too much?'

'Whadyoumean?'

'You're always trying to organise the world in your thoughts. You're upset about things you have no power with. You read something in the newspaper and it makes you ill. You watch the news on television.'

'It's an addiction, Mipi, like heroin.'

'But heroin at least makes you high.'

'In my country people watched the news as an alternative to doing something to change the way things were.'

'To change things. It's so Western, Abraham. You're always being so frustrated. It affects the way you make love.'

'I suppose so. I wouldn't win prizes.'

'You see – all the time you make judgements.'

'It's a rehearsal, for when we all stand trial up above before the Old Bastard. We only have a lifetime to prepare our case. You know the defence lawyer will be an asshole.'

'It's the Judeo-Christian religion,' she said. 'It fucks you up. You don't understand who I am. You don't understand women. You don't understand the East at all.'

'Guilty as charged. I blame society.'

'You have to be one with the world. Just accept there are no contradictions. It's an illusion. There is always harmony.'

'Not in Jerusalem or West Hampstead.'

'Everywhere. You just don't know how to look.'

'I love you, Mipi.'

'I don't love you, Abraham. You're simply making a category again. Just accept the way we are now. Tomorrow it won't be appropriate.'

Back to the Singapore Stock Exchange. Vegetarianism and Investment Accounting, Spot Margins, Gilt Edged Bonds, Hypothecation, Equity Cults and Long and Short Sales. She informed Blok she was going to marry a third cousin, who had a bank in Bangkok. ('She's going to marry a bank in Bangkok?' said Asher. 'Oh God, I'm sorry, Avram. Come on up, Jane and I'll make you our best Spaghetti à la Theo.') 'I had a sweet time with you, Abraham,' she said, kissing him lightly on the cheek. Her landlady Rosamunda gave him a sympathetic look as he shuffled out the door.

So much for the Big Bang.

The following week Blok, Asher and Jane, chaperoning the London College Film crew granted leave, by a reluctant Henry Gibson, to shoot their term documentary in the summer break, travelled up, in convoy, to Cheetham Common, joining the Professor, Jacqueline and a swelling band of hundreds of women, men, and others, surrounding the American Nuclear Base . . .

★

PROTEST AND SURVIVE. The woven web. The swamped mud. The self disenfranchised. Blessed are the chic. The bobbing sea of woolly caps and denim overalls. The undulating play of planned absurdities. The challenge of the imagination: EMBRACE THE BASE. STOP US 'STROKE' MISSILES! WOMEN SAY NO TO NUCLEAR GENOCIDE! Strange rituals among the concrete silos: DARE TO GIVE, DARE TO DREAM. Sphinxes, hippogriffs and salamanders, mermaids, keening sirens: the meek, the mild, the softly melancholy, the odd, the marginal, the rara avis. Amoratas of the earth, fresh from die-ins in black robes at the Stock Exchange, dancers at dawn on blocked off ley lines, loyalists of slumbering goddesses, weavers of wool on iron fences. (Never in the field of human conflict has so much been knitted by so many for so few.) The self-appointed gypsies of permanent residence, with their foldaway tents, jerry-built 'benders', inflatable beds, foam mattresses, folding garden chairs and tables. A thousand and one umbrellas. Portakabin refugees, with seeds for planting, fruit preserves, camp stoves and primuses, a hundred and one do-it-yourself kits, torches, tarpaulin and old cloth, two thousand tin cups, plates, bowls, garlic crushers, woks, can openers, Swiss army knives (no Swiss army), sacks of rice, lentils, barley, cratefuls of tinned reserves. Baked beans, spaghetti hoops, tuna (no South African pilchards), organic foods, Bovril, Bisto, Marmite, cocoa, Be Ro flour, powdered milk, baby foods, babies (to whom War is harmful), jumbo packs of toilet tissue, refuse bags, sanitary requisites, tampons, gels, organic disposables, specula, towels, two and a half thousand toothbrushes, musical instruments. Tambourines, flutes, castanets, accordions and triangles, personal walkwomans, (womuns, or womyn), a thousand and one badges and symbols, emblemata, stigmata, coloured balloons, books on holistic medicine, poetry, well-body manuals, womyn's novels, phenomenology, annals of ancient matriarchies: Hecate, Aphrodite, Bast, Rhiannon, Isis, the Great Witch of Barclay, the Venus of Wickenburg, etcetera. The old mum with the billion daughters, Jehovah need not apply. Allah is out. Jesus may kibitz for a while, as the cycles of the moon are retrieved, the vernal equinox, the harvest bounty. Loitering with intent, we have converged upon the great blot upon the landscape, the storehouse of death, the male dominion, Hiroshimas in boxes and assembly lines, Theatres of War, forceful modernisations, states of police and armed mites, the rape of the earth, planned carcinogenesis, fallout of brain and malformed babies, nuked apes, Mutual Assured Destruction, Lunch on Warning, First Shrikes:

TURN BACK THE 'STROKE' MISSILES!
WOMEN FOR PEACE!
END WAR!

. . . 'She always wanted to hoover the carpets on a weekend,' Asher expatiated, 'when all I wanted was to put my feet up and

87

relax with a Philip K. Dick novel. I was almost driven from the house one day because of a silverfish in the toilet . . .'

'I would have driven you out as well,' said Art Mattock. 'What you needed was a personality transplant.'

'Exactly what I got, she took her personality and transplanted it elsewhere.'

'You ought to be in a museum.' Jane Springs rustled in the dark. Inhospitable hedgerows crowded in on their sleeping bags on the periphery of the encampment, exiled to the margins due to the strict policy of Women Only in the Camp itself. 'So what do I care!' said Asher. 'I'm allergic to communal singing.' Armies of insects, the true wretched of the earth preparing for power, reconnoitred their orifices. From the sprawl, the faint twang of guitar strings, a baby's cry, a burst of song, the reassuring burr of the BBC Overseas News:

'. . . however, despite the Golkar Party's overwhelming majority in the Provisional People's Consultative Congress, President Soharto's problems have been exacerbated by a growing economic crisis . . .'

A dog barks from the village across the common. The watch-lights of the adjacent airbase fence, a few hundred yards away, cast little pools along the wire. A crackle of static hangs in the air. The blue flicker of police lights can be dimly glimpsed through the trees. Asher is not assuaged.

'The countryside! God rot its soul!'

'Don't worry, you'll get your money's worth tomorrow.'

'I was afraid of that.'

Jacqueline sits on the damp but warm bank by the hedgerow smoking a cigarette, her plaster-covered leg stretched out before her strewn with the signatures of well-wishers, messages of sisterhood and a political cartoon of Margaret Thatcher in traction, drawn by a national daily's scribe.

'I can't believe they'll bring the missiles in with all this razzmatazz,' says Jane.

'They always keep a date,' says Jacqueline.

'Isn't this a sneezewort?' Mattock muses, shining his small pocket torch on a patch of weed.

'I wouldn't be surprised,' says Jacqueline.

88

'I'm sure this is meadow eyebright,' Mattock rustles on, 'hot medicinal stuff in the old days.'

'This used to be Goddess turf, so they tell me,' puffs Jacqueline, 'Until the Christians came.'

'Very ecumenical,' says Asher.

'It takes all sorts to fuck a world.'

The counter-Patriarchal Revolution. The Fear of God introduced not only God, but Fear. Before, everyone frolicked in Arcadia. Phallocracy buries love, affection, true divinity and solidarity. Yea!

(Deep in the undergrowth, something stirs.)

'The old herbalists used it to cure eyesores, glaucomas, even blindness,' says Mattock. 'The earth is full of surprises. You never can tell what's just under your nose.'

Hog's fennel, wild garlic, canadian fleabane, mouse-ear hawkweed and yellow foxglove. Small caterpillars crunch their way through buds. Aphids leap from stems. Stoats, hidden, consider their moves. In the bosom of Nature, never a dull moment. Moths fluttering against the lighted panes of caravans. A night beetle forages in a cardboard box of peace badges. Two and a half thousand nocturnal tremolos trembling. The night domain of those faery forces shunning the hairy male stench of day, migrating leprechaunettes unreeling threads, Snow White studiously evading dwarfs, Red Riding Hood laying wolf traps, the Sleeping Beauty emitting smoke signals, princesses putting out the peas.

(Static crackles on secure wavelengths. Deep in concrete, VDUs flicker.)

'Nothing'll happen here,' growls Asher. 'This is never-neverland. Wishful thinking and wet dreams is all.'

'Speak for yourself,' says Jacqueline. 'Do you need a Kleenex?'

'No,' he ripostes. 'I'll wipe it on the grass.'

'Put a sock in it and let us get some shut eye,' moans Jane.

'Peace,' scoffs Asher, 'it's an old wives' tale. The predator gets my vote every time. Sylvester is always preferable to Tweetie Pie. God! Those wonderful screenings at the Piccadilly Circus Classic. Get that fucking canary! I'd shout, from the stalls. Don't let the bastard get away! Three shillings and sixpence. You got your jollies cheap those days. Not like now, littering half the world.'

'What the fuck does that man want?' Jane throws a boot at him.

(The night is young. The days are old.)

Gossiping in the small hours, Art Mattock and Jacqueline, an odd twosome, the tall, rangy woman and the small dumpling man with his floppy hat: 'Remember, Jackie? Amarillo? Albuquerque? Sioux Falls? Sonoma City?'

But Jesse James is laid in his grave.

(The Jesuit, still hiding in Art Mattock's attic, having completed William Gaddis' The Recognitions *and moving on to Musil,* The Man Without Qualities. *'Chapter One: Which, remarkably enough, does not get anyone anywhere . . .' 1265 pages to go. And after this: Proust, Vargas Llosa, Fuentes'* Terra Nostra, *and on, and on . . .*

(Or Che Guevara, leaving the Moroccan Pâtisserie and stumbling down the Boul Mich towards the Seine, nodding vaguely to other lost compadres slumped in the open-air cafés . . . pulling at the leather patches on his sleeves, fingering his beard, adjusting his beret . . . Can there be three, four, five Vietnams, without drowning in blood? Or is the Revolution merely a fad, culminating in boutiques and coiffure? Clicking his old Polaroid at the tourists gaping across the river towards the Cathedral: One franc for a souvenir, Monsieur . . . They push by, blindly . . . the quasimodo pealing of bells . . .)

'Weird times, Art, weird times.'

'Daffy Duck, Bugs Bunny, Porky Pig, Droopy, Foghorn Leghorn, Donald Duck . . . those were real revolutionaries, Goddammit . . . !'

The other boot sails through the air.

Blok, sitting a little way off with Isolde, the Venezuelan film student, both unable to sleep, although the rest of the school film crew, Icelandic Annie, Harald the Swede and Mahmud the Iranian Prison buff blissfully snooze by their equipment pile.

'Do you want to walk a bit?' he suggests. 'Nobody'll swipe the stuff.'

They amble off into the darkness, away from the vast stagnant assemblage.

'What do you think of all this?' he asks her.

'It's necessary,' she says. 'Somebody has to speak up.'

'Will it make a difference?' he asks.

'Perhaps, to those who speak.'

Her face is dimly lit by her Gauloises ember, blue smoke wreathing into black.

'You are uncomfortable,' she says, 'because it is the women who are doing things, while the men are talking their usual rubbish.'

'No,' he says, 'that seems quite natural.'

They move through a gap in the hedgerow into an open meadow, sitting on the slope of a small grassy mound. The eternal trill of invertebrates.

'Why did you come from Israel to England, Avram?'

'Who knows. And you, from Venezuela?'

'It is quite nice, Venezuela. There are mountains, prairies, the Orinoco . . . but it is just one part of the world. I wanted to get the wider picture . . .'

'And did you get it?'

'A little. Until the Malvinas War. And then this place was just like home. Loud voices and macho screams for blood. It's all the same, just deeper lies.'

(Deep in the copses, engines rev.)

'Your friend Asher. Did you know him in Israel?'

'No, I only met him here.'

'He is the only man I know who drinks to make the impression that he is full of despair. It is an excuse to make you feel he makes excuses. He wants to turn himself into a stereotype. Do you understand what I mean?'

'I suppose so.'

'He did some good work, and could do some more. But instead he wastes his life at this shitty film school. He wants us to feel that is tragic and sad. But for me, it is just infuriating. And that Henry Gibson? my God, that is another . . .'

'He's a man who cares too much.'

'Then why doesn't he show it, instead of playing the clown?'

Poor Henry Gibson, sending his summer film crew out with a forlorn benediction. Waving his bib mournfully at them as he made off to meet his fate, or rather his arthritic wheelchair ridden aunt, or so he claimed, in Bournemouth. Think of him with his little bucket and spade, moving gravel, on the shingle. His striped bathing suit. Making Monsieur Hulot look like a model of emphatic masculinity.

'Real men don't swing from toilet pipes,' Blok murmurs.

'Do you have a girl friend, Avram?'

'I was going out with a girl from Singapore, but she has gone off to marry a bank.'

'And this Jacqueline, the American lesbian? What is this you and Asher have with her?'

'We used to know her sister. It's part of our legend.'

'And the Professor?'

'An ectoplasmic vision.'

'Have you always been like this, Avram?'

'Only since I was drowned at birth.'

'It is ridiculous,' says Isolde, 'this gender war. You should throw away the rubbish that is in your mind. Your hierarchies, that are so convenient. You should listen to what half of humanity has to say.'

'No thanks, the other half were bad enough.'

They fall silent, the only sound heard for a while the tight-lipped sucking in and exhaling of her Gauloises. Then, imperceptibly, almost as if it comes from their bowels, a low, distinct rumble.

'What is that noise?'

The low growl and indiscreet coughs of heavy trucks in convoy oozing out of the night. Pin-point lights appearing around a copse, motorcycle riders preceding a snub grey police bus and army personnel carriers. Then the juggernauts: the great oblong boxes swathed in tarpaulins, flickering red warning lights either side . . .

'Bloody hell,' says Isolde. 'Is that . . . ? weren't they supposed to be flown in, tomorrow?' She leaps up. 'We'd better warn the camp!'

(The Redcoats are coming! The Federales! The Huns! Ride like the wind, muchachas!*)* 'We have to get the camera out . . . the sungun . . . come on, Avram . . . This way . . .'

But out of the dark, the woods explode. A policeman or policewoman from behind every tree, from under every stump, rock or stone. Go get 'em, Officers of the Law! From clumps of grass and from cow parsley leaves they issue, squeezing out of mole mounds and rabbit holes, sidling like sap from oak, ash and thorn, rising on the waning moon, influenza oozing from sneezewort, blind man's bluff from the meadow eyebright: truncheons out! eyes right! As the trucks roar up the main road . . .

All lights suddenly turned on in the air base. Searchlights on towers flooding the peace camp. Cries of confusion and premature awakening. Bulldozers grind up the approach road. A portakabin lurches and collapses. Washing lines fall. Dogs and babies howl. Voices of authority call through a megaphone, incomprehensibly. Several women fall out of treehouses. Tents and makeshift shacks, made of ingathered branches, fall to the cutting edge of the raid. Blok and Isolde, crouched like the spies who are too late at the promised land, watch as the curtain is torn aside. But not fast enough. For a few dozen of the women, rallying swiftly to the cause, have already rushed en masse to the main gate and thrown themselves on the road. The motorcycles screech, skid, stop. The police bus, drawn up, disgorges more uniforms, wading in to the lying, sprawling, sitting womyn, wielding power, pulling arms, legs, sweaters, trousers, boots, shawls, caps, hair.

'Yorg! Borg! Morg! Gorg!' rasps the megaphone.

The womyn begin to sing. The searchlights pan over banners coming into battle from the encampment: CHOBHAM GRANNIES FOR PEACE. PAN – PAGANS AGAINST NUKES. PAX CHRISTI. SAVE THE EARTH. TREES ARE LIFE. CONCRETE DOESN'T GROW FLOWERS. Behind the wire, troops run up, hup, hup, hup. The womyn in the road begin to keen. A helicopter thrums in the air.

Blok and Isolde, searching for their group and the College camera crew, sidle round the flank, but all is mêlée and confusion.

'It's the "Stroke" missiles!' the womyn shout. 'Lie down in front of the trucks!'

The nuclear deterrent. Womyn and police meet in battle waves. Banners and uniform caps fly. The helicopter hovers lower over the encampment, its wake collapsing tents, sending cups, saucers, clotheslines, bits and bobbed hats flying, dust and grit flung in eyes. The police wade in, trying to part the sea, which closes in behind them, their boots sinking below the press of protestant thighs, torsos, armpits, the massed resistance of passivity. A collective sigh runs through the forces of law and order, as they begin the herculean task of hauling the womyn away, one by one, by their limp and heavy limbs, while the incoming missiles are stalled impotently on the approach road.

'Jacqueline . . .' Blok remembers her, trapped in plaster. The Professor, *et al* . . . he crawls forward, Isolde by his side. 'That caravan . . .' she shouts. Mahmud is sitting on its steps, his hands plunged in a black changing bag, Icelandic Annie waiting with the camera, Big Harald the Swede with the sungun.

'We shot one whole reel . . .' she breathed at them, 'by the searchlights . . .' Asher calls out from behind a tree: 'One point seven! one point seven! look out for that depth of field, Goddammit!' The Professor rushes up, panting, his floppy hat clasped in his hands, protected from the chopper's rotor.

'Memories, Art, memories!' Asher shouts to him.

'1972! A riot in Rawalpindi . . .'

'Where's Jacqueline?' Blok asks, breathlessly.

'She's with Jane in the front line,' says Asher, 'gammy leg and all. Jane carried her into the fray. You should have seen them, Avram, the spirit of Boadicea . . . Joan of Arc . . . Big Mama . . .'

'But she has a broken leg!' Blok cries. 'We'd better go down there . . .'

'This is women's work, Avram,' Asher reminds him. 'We just stay behind and knit sweaters . . .'

'Fuck! I have torn the film!' shouts Mahmud, flailing in the changing bag.

'You won't get back down there anyway,' the Professor tells them. 'The cops have sealed off the road and they're cutting through the camp. You'd better grab all your things and let's go. I've reconnoitred this area, I know how to get to the village, and my car is there.'

BLOK: 'But we can't . . .'

HARALD: 'But we have our hired van . . .'

ART: 'You'll get it in the morning, if the missile trucks haven't flattened it. Then it's the glories of Insurance.'

MAHMUD: 'Damn! Damn! Damn!' Adding several chords in Farsi.

'Let's go.' The Professor ushers them on, collecting bedrolls,

94

accessory boxes, knapsacks, jackets. 'This way.' Pushing them through the hedgerow, away from the war, into the small hours.

Dong! Dong! Dong!

(Che Guevara stirs, jarred by the echoes of foregone clashes, consequences not quite ensued . . . One must keep faith, even if only in dreams. I have seen the future, and it is not quite me, but perhaps someone with the same face and much fiercer means . . . Or, perish the thought, gentler forms . . . ? He drifts off, deeper and deeper, into the morrow's banner headlines, the blind leading the blind, the deaf bellowing at the deaf, cripples beating each other to pulp with their crutches. Viva la muerta! *But, at the deepest level, a brazen amniotic song . . .)*

Dong! Dong! Dong!

Three a.m. Two and a half thousand bells. And the world in turmoil again . . .

★

Document:
INTERDEPARTMENTAL TACTICAL SUPPORT GROUP (ITSG): (ASG56/g/735f/12). Operation Headbanger. Cheetham Common, 7/83.

> **Particular problems arising from the combination of IPMs (Irregular Political Movements) planning QLAs (quasi-legal activities) at or around the area of Cheetham Common in July–August 1983. The following groups have advertised their intentions in various extremist publications:**
>
> **The Campaign For Nuclear Disarmament, affiliates: Christian Nuclear Disarmament, Methodists Against the Bomb, European Nuclear Disarmament, Unwaged Mothers Against the Bomb, Women Against the Bomb, Women For a Nuclear Free Europe, Anglicans For World Peace, Catholic Peace Pledge Federation, Lesbians and Gays Against Genocide, Wages For Schoolwork, Humanists Against the Bomb, The Ecologist Party, Jews For Nuclear Disarmament, Bradford Peace Studies Anti-Nuclear Group, Ad Hoc**

Out of NATO Committee, British Peace Federation. The usual Communist Party fronts.

Cheetham Col Carnival Council (4Cs), planning Bank Holiday Rock Festival and Summer Solstice Celebrations at the Neolithic Monument of Old Cheetham (Coordinates 35.6/47.9). Various eccentric and occult groups have announced parallel convocations: Druidic Council of Great Britain, the 'Serpent Power People', the Federation of Saint George, the Sisters of Hecate, the Brotherhood of Odin, the Hellfire Club, the League of Dowsers, the Federation of New Age Workshops, the Cosmic Crystal Group, the Followers of Adonai the Avatar, the Mistresses of Dianne. Large numbers of hippies and 'travellers' are expected to attend. The obstruction of main roads and bypasses in an inevitable outcome. A Viking Convocation or 'norlsraeffel' might also be held along the Cheetham 'ley line', and Intelligence reports suggest plans for an attempted burning of 'holy trees' by an unaffiliated group of Danish Pagans from Aarhus.

We need not stress the acute difficulties which can be caused to the maintenance of law and order and to the security of the Cheetham Common Air Base, given the expected arrival of the second consignment of STROKE Missiles from across the Atlantic on the same weekend. It is up to our ITSGs, therefore, to maintain strict security of the Base and its environs, *whatever the cost and consequences*, to contain the QLAs.

Copies to --- (list enclosed) . . .

In the blue corner: the Chief Constable of Greater Cheetham, Sir Francis R--r, RSFRP, FRSB, DDGG (ret), KCEGB, MGCCC et cetera, Chairman of the Royal Society for the Protection of Basset Hounds, cornet player in the Greater Cheetham Police Band, Candidate for Elevation as a Loyal Mason of the Thirteenth Degree (Royal Arch), et cetera, sweating deep in his Operations Bunker, his thumbs pressed against the closed lids of his eyes, deepening the whirl and swirl of his floaters, forcing the inner patterns to encode the widening disclarity, the conspiracies of his tormentors in all their manifold demon masks, as the Cheetham Common stigmata downloads to the mainframe at Scotland Yard: a welter of false names, false ages, false addresses, false evidence, false identities, clues from lists and notes found in the parked Avis van: Katzman, Ferrara, Hozbzadesh, Sjarlbergson, Olinsdottir, Blok. Search. Search. Search. Immigration history, deep background, global cross-referents, associates, medical, educational, military service records, birth certificates, X-rays, mental health records, blood, urine and faecal test forms, tangential cusps with proscribed and/or subversive organisations and persons, past, present or potential. Chromosomal maps, gypsy prognoses, analyses of dreams. What makes a man a man, a woman a woman, an object of official scrutiny. The matrix of a single human been, just one more problem, one more point on the graph . . .

Moop. Neep. Barp. Feep. We'll soon have you all in the target range!

★

'Tyranny? Oppression? Brutality? In this, our Green and Pleasant Land?'

Henry Gibson had entered one of his most incredulous modes, taking his spectacles off and wiping them on the unwashed curtains of his ground-floor sitting room, in which there was no place to sit, cluttered as it was with leaning piles of books in three European languages which seemed to have been bought for weight at a second-hand closing-down sale. German language courses, dog-eared 1950s travel books, crumbling editions de Minuit, Readers Indigestibles, the Everyman Library, Collins Classics, Thomas Nelson & Sons, the earliest Penguins, with their back cover advertisements for Norvic Shoes and a plug for Harold Nicholson's *Why Britain Is At War* – 'copies of this should be showered on all neutral countries and presented in bundles to Pacifists' (Sir Hugh Walpole in the *Daily Sketch*).

'*Non!*' He thrust his right hand inside his jacket, over his heart, thrusting his snub nose into the air. '*Après moi, le Deleuse!* Which reminds me, when is that fucking plumber coming . . .' removing his hand and thrusting it bravely into a mound of envelopes, invoices, notes and bills, knocking them off their shelf and following their scatter on to the unhoovered shag pile, doubling up as the dust met his nostrils. 'Ach-choo!' More books cascading down: *Three Men in a Boat, The Innocents Abroad, Around the World in Eighty Days. Diary of a Nobody* by the Grossmiths. Cedric Belfrage: *Away from It All. Back To Methuselah* by Bernard Shaw. Robert Owen's *A New View of Society*. Richardson's *Clarissa* (in four volumes). *The Rubaiyat of Omar Khayyam*. Ethel Mannin's *Confessions and Impressions*. Captain von Rintelen: *The Dark Invader*. Ernest Bramah, *The Wallet of Kai Lung*. Sir Walter Scott's *Old Mortality. I Was Hitler's Prisoner*. Eric Muspratt: *Wild Oats*. Forgotten and neglected witness to things that have had their day –

> One moment in Annihilation's Waste,
> One moment, of the Well of Life to taste,
> The Stars are setting, and the Caravan
> Starts for the dawn of Nothing – Oh, make haste!

'Jacqueline and Frida are up before the beak at Cheetham ten days from today, Henry. We ought at least to get our film crew there. Pretend there's media attention . . .'

'Dahlings! I have my own problems!'

Yes indeed. The cash-budget-liquidity-flow crisis of the London College of Cinematography having really come to its crunch, deflating the features of bursar Duguid (Melancholy Jove) as he drags the corridors like a spent balloon. 'Studio Film Labs want their moolah, Henry! Genuine coin of the realm, or else!' 'I'll give them my personal IOU, a thing I rarely give to strangers.' 'The time for bad jokes is past, Henry.' 'Tell that to the BBC.' Creditors mass in Drury Lane, with battering rams, mangonels, poison pens, flaming torches. Fusillades of Last Notices To Pay penetrating the embrasures. 'The staff are demanding a bankruptcy meeting.' 'That's about five years overdue.' 'Wake up, Henry, this is serious!' 'Ba-be-do, ba-be-do, ba-be-do . . .'

Puff, puff, puff. Pipe smoke and old men's coughs in the air. Sonia Prang's Robert chasing a smoke ring. Go getim, boy! Woof,

woof . . . Are we all here? I would like to know, puff, puff, what plans our Director has given that the College ah, puff, puff, is due to open in five weeks' time for the new intake of stoodents, are we goin' to tell 'em their money is goin' to be sequestrated right away by the commissioner of debts? Puff, puff, puff. Thank you very much for your contribution, Del, you've raised an important point here . . . if I may address the meeting . . . shouldn't we first discuss . . . ah, um, as the representative of the ACTT shop here, I would really like to say . . . if I may follow Orde's point, Mr Chairman, have we in fact got a Chairman, ah, Chairperson, sorry, Sonia . . . get on with it, for God's sake . . . Did Asher say 'wankers'? Did you say 'wankers', Asher? I really think that was uncalled for . . . Gentlemen, gentlemen, ladies, we are all, so to speak, in the same boat here . . . the *Titanic* I would say . . . I suggest we all keep our nerve, stand firm, not panic, put our shoulders to the wheel . . . point of order − I strongly urge we elect a Chairperson . . . vital meeting . . . College future at stake . . . Oh God! . . . I vould like to esk . . . second the motion . . . Oh really for God's sake, Frank . . . About ziss roomor zat ve vill not get paid ziss muns . . . We're in a voting situation now, Lech, we can have your contribution later . . . Bot . . . Have we decided to vote? When did we decide to vote? What are we voting for . . . ? Can we have a show of hands? Are you counting Bill . . . ? I thought you were . . . all right . . . Put that dog's paw down, for God's sake . . . woof, woof, woof . . . is that an abstention, Avram?

> Ah, fill the cup: − what boots it to repeat
> How Time is slipping underneath our Feet,
> Unborn Tomorrow and dead Yesterday,
> Why fret about them if Today be sweet!

Henry Gibson gives voice from the toilet. '*Allons, enfants de la patrie-ee, le jour de gloire est arrivé!*' Joining Blok and Asher in a brisk night amble up the hill, down Pond Street, round by the British Rail station and up South End, Willow Road, to converge upon the Motherland Punjab Tandoori in B— Gardens. And Gibson's plaintive cry:

99

'How does one get these fucking students to pay, Asher – short of attaching electrodes to their balls?'

'We should consult our Mahmud about SAVAK and Khomeini's Pasdaran . . .'

'Ah! when we were young and innocent . . . Remember, when we first met, Asher – you a young struggling Israeli would-be cineaste, me, a humble freelance editor, living off past glories . . .'

'And fishfinger commercials . . .'

'The salty whiff of the briny . . . the Young Socialists' Right to Work march from Glasgow to Downing Street, when was it, '71? Raggedy jeans and Doc Martens boots . . .'

'Heath oot! Heath oot! Heath oot!'

'Ah, those aching toes, corns, bunions . . .'

'We did our bit.'

'Our smidge.'

'Our morsel. And what have you done for the working class, Avram?'

'Ah, um . . .'

'Betrayal. Obloquy. Disgrace. What would Grierson have said?'

'"It taks more ways to skin a cat, laddie . . ."'

Remember! when movies were movies, Henry, and not smears on cathode ray tubes . . . when stars were stars, directors directed! You knew who wore the pants, by fuck! Cecil B. de Mille, on the set in a solar topee and heavy boots with puttees and spurs. They say he kept costs down on *Sign of the Cross* by feeding real Christians to the lions . . . Fred Niblo, John Ford, Howard Hawks, Wellman, not a crumb of quiche passed their lips . . . But who cares nowadays, who worships with real passion at the cathedral of the magic light beams . . . ? Nobody wants to do any more, only yak and scribble . . . where is Erich von Stroheim when I need him? I picked up the latest copy of *Screen Monthly*, Henry, you wouldn't believe it, I couldn't even understand the Table of Contents . . . Do you realise looking at the family snaps is a 'scopophilic regime'? You have to progress with the times, Asher . . . Give me regression any day . . .

'So what do you want out of Life, Henry Gibson? What are your three wishes, bismillah?'

'Ohhhhh Gaaawwwwwdddd . . .'

'And you, Blok? And don't talk of laying Jacqueline . . .'

'Welllll . . .'

'What was it Raymond Chandler wrote? . . . "I needed a drink, I needed a lot of life insurance, I needed a home in the country. What I had was a coat, a hat and a gun." Of course, the gun would come in handy . . .'

'I need a large manhole to open up at the College,' Henry Gibson mused, 'and swallow Del Rushforth, Clapper, Klaus Lager, Nobbie Marx, Van Nest Polglase and all . . . how do they all find me? Why do they all seek me out? Why me? Whom have I raped, despoiled, slaughtered? Am I so maimed in soul, crippled in mind and body?'

'Underdogs, finding each other's buried bones,' said Asher. 'Confess – you have been touching yourself again, my son. Retribution is certain.'

'Mercy! Mercy! Mercy!' Henry banged his forehead on the table. 'Take pity! I am an only child!' The waiter stood by, hesitantly, with steaming dishes. 'Go ahead,' Asher told him. 'This is quite normal.'

Is there life after lamb jalfreezi? Staggering back, along the quiet summer lanes.

'It used to be so simple, Goddammit!!'

Yes, granny give Chubby a nice ball on the beach. Chubby waddle over the gravel, with his weenie plastic pail, thwowing ball at doggies, woof. Other kids not like Chubby, but he has his own dweams. Later Daddy will give him Kodak Bwownie Eight. Chubby shoots sea shore. Looks out to sea, through Auntie's telescope. Watches boats, yachts, ships. Gets seasick watching. But it's all for the best. Mummy says you can't change yooman naicher. Wot can't be cured must be endured. Blood's thicker than water, when all's said and done . . .

★

Indeed! '*It was this unity,*' wrote the bald French philosopher (Asher struggling despite it all to scoop out his meaning), '*that was shattered at the beginning of the nineteenth century, in the great upheaval*

101

that occurred in the Western episteme . . . Things first of all received a historicity proper to them, which freed them from the continuous space that imposed the same chronology upon them as upon men: nature no longer speaks to (man) of the creation or the end of the world, of his dependency or his approaching judgement; it no longer speaks to him of any but a natural time; its wealth no longer indicates to him the antiquity or the imminent return of a Golden Age; it speaks only of conditions of production being modified in the course of history; language no longer bears the marks of a time before Babel or of the first cries that rang through the jungle; it carries the weapons of its own affiliation. The human being no longer has any history . . . by the fragmentation of the space over which Classical knowledge extended in its continuity, by the folding over of each separated domain upon its own development, the man who appears at the beginning of the nineteenth century is "dehistoricized" . . .'

(MICHEL FOUCAULT: *The Order of Things*)

But who appreciates the Keepers of the Peace, mused the Chief Constable. No one gives any credit nowadays. Remember the bobby on the beat, the protector of the innocent, the arbiter of community conflicts, the Man of Authority? Today they piss on it all. The rising pus of Crime, viciously targetting the old, the crippled, the sick. The total collapse of hierarchy, not to speak of 'civil disobedience', the self-criminalisation of the middle classes. He opened his eyes and rose painfully from his seat, leaning on his cane so as not to place weight on the foot crushed by the womyn protestor's plaster cast. And I was only trying to pull her out of harm's way in the scrum! Crash! the infernal thing comes down without mercy. Of course, I would not press that charge . . .

Oh, Lord! Consider mine affliction, and deliver me, for I do not forget thy Law!

But no redeemer appeared. No Lamb of Bethlehem, oozing through the Operations Room walls. No Archangel Gabriel, with flaming sword, elbowing aside the filing cabinets. Just the quotidian hustle and bustle of another day in the eternal War with Chaos . . .

★

102

'You crushed ze Chief Constable's foot! *Ach, Liebling!*'

'It was an accident. I slipped. The big oaf was trying to carry me off on his own, on his big rugby shoulders . . .'

'Beauty and the Beast, Jackie! You were lucky your own leg didn't break again . . .'

'He has very fragile ankle bones, it seems . . .'

'Well, at least he didn't press charges. A gallant of the old school . . . !'

'A male chauvinist pig!'

'A Mason of the Twelfth Degree, they say, Art.'

'A Most Excellent Master! tried by the capstone . . . he gains admission by the twelve knocks. Kneeling on both knees, hands on the Bible, square and compasses. Just wait till he climbs up the Order's ladder, to the Eighteenth and Nineteenth Degrees . . . Knight of the Pelican and Eagle and Grand Pontiff, and on and on from there . . .'

'The never-never-land of Authority . . .'

'The laugh is that that's the real world. It's us who are floating in the fantasy . . .'

'Them's fightin' words, pardner . . . Hey ho. So you're off back to Brooklyn, Art.'

'My little home in Avenue L,' confirmed Mattock. 'I can't leave the Jesuit too long on his own. You know what he's like. After a while, he gets restless.'

'It was good to see you Art. Any time.'

'And any time for y'all, Jackie. Blok, Asher included. I've got plenty of room there, even with the Jesuit. My Armenian friend Van is due in a few weeks. The Salvadorians are coming, but just for a short while. They are trying to charter their own *Granma* and set sail for Central America . . .'

'You'll miss Hiroshima Day.'

'Thank God.'

It came and went, followed by Nagasaki Day. The Professor left, a week before, waving goodbye from the passport booth at Heathrow Airport, boarding Pan American Airways back to the Land of Opportoonity. Jacqueline, and Frida von Weiszacker, in wheelchairs, joined thousands of women converging on the nuclear

103

airbase, singing, keening, keeping silent vigils and hanging baby clothes and toys on the fence. The Chief Constable keeping a safe distance, hobbling about by his command van, or hunched inside, scanning video close-ups. (His elevation as a Royal Arch Mason [of the Thirteenth Degree] having in fact already taken place, two weeks previous.) 'Calamity' Jane Springs had also adopted the cause, and pushed Jacqueline's wheelchair in the vanguard. Asher remaining behind, fuming silently, locked with his books and bottles in Inglenook Road. And Blok, too, back out of the battlefield, walking the streets of London again, pondering his legitimacy. He had already reported for the second time to the Aliens' Administration Office in High Holborn and duly registered his foreign national status. The days were warm, hazy and rain-free. Young men walked about the streets bare breasted, young women, to his chagrin, with slightly greater modesty. He had written a long overdue letter to his father in the Holy Land, now permanently domiciled down on the co-operative farm of Aunt Pashtida, and in the custody of Mama:

'How can one engage these problems? Nuclear War, total devastation, the end of all disputes and conflicts . . . There you are, on your little patch of earth, scrapping with the Arabs for a few hundred square yards, shooting each other's balls off for the inheritance of "history", while here the end of all history could come any time, by the mistake of some computer . . . Do you think women can save the world?' He did not need to read the answer, which came within two weeks: 'Not if your mother can help it.' An older war by far raging down there by Kfar Pippin's manure piles . . .

But Blok kept only a fitful eye on the continuing miasmas of his abandoned Homeland: the Israel Defence Forces bogged down in the Lebanon quagmire, the Prime Minister, Menachem Begin, hidden in his bedroom since the war of 1982, smuggling out a scrawled note containing his resignation, enabling his deputy, another ex-terrorist and an ex-secret policeman, to take over the ruination of his country. Elections were not due until well into the next year, George Orwell's 1984. The year of sexpol, double-think, newspeak and thoughtcrime. Some thought it had arrived long ago. The current Prime Minister of Great Britain, among

104

others, was said to have schooled herself along those lines; promises of life, liberty and property for all, co-existent with death, helplessness and poverty for so many, and so on and so forth. The world burning on a low flame: a coup d'état in Upper Volta. War between Libya and France in Chad. The overthrow of a mad episcopalian right-wing President in Guatemala by equally right-wing generals. Assassination, in the Philippines, of an opposition leader who had just stepped off the plane home from exile. War continuing in Afghanistan and Angola. Although not all was grief and grumbling. The stock market was buoyant. Unemployment stable. Inflation a mere 4.2 per cent. The British theatre flourished, though the Arts were constrained by reduced subsidies from Government bodies. British films were undergoing a successful renaissance. A new television channel had been opened, to cater to minority interests and the intellectually dispossessed. Many important scientific discoveries were being made, on an ongoing basis. A recent report proved Napoleon had not been poisoned by arsenic, the presence of which in the dead ex-Emperor's body could be shown to be due to moulds in the wallpaper of his room in exile at Saint Helena. The American space probe, Pioneer Ten, was still sending messages of its progress on its way out of the solar system. Scientists hoped it could find the elusive tenth planet. In 10,503 years it would be passing the first celestial orb beyond Our Sun, Barnard's Star . . .

But still Blok was not satisfied.

'You just have to take it as it comes,' said Walter, 'the ups and downs of life. The ebb and flow. Just when you think life has got you, mine boy, just when the baas seems to have the whip in his hand, a voice speaks from inside and says: Hell, no! I am going to make my own way!'

Another visit to the Willesden Green conclave, Blok on the sofa which had once sustained Joshua Nkomo, Asher sipping his dram on the floor.

'Self-determination,' said Annie. 'It would be nice if we could all have that.'

'Each man and woman a nation,' said Asher.

'I knew a man in Jerusalem once who tried that,' said Blok, 'but they threatened to repossess his TV set and he hanged himself in his apartment.'

'How do you like that,' said Walter. 'It is sad to find what some people value. I knew a woman in Cape Town who starved herself to death because her pet chicken was stolen.'

'That was a completely different matter,' said Annie. 'You cannot compare the situations . . .'

'No, but some people have everything but are never satisfied, and others seem to have nothing to lose . . . Remember that man in Soweto who sold people plots on the moon? He said the UN had decided blacks had had such a raw deal on Earth they would get special discounts elsewhere. Now there was an enterprising chappie . . .'

Oyez. Oyez. Oyez. The gentle haze of the ides of August failing to dispel the growing frisson of doom and gloom at the London College of Cinematography, with crisis meetings breaking into holiday time:

– Are we to understand, Henry, puff, puff, puff, that the Goddamn accountants want to close us down for one term, on the pie in the sky promise of our openin' for the next term after that? . . . Seems to, Del, la forza del destino . . . La forza del shit, man, puttin' the stoodents out on the fuckin' street, is that what we're in business for? . . . No, Del, that's certainly not our intention, but we have to clear the income from those whose fees are overdue . . . the charity commission . . . balancing the books . . . we're all risking our livelihoods here . . . Same sitooation, I remember, at Gainsborough pikshers . . . or was it with Vincent Korda? . . . Eggscuse, pliss, bot about our celeries . . . we all have to take the rough with the smooth . . . Fuck that one for a lark, Gibson . . . as the ACTT shop advised . . . or was it Zoltan? . . . wanton incompetence . . . bot really, how can ve eggspect . . . we're all in the same boat, Lech . . . Boat? this fucking leaking tub?? Man Overboard! . . . Paddle like hell for the shore . . .

Shrinking options . . . what's left? Blok had had one hour with Jacqueline. Sitting with her on the old cinema seats in Walter's garden, among the debris of old crates and electrical goods, listening to the trill of English summer birds, watched by the fat cats on fences. Her plaster-clad leg thrust out before them, like a great white medal of honour, or a massive plaster-cast erection . . .

'A long way from the talking fish, Avram.'

'But we're no closer, Jacqueline.'

'You, you're a chaser of impossible dreams, Avram. Even more than Asher. There's a man who lives that Groucho Marx joke, you know – he won't join any club that would have him as a member. But you're a genuine outsider. I don't know whether to envy you or to feel sorry. You're chasing me because I can't say yes. But you'll find another Malayan bank, Avram. Things happen to you. You have that aura.'

'I don't see any light.'

'It's invisible. Like Claude Rains. All you see are the bandages.' She paused. 'You know, when that big policeman carried me away from the crush, up at Cheetham . . . He carried me like a cross, almost willing me to drive my cast into his foot . . . Another man in search of some impossible dream. I could feel him sweating, oozing sincerity, a believer in the Law, that mad search for a lost nirvana of Order, Discipline, cosy certainties of a dead past. Imagine the man, defending with all his energy the weapons which can put paid to it all . . . and us, fighting the Pacifist Wars . . . We're all locked in a common irony, all part of the same absurd farce . . .'

She embarked back inland, rejoining her troops, leaving Blok behind, dividing his time between Walter'n'Annie's kitchen and Inglenook Road, keeping Asher company in the aftermath of 'Calamity' Jane's defection to militant feminism in her spare hours off the negative cutting bench. Idling while the Film College failed to open, dipping into *Why Not Eat Insects* and the nostalgic domesticities of *101 Things For The Housewife To Do* (A Practical Handbook for the Home):

Selecting Furniture
Bedroom Furnishing
Furnishing the Day Nursery
Making Loose Covers and Fabrics for the Home
Fitting Curtain Hooks and Rails
Needle Weaving

Decorative Stitches
Washing and Ironing by Electricity
Carpet Sweeping
The Care of Household Brushes
Window Gardening
Putting Up Extra Shelves in the Pantry
Making Wastepaper Baskets
Care of the Sewing Machine
Darning Table Linen and Towels
Cleaning Pots and Pans
Repairing Broken Crockery
Fixing Tiles and Repairing Fireplaces
Keeping the Gas Stove in Good Condition
Dealing With Moths
Exterminating Mice and other Household Pests
Building Dolls' Houses
Care of the Teeth, Hands and Feet
Preventing Double Chin by Massage
Massaging the Scalp
Pressing Out Blackheads . . .

His delicate reveries interrupted, nevertheless, by Asher's post-midnight bottle imp blues:

'AMERICA, Avram! There can be no question – we should take up Art Mattock's invitation. I mean, what are we doing here, you tell me, brother, in this pisspot land of bankrupts and insolvents keening for long lost empires? Walter is right! We should determine our own destiny. We should grab our fate, by both balls! Let us listen to the wise and stirring words of Franz Fanon, the Martiniquan shrink and rebel who said: Let us spend no more time in sterile litanies and nauseating mimicry! Let us leave this Europe where they are never done talking of Man, and yet murder men everywhere they find them, in every corner of their own streets, in every corner of the globe! Look at them swaying between atomic and spiritual disintegration! Of course, he had a different destination in mind, but who are we to stand on literary niceties? Let us indeed plan our escape from this dump . . . The land of Tescos and the Thin Blue Line and Petty France, endless nostalgic smalltalk and the Royal Family and wads of butter unmelted in mouths . . . The straightening out and straitening in of all discourse, BBC and *The Times* and *Hansard* and Radio Four and Any Questions which Comes Tonight From Buchenwald . . . Oh yah: In our team tonight are Reichsführer Heinrich Himmler, unsuccessful chicken farmer and one of the initiators of the controversial Final Solution, Ilse Koch, wife of the camp kommandant who has a unique line in interior decorating, Alfred Rosenberg, distinguished ideologue of the National Socialist Party and author of the best selling *Myth of the Twentieth Century*, and an inmate, Ebenezer Fishstrudel, of Punishment Block 34. Our audience is made up of inmates, guards, clerical staff and the good burghers of the nearby town of Schloss-Scheisse. Can I have the first question please? Eva Braun – does the team think the bad image our camp has recently acquired in the outside world is in any way justified???

'Nein! Nein! Nein, Avram, one must give this putrescent kachkeval the unequivocal thumbs down. America, laddie! Where men are men, and lesbians fight each other topless with spike-tipped gloves in mud wrestling emporiums. The land of kill or be killed, the call of the wild, where the poor are as well armed as the rich and can toll the bell for their oppressors. Let us leave the wretched of the earth and even poor Henry Gibson behind, to wrestle his salvation between the balance sheets . . . And perhaps they can find their Prince of Hope in some manger come the jingle bells of Yule . . . We have four months, therefore, until the New Year. What have we got to lose? This deadbeat apartment house and street of mattress burners has got to me up to here. My darling Jane has deserted me for the duration of the legal wars at Cheetham, which will end in their pleading Defence Against Genocide and ingathering a fifteen-pound fine. A decidedly cold winter looms, Avram. It is Yin and Yang, the two Chinese illusionists. The organs of the body devouring each other. Or shall we join the Dinosaurs of West Hampstead and sup on Kalamata olives and memories while we wait for the world and catch up with our revolutionary insights? Let's go, baby! Let's go! It is better to arrive than to travel hopefully. The nest egg is fattened, the brochures are stockpiled – I've been thinking about this for

109

some time – a cross-continent run, what do you say – New York City to San Francisco and back . . . I've only done it once, but round about, not non-stop. The straight line always connects the two dots, or it did, until the new mathematicians came along and destroyed all our certainties . . . So speak to me, Avram. Shall we go forth and multiply our experiences, or are we just nailed to our trough?'

Indeed, temptation definitely lurked in the old Greyhound bus schedules, magic names and insignia vaguely stirring in Blok's memory and bowels: Ottistown, Schenectady, Syracuse, Nineveh, Tuscaloosa, Jackson, Little Rock, Yazoo City, Modesto and the Yosemite National Park, Half Moon Bay and San Luis Obispo, Las Vegas and Butte, Montana and Anaconda, Amarillo and Wichita Falls . . . Legends and hopes that might despite it all jog, somewhere, a genetic wanderlust . . . Can one dare? Can one tear oneself away? Can one be two, three, infinite beings, endless shards of flying angels . . . ?

He tosses and tosses and turns . . .

★

WE HAD A DREAM, that we carried about in a faded old valise, putting it down every few hundred paces, taking it out and examining it in the cold grey light of day. Multi-hued, it rippled vaguely, causing blurring of sight and eyestrain. Emitting strange rumbling chords, like an orchestra tuning up for a piece not yet decided on. It oozed, leaving sticky puddles on the road. We folded it up, tucked it back in the bag, which was becoming heavier, even with the leakage, with every step we took . . .

(The Jesuit, wrapping himself round novel after novel, from Cortazar to Camus, Celine and back. Becalmed by the heat, working his way on through the Professor's stash of academic esoterica: History of the Train Driver's Union of Dahomey, *by Basile Gnasounou Ponoukoun;* Sociologie de Brazzaville Noires, *by Balandier; Lugard:* The Dual Mandate in Tropical Africa; *Sa'ad ed-Din Fawzi:* Origins and Development of the Labour Movement in the Sudan; Le Mahdism en Afrique Noir *by A. Le Grip;* Statistical Abstract of the Union Minière du Haute-Katanga *(1953); J. B. Danquah:* The Akan

Doctrine of God; *Franklin:* Negritude – Réalité ou Mystification; *Schaar:* The Hunza Cult of North Badakhshan. *Slowly his eyelids droop, his hair begins to crinkle, his hands weaken their grip upon the hard covers, as the minutes, hours, days pass . . .)*

(Che Guevara, tumbling in his Paris garret, shaking his fist at the airliners coming and going in the north-western sky . . . There will be a day of reckoning! (Take your piktsher, señor?) You may laugh now, but our day will come! He idly thumbs through an old tourist guide. Go West, old man, Go West! Begin again at the source . . . If at first your success spoils, fly, fly again . . .)

'Who goes there? Who dares approach the Outer Veil of Our Sacred Tabernacle?'

'Three weary travellers from Babylon.'

'How will you enter here?'

'By the password that we received in Babylon: I AM THAT I AM . . .'

(. . . the Chief Constable, staggering out of the inner vault of the Masonic Lodge on his gammy leg, carrying the world on his shoulders, accepts the congratulations of the Grand Master and his Priests: 'And behold! the Angel of the Lord appeared in a flame of fire out of the midst of the burning bush – and the bush was not consumed . . .' All cry: 'A pot of manna! Holiness to the Lord!' While, outside, the Priestesses of Diana cavort and gambol, hopping about on their crutches, high fair voices singing defiance, while, in the dark below, goblins toil, whistling as they polish the binary warheads, the launching pads, the hydraulic gears . . .)

Can one be truly 'dehistoricized'?

Is there a balm, after all?

II
Purgatorio . . .

AMERICAN EXPRESS

He pushed the picture out of his mind, it was a false memory. He was troubled by false memories occasionally. They did not matter so long as one knew them for what they were. Some things had happened, others had not happened. He turned back to the chessboard and picked up the white knight again. Almost in the same instant it dropped onto the board with a clatter. He had started as though a pin had run into him. A shrill trumpet call had pierced the air . . .

GEORGE ORWELL: *1984*

Go Greyhound – And leave the driving to us!

Greyhound Lines Inc, Phoenix, Arizona

Having left Mr and Mrs Joy proceeding to Carmel, Blok toiled alone up the Big Sur footpath. The Pacific breakers roared and played against the rocks behind and far below him, the sea hidden by the abundant coastal pines. The cry of the migrating whales was drowned by the harsh resonance of artificial birdsong broadcast from loudspeakers hidden in the trees. Here he could forget the dolorous road that brought him here, the shifts and shafts of fortune, the ebb and flow of time, the wishful thoughts and rude awakenings and just be, in the fresh mountain air, uncurling, like a hibernated hedgehog, his inner ball of spines . . . Looking up, he spied a small sign nailed to a cypress tree, which announced:

Irving Klotskashes ☐👉

He followed the winding, narrow gravel path, overgrown by weeds. The loudspeakers in the trees were now emitting a full, though *sotto voce*, panoply of cinematic FX: frogs croaking, owls trilling, scorpions performing intercourse/lunch, hunchbacks lurching into graveyards, coffin lids creaking, the chink of amontillado glasses, the walling up of men of goodwill in niches, spiders weaving webs, vampires brushing their teeth, cats purring, the twanging of jews' harps. Way ahead, above the trees, he could just make out a twirl of thin blue smoke rising to vanish into the clear sky. He readjusted his knapsack over his shoulder and pressed on, through the undergrowth, towards the smoke, determined to ignore the geneses, foretastes and antecedents of the two preceding years –

'I love you!' The cry of the crew-cut, grey-suited, black tied youth who approached Blok and Asher in the concourse of the Port Authority Bus Terminal, thrusting a folded leaflet into Blok's hesitant left hand and seizing his right in a grip of cold rubber.

'God loves you! Jesus Christ loves you! You must be born again, says John, Chapter 3 Verse 7.'

'Crucify him! Free Barabbas!' Asher answered, pulling Blok towards the escalator leading to the departure gates.

'God forgives you!' the youth shouted after them, as they descended to the lower level. 'Jesus loves sinners most of all!'

There is no accounting for taste. Asher took the leaflet from Blok and threw it in the garbage bin at the Greyhound westbound platform. The offer spurned, the passengers settling like bugs in a mattress as the bus crawled through the Lincoln Tunnel, straining for the blob of night at its end, the glinting lights of Hoboken and Newark, the great swathe of the motorway beyond, the belly of the wide open spaces . . .

They had arrived by Pan Am Clipper on stand-by tickets, camping out for two nights at the airport. The Captain flew them at 30,000 feet above the Atlantic ocean, with minimum turbulence, picking up a tail wind over Newfoundland. The stewardesses offered them hot towels to place over their faces as the aircraft descended towards John F. Kennedy Airport. A small, wart-nosed Immigration Officer checked their names against a large, dog-eared book upon whose cover a handwritten note was paper-clipped indiscreetly: 'Hassan Abu Rugheila – Refer To Phase Two.' Blok and Asher were, however, waved through without even a request to see the signed letters by Henry Gibson on behalf of the now suspended Film College, vouching for their return.

'What's the purpose of your visit, sir?'

'Touring the United States. Seeing friends.'

The Truth, such as it was. They took the train from the plane and exited at 34th Street to change to the D train which would waft them back south to Brooklyn. 'Straight lines come later,' said Asher. The miraculous din and dynamo of the Metropolitan

Transit Authority. The rainbow hordes of New York, hemmed in by graffiti:

The girder webs, Manhattan and Brooklyn Bridges, financial towers and brick warehouse walls, the gleam of muddy East River, then the long cavernous tunnels, stops and starts, deceleration and acceleration, the passengers jerked about like rag dolls, the spiderweb junction of DeKalb Avenue, swathes of platforms, peeling, scrawled walls, the poor and the black, shopping bags and trombone cases, madam butterfly hairdo, a chinese lady in a paper bag, black youths rushing from carriage to carriage, a fat poor white man rolling marbles down the aisle, an intense young black woman reading Alice Walker's *You Can't Keep A Good Woman Down*, an Old Puerto Rican man bolt upright and asleep, a lady in tattered furs eating grapes, a black man in overalls gazing at the offers of quick courses in business, accounting, hairdressing and the Law. The legion of the tired. Asher jogging Blok's elbow, rolling his eyes, proclaiming soundlessly: the Real World, Man! this is it! You've been here before, have you not, Avram? Well, here's your chance to start again . . .

Atlantic Avenya. Seventh Avenya. Prospect Park. Parkside. Church Avenya. Beverley Road. Cortelyou. Newkirk. Avenya H. Avenya J. Exit here through the creaking barred door into a time-space warp of the familiar, a recognisable but incomprehensible language, shouting its claims, offers, denials, the Jewish fishmongers and grocers, Yiddish bookshops, bagels with or without lox, the black-coated figures with beards, the head-scarved women, the commerce of shoes and slips and sealing wax, cabbages but no kings . . . Blok and Asher, staggering through the late evening, past the elevated railway tracks to the quieter haven of large detached house-and-gardens, leaf strewn pavements of this fall, October 1983 –

'Welcome to the funny farm!'

The Wacky World of Art Mattock.

'Urf urf urf!' An immense German Shepherd nuzzled Blok's groin. 'Don't take any notice of Pedro, Avram, he's permanently randy. You've made an instant friend there, haven't you, Pedro? Avram will take you walkies . . .' He uncoupled Blok from the dog. 'I'm looking after the wretched mutt for a friend, temporarily. If he's not reclaimed I'll give him to my Palestinian grocer. He needs him in this part of the world. Let me show you the burglar alarm. It's a little tricky. If you trip it, the phone rings, and you have to give the code number. If you get it wrong, the cops arrive in five minutes. They shoot first and then read you your rights. The Salvadorians loved it. They said it was the safest safe house they had ever been in.' But the Salvadorians had mostly left, leaving only Orlando and Clara, who were invisibly ensconced in the third-floor bedroom, just beneath the Jesuit, who was still in residence, chewing his way through the Norton Sigmund Freud Library, having completed *The Ego and The Id* and proceeding through *Inhibitions, Symptoms and Anxiety*. The second guest room, on the second floor, was taken up by 'my good friend Van, the Armenian Anthropologist. His full name is Vahan Djerdejkian. We go a long way back, Van and I. But that's later. I'll put you down on the ground floor.' This was a large dining room-cum-salon filled with African masks and statuettes and Indonesian phallic sculptures. 'These were done from life. Can you imagine?' More room was taken up by piles of boxes and clusters of art deco lamps, from the tinkling midst of which a morose North African youth rose to shake their hands limply. 'Asher, Avram, meet Allah al-Din. Aladdin, who else? His father

120

was a romantic. Aladdin has the basement for the moment. The Haitians have gone south for the winter. But they may be back in the spring . . .'

Go south! Go west, young man! The land of migrations and landrush. . . (Thrum, thrum, thrum, the silver bus with its iconic leaping greyhound backs away from the Port Authority Platform, to the drawled invocation of the middle-aged, middle-american driver: 'Ladies an' gennelmen, this is your thru bus from Noo York to San Francisco, calling at Noowark, Philadelphia, Harrisburg, Breezewood, arriving Pittsburg at 2.40 p.m. Calling at Youngstown, Cleveland, Toledo, South Bend, Chicaga. Change at Chicaga for Milwaukee, Minneapolis-St Paul, Indianapolis and Cincinnata. Calling at Moline, Rock Island, Davenport, Iowa Cita, Des Moines, Omaha, Grand Island, North Platte Nebrasker, Cheyenne, Laramie, Rock Springs, Salt Lake Cita Utah and all points west. Arriving at San Francisca on Thursday mornin'. There is a rest room located at the back of the bus for your convenience. Cigarette smoking is permitted in the last three rows of seats only. Cigarettes only. No pipes or cigars. Marijuana smoking is not permitted on this bus. This is a Federal Law. Certain States do not permit smoking in any part of the bus and you will be dooly informed. Hope you have a pleasant trip, folks, and thank you for going Greyhound . . .')

'. . . You want to do the whole trip in one go?' Art was incredulous. 'You're meshugge. You'll be dehydrated. By the third day you'll be pissing out of your nose and follicles. Your arse will be coming out of your ears. When I did the northern route, through Montana, I walked for weeks like the Hunchback of Notre Dame . . .'

'. . . When I crossed Afghanistan by bus,' recalled Van, 'we had to throw dead chickens out of the windows. The passengers began ritually slaughtering the animals on the seats, to avoid wasting the meat. One woman gave birth to twins, half way up the Khyber Pass. Midway they discovered I was a Christian. I only got by by dissimulation, reciting the Koran, day and night . . .'

'. . . When I crossed the Sahara, by taxi,' said Aladdin, 'on the fourth day, we saw real mirages. I saw a big multi-coloured soda

121

fountain, with a Pepsi–Cola sign. But it turned out to be a genuine kiosk, franchised by a German named Teisch, at el-Dar . . .'

A buzz at the door interrupted this kitchen table evensong, as Art disengaged the alarm to admit two Black Muslims, students of his course in Central African history, who had come to consult him about some obscure pre-Koranic exegesis of the concept of *asabiyah*. They stayed to marvel at an odd piece of charred fossil wood the Armenian Van had in a plastic bag on the table, which he claimed was a genuine fragment of the lost Noah's Ark. 'It has been carbon dated,' said the tall Levantine, 'to 3,600 BC. I got it off a Turkish soldier who was guarding the artefact in a secret warehouse in Kagizman. The Ark was brought there in the late Forties to prevent its discovery by new expeditions. They have some skeletons, too, but they are in Ankara, at the Air Force Headquarters.'

'Well,' said Art, 'whadaya know.'

The Jesuit sat, stony faced, at the end of the log table, nursing a small tumbler of brandy, his black false beard by his right hand, ready for use at any threat of officialdom. Earlier he had tried to draw Blok and Asher out, laconically, with some queries on Middle East politics. The years of his semi-martyrdom to his Faith were etched like tyre grooves in his stretched tanned cheeks and forehead, and the gnarled, small fingers of his hands. Blok found it difficult to envisage him with the ebullient, combative Jacqueline. His wars seemed to be taking place internally, in some dark battlefield of the soul.

'I spent six months in Jerusalem in 1970,' he had said, quietly. 'Staying at the Casanova Hotel. A misnomer, you had to be in bed by eight thirty. The city was quiet, but with an underlying tension. I felt it was a very tentative sort of society, both for Jews and Arabs, I reckoned. I felt as if these two very ancient cultures gave off a terribly ephemeral air. Both terrified of vanishing into thin air. Or is that just my own prejudice?'

In order to have a view, one must first have windows. Blok recalled and quoted a note scrawled by a dead man: 'IN THE COUNTRY OF THE BLIND, THE ONE EYED MAN IS HALF-BLIND.'

'Everyone wants to be what they're not,' offered Asher.

122

'The past,' said Aladdin, 'that is the criminal.'

'The past can be a helpful crutch,' said the Jesuit, 'but the able bodied shouldn't need prosthetics.' He related a bus ride he had taken in Jerusalem when several ultra-orthodox Jews, in full regalia and beards, had demanded that the bus should turn back to its depot because some of the women aboard, being in their menstrual period, were endangering the souls of pious males.

'How could they know?' Art Mattock asked. 'Could they smell it?'

'It was an object lesson in sensitivities,' said the Jesuit. 'I understood how complex life is for them. It's a fallacy that those who find their "truth" are blessed with grace and calm harmony. Look at our own evangelicals.'

'They're sinning in their thoughts all the time,' said Asher, 'and they know it. They know just why they're damned.'

'God is often difficult to make out,' said the Jesuit. 'One has bones to pick with Him all the time.'

'Let us drink to that Great Autopsy,' said Art Mattock, bringing out the brandy. Remaining to reduce the level in the Armagnac bottle after the Black Muslims, suitably bemused, had left and Pedro, on the kitchen floor, had flaked out, snoring walkies in his canine paradise. (The Salvadorians, Orlando and Clara, stayed in their room at all times.) They exchanged the latest news of Jacqueline: acquitted, with Frida von W., of affray, but fined twenty-five pounds sterling for trespass and criminal damage to a fence post. 'She'll probably stay on for a few months in England, before joining us here,' Art said. 'We shall be well shot of the Atlantic coast by then,' vowed Asher. 'The West Coast, San Francisco, Big Sur and the oranges of Hieronymus Bosch.'

'You are doing the right thing,' said Aladdin. 'Politics is a stinking bag of pus.'

He ought to know, for, according to Mattock, his brother had been the Tunisian President Bourguiba's official taster. He had expired, after a contaminated couscous, though officially no foul play was proven. Now the young man could not bear to touch his national dish and was convinced the President's secret police were stubbornly on his tail. Deep into the night, he played melancholy Berber tunes on his guitar, which he recorded on jealously guarded cassettes and sent, with no response, to radio stations and music companies, though sometimes they were wiped out in the night by mysterious magnetising forces which drove Aladdin to despair . . .

'Ah, paranoia!' sighed Art. 'Have I ever told you my Algerian story? It was some years ago, crisis times as usual . . . I was just passing through, making a stop-over on a flight from Bamako to Paris. Unfortunately an attempted assassination of President Boumédienne had just occurred. They were rounding up the usual suspects. The CIA, of course, was blamed. American citizens, even small, weedy, harmless ones like me, were not popular. I was hauled out of the transit lounge and given the works, the most thorough search I have ever had in my life. My suitcase was dismembered, its lining cut to ribbons, my camera and transistor radio were demolished. My batteries were taken away in a small plastic bag held by a sweating cop with tweezers. My electric shaver was dropped in a pail of water. My little Malian figurines, which had been given me as a gift by the Minister of Culture, were sealed separately in metal containers. I was strip searched. A metal rod was passed through the remains of my hair. My shoes were shredded. My pockets were turned inside out and examined by infra-red sensors. They passed the rod between my toes and fingers and then my crotch, carefully parting the pubic hairs. Then, as I was bending over, with the Algerian customs officer's gloved finger shoved deep up my ass, I asked the man: "What's all this about? After all, I am only in transit!" He replied, "*Cest la politique, monsieur.*"'

Indeed. The brandy bottle emptying, the reminisinces flowing, even after the Jesuit had retired upstairs with the *Psychopathology of Everyday Life*, Van musing fondly: 'I really love that man, Mattock. Do you remember, that first time we all went together to jail?'

'Tell 'em the tale, Vahan, tell 'em the tale.'

'Ah, yes . . .' the Armenian lent back in his chair, eyes glazed with nostalgia, Asher and Blok all ears, Aladdin strumming fitfully, the dog kicking in his own dreams. 'We were all three accused of plotting to kidnap the Secretary of State Henry Kissinger . . . I was a student of Art's at Columbia – 1970, we all went down to Washington for the big picket of the White House, after the killings at Kent State . . . that day Tricky Dicky himself came to try and talk to us, mumbling about his football . . . The Jesuit told him he had betrayed God by continuing the war and bombing Cambodia.'

'I fell asleep, while you yapped on,' recalled Mattock.

'Some days later our group met to discuss how to continue the protests. But we were joined by a weird wild young man who kept demanding violent action. We sussed out immediately he was an FBI agent. So we began hatching absurd plots, to fool him. We said we'd kidnap Kissinger and hold him in a ranchhouse in New Hampshire until the United States withdrew from South-East Asia. The next morning, at four a.m., we were all woken up and arrested by Federal agents. The three of us found ourselves together in a small cell with four colossal muscular black guys. "What you in for?" they asked with contempt. "They say we tried to kidnap the Secretary of State," we told them. The news spread throughout the whole jail. Overnight we became the kings of the penitentiary.'

'I became the Miss Abby of Cell Block 21,' said Art. 'I had to write a million letters. But the trial was a farce. The evidence was so absurd, when the Prosecution had finished our lawyer just said: 'The Defence rests.'' We were all acquitted *tout suite*.'

'The police agent later joined the Maharishi,' Van added. 'Today he is trying to promote World Harmony in the Philippines.'

'Was that the year we had the Magic Mushrooms?' asked Art. 'The Hopi Commune, at Escalante, remember?'

'I remember absolutely nothing of that,' said Van.

Perhaps that's best, perhaps that's best . . . The tentative night life of Mattock's Brooklyn. And the phone calls, flooding in day and night, puncturing the already jangled household nerves. ('Take 'em all down. My answering machine is broken.') Cries for help from all corners of the globe: 'Hey, tell him it's Jonathan, from the Bronx, it's OK.' From Texas: 'Hail! Ah missed him agayan!' From Ougadougou, crackling via Paris: 'Tell him the Minister of Justice will not be able to attend next week's seminar. The militia are too active.' From Cairo: 'Tell Art Mahmud says it is still too damned hot here.' From Lisbon: 'I need those figures

125

on nuclear proliferation. Does he have the Alamo File?' From Rawalpindi, a coy cipher: 'Tell Art I cannot find those pots.' From Katmandu: 'Oh God; well, I suppose I shall just have to fend for myself.' From Geneva: 'Ah hail! Missed him agayan! Ah don't seem to have much luck, doo ah?' And several calls from a man with the same voice and accent, leaving messages under different names: 'Tell him Yahya called.' 'Tell him this was Yefim.' 'Ah . . . tell him Baruch will call again.' 'Jose. I will call back.' 'Vasil here. I'll call again.' 'Tell him Ishmail called.'

And the walkies Pedro took Blok on, tugging him powerfully on his leash up Ocean Avenue, the flat wasteland of shops and garages and gas stations, leading on for ever. 'You stupid mutt! I want to go back! This is dangerous!' 'Ruff! Ruff! Ruff! Ruff!' Or, leashless, discovering, some miles downwind, near the end of the D train line, the enticing ethnic island of Brighton Beach memoirs, a blob of Russia on the Atlantic under the El – the Ukrainian Tearooms, the Georgian Kebab Restaurants, Cyrillic signs over the potholed road, stalls of Uzbek cassettes strung across the boardwalk, street kids shouting abuse in Estonian, old men with rolled-up trousers on the sand, smoked raw fish, caviar and kasha and Mrs Stahl's Knishes, and an aged Jewish man in a black suit and homburg, hobbling by, humping a battered ghetto blaster blasting Hassidic melodies and tear jerkers before the haze of Coney Island . . .

Amerika! Ye hungry, huddled masses, yearning to be free . . . Go! Go! Go!

'. . . Forget it all, Avram! Give nostalgia the elbow! Regard everything behind us as closed, including our arseholes, comrade! Amerika! Only what lies ahead is real!'

Empty your brain and let the vibrating hum of the Greyhound clear the cobwebs, dust the drawers, sweep the cells clear! The evening departure, snaking through the night out of the Lincoln Tunnel across New Jersey, past Burnt Mill, Potterstown, Lebanon, Clinton, Bethlehem, Fogelsville . . . the passengers crumpling slowly into their clothing, slumping amidst each other's spent odours, rustles, creaks, coughs, sneezes, farts, burps, whispers, snores . . . the luminous icon billboards appearing out of nowhere on the freeways:

126

THERE'S A MIGHTY GO IN THE WORD GOSPEL
SOME ARE WISE AND SOME ARE OTHERWISE
THE ELKS OF FOREST LODGE SALUTE
JERRY OGDEN,
JUTLAND CITIZEN OF THE MONTH
UNFAIR TO TICKS AND FLEAS

The demon Asher still whispering in Blok's ear as he attempts to sink below the waves: 'What do you think, Avram? Tell me, when was the last time in your life you were madly, deliriously happy? Does there remain the slightest vestige of an innocent pleasure?'

The policewoman, in Jerusalem? Chance encounters, out of the blue? The first falafel? The first fuck? The first turd? The first suck? How much further should one go? Warmly ensconced in the womb, with all conveniences and services on tap, round the clock. Or were there other times of immersion, in love, in faith, in community? The forgettance of things past: their last night at Art Mattock's refugee camp, when the erratic and paranoid Aladdin had accused Asher of erasing his taped cassettes of melancholy Berber songs in the night, whether as part of some Zionist plot or as an agent of Tunisian Intelligence he would or could not say. All he would divulge to Blok, whom for some reason he felt he could take into his confidence, putting an arm around his shoulder was: 'Your friend has brought X-rays into the house.' Blok reported this to Asher, who merely said: 'I wouldn't rub that boy, God knows what genie might appear.' A prescient point, as it proved, when, two hours later, at the stroke of three a.m., Allah al-Din pursued Art Mattock with a carving knife around the bedrooms and up and down the stairs, overturning the art-deco Hubbard lamps, smashing Nuart shades, foaming at the mouth and bellowing his hallucinations: 'Youssefist spy! Neo-Destour agent!' The Professor forced to defend himself with one of his Indonesian carved phalluses, modelled, luckily, on a well-endowed Javan. Pedro leaping about between the two, tonguing whatever flesh he could find. Van darting about, waving a salt cellar. Finally the Jesuit leapt on the berserk North African from on high, disarming

127

him while an unhinged window tripped the house alarm system, Blok rushing to the ringing telephone to bark the code: 'Nine-One-Five! Nine-One-Five!'

C'est la politique, monsieur . . .

. . . Cleveland, Ohio, three a.m.: rest stop at the Greyhound Station Men's Convenience. Noxious puddles on a cracked floor. The steady drip of a tap, hopefully of water. The heave and strain at an encrusted bowl, staring at the scrawled graffiti above the broken lock on the scuffed door:

> 'You think you cute so you piss on the floor –
> be a hero and shit on the ceiling.'

Also:

> Black Revolutionary taking a shit, 5/17/79,
> KKK FUCK YOU PUNK.

Onwards, into the unknown . . . Elyria, the James W. Shocknessy Turnpike, Toledo, Elkhart Indiana, South Bend . . . Beware of the hun in the sun . . . the chattering flow all about them, rotating with the combustion engine: . . . my mouth's too small, I only have twenty-three teeth . . . everyone has a plate nowadays . . . I told him, you can't bite the pizza from both ends . . . head shop he said, I didn't realise . . . as a baby, she looked like Gerald McBoing Boing . . . hominy grits'n'hash browns . . . just a decent world, that's all . . . give her a clinch, she bakes a smile . . . a dollar a day . . . mud wrestling . . . perhaps ah should have had braces . . . a life for a life . . . an I for an I, man, no shit . . . suffering from death lag, coming over from Europe . . . always wanted to visit Guatemala, you can take the Greyhound down south to Mexico City, they call it Transportes del Norte, you go down from Brownsville to Matamoros, then to Ciudad Victoria, Tamazunchale, Zimapan, San Luis Potosi, Guadalajara and Mexico City, I can tell you that's some journey, and from then on you're on your own . . . I know they have killed a lot of people there, people talk about Nicaragua but what about all the rest of those Godforsaken places, people who are real poor, look at us here, I don't think we can criticise when people try to better themselves, after all it's our birthright, the Declaration of Independence, do they teach any of that over in England, I'm a teacher by the way, I used to work in New York City but I can't take all that any more, when you really think . . .

Don't think! Just let it happen! Just lie back and enjoy the view . . . But as they approached Chicago, rolling through untouched vistas of inter–urban decay along Interstate 90, the drum of incessant traffic, the powerpunch thrust through the arse from the bus engine, Asher suggested a strategy of achieving contact with two robust sweatshirted girls some way behind them, who had been sleeping curled up in each other like cats for virtually the whole route from New York, only spilling out reluctantly at Cleveland where the bus was driven off to be cleaned, leaving Blok to wrestle with the toilet graffiti and Asher to queue wearily for the Rest Stop Hamburgers which flopped, like reheated turds, on to little plastic plates. 'Eat! Eat! don't ponder!' But now the damosels appeared to have woken, shaking their old–style flowing locks, black and blonde, like a vision from the old rucksack past (ahhhhhh . . .), though these lassies were probably just burning their dolls in the days of Kent State gunpowder and Tricky Dicky on the lawn . . . But Asher said: 'This is what it's all about, Avram. Fucking on the Greyhound, that's legend. The rise and fall of cunt on cock as we cross the Rocky Mountains. John Wayne on his hoss. Mark Twain on his River. It all comes down to basics, man.'

'It's OK by me,' said Blok.

Yus! Chicago! Great towers peeking through a maze of sky-ways, the tangled junction of Dwight D. Eisenhower Express-way, pushing through steaming midday bustle to the Terminal at North Clark and Randolph, exiting up several levels of milling humanity in search of the Burger King franchise ('this is a schayduled rayst stop . . . you have fifty minutes . . . fifty minutes . . .') – 'Goddammit, Avram, where have they gone??' searching among the hordes of travellers and tramps slumped in curved plastic chairs before individual televisions disgorging blurred and snowy major league football in miniature for two bits a peek. Tinny announcers like trapped homunculi in bottles vying

129

with the sludge of Terminal sound, the crowd pouring every which way, slight men in suits thrusting ubiquitous leaflets into their hands:

THE NEW AGE MOVEMENT –
TIME'S TRAGIC TOLL –

The Bible has promised God will send a Redeemer, and He is come right now. He is among us. His agents are everywhere. They have infiltrated government departments and defence and security estab-lishments. All churches welcome these new Preachers of Peace, Tolerance and Unity. But who is The Christ?

Who indeed?

'Where the fuck are those dames??!!'

'They might have got off in Chicago,' Blok offered, unhelp-fully. 'Perhaps they are Chicagoeens.'

'Not so. I saw them leave the bus without baggage.'

'Maybe they're travelling light.'

'What is it with you, Avram? Are you addicted to drought?'

Onward, the rainmakers. Achieving only enough time to purchase a phallic hot dog before rushing back on the bus. The two ladies comfortably giggling in their seat, with their juicy Burger King packets.

'Aaaaaarrgghhhh!!!'

On, on, on. Out of Chicago, across Illinois flatlands, nada, nada, nada but cars, autobuses, container trucks coasting along the Interstate Highway: Joliet, Ottawa, La Salle, Peru, Princeton, Annawan, the Quad Cities . . . The two girls had long digested their burgers, and were now engaged in conversation with a middle-aged man in a faded grey jacket with elbow pads, who had got on in Chicago and taken the back seat, by the toilet. A mournful, Hispanic lined face with a grey beard and blackish-grey hair protruding from beneath a large black stetson. A shade of familiarity, as if he had stepped out of a bygone age and other dreams . . .

Asher fumed: 'Shit! Shit! Shit! Magic mushroom time! Che Guevara there has scooped the pot!'

130

Indeed? The old tattered hero/bogey, risen from his café exile, another genie of a tarnished lamp which only glimmers dimly in the night?

Onward! Onward! Into Iowa, from Davenport towards Iowa City, Asher still wide awake and restive, Greyhound-lagged and mindstewed –

'Death, Avram . . . have you imagined the outcome? The black-clad figure, playing chess. Grandmaster Todt. Have you considered the consequences? Ingmar Bergman ad infinitum. Virgin springs. Summer night smiles. Bring on those big-titted Swedish floozies. Ah, that winter light. The shame. Switching personas in the sand. Calvinist logic, sins abiding. A million wrongs to make a right. And yet orgasm does ensue! Do you believe in survival after death? Don't answer, we are too close to banality . . .' He furtively removed his little flask of booze from his shoulder bag and imbibed alone, Blok declining the offer, but looking out for the driver's roving eye. Asher drank, and fell asleep throughout the Iowa plains, and when the next rest stop was announced ('donuts here are mighty fine, folks, twenty minutes, twenty minutes only'), Blok alighted alone and sat close by the table at which the two girls were being entertained by the stetsonned usurper, who was speaking in a slow, accented voice, having taken out a large cigar, clipping the end off ponderously and patting in his pockets for a match. He turned to Blok.

'Hey man, got a light?'

Oddly enough, Blok had a set of matches from a Chinese Restaurant, the Hunam Taste on 81st and Broadway.

'Have a seat, man. Are you going all the way?'

He introduced himself as Carl, the girls as Dominique and May.

'I'm going with my friend to San Francisco,' Blok said.

'A pretty town, but overvalued. The ladies and I are headed for Los Angeelees. We change schedules at Salt Lake City.' Sucking the long cigar alight with a deliberate expertise.

May, the blonde, explained softly: 'We're not looking for nothing in particular. All we want is a good time on the beach, with lots of surf, sand and sun.'

'Los Angeles,' said Carl. 'That's the real nothing, none of your cheap imitations. The atmosphere of pure nothingness blankets

131

the city. Miles of nothing. A massive emptiness over great distances of urban and suburban zilch.' He blew a smoke ring, the first genuine one Blok had ever seen.

'I think we have to get back on the bus,' said the raven-haired girl, Dominique, quietly.

They carried aboard donuts and milk cartons. Asher still stretched across both seats, Blok joined the grouplet in the back.

'At the end of the day it doesn't matter where you are going,' said Carl, 'the important thing is just to go. Ain't that the essence of America?'

'Marlon Brando, *The Wild One*,' May corrected the quote: '"We don't go anywhere, baby, we just go".'

'I have some interesting stuff here for that purpose,' Carl revealed briefly a flash of a white powdery substance in a little plastic packet. 'Ready for take off, warp nine.'

'No, thank you,' said Blok.

'It is top-quality cocaine,' said Carl, looking hurt at the refusal.

'The Happy Hour,' said May, grinning at Blok.

'Well, a little sniff perhaps,' agreed Blok.

They took turns in the toilet. Blok sat, on the seat warmed by the travelling ladies, trying to balance the small sliver of silver paper and the small paper cone, while five feet below, the asphalt rolled. The lock on the door creaked and clattered. Someone's false teeth had been left in a glass. He had taken down his trousers and underpants in case someone burst in none the less. The pungent chemicals of the toilet sloshed upwards towards his arse with the yaw of the bus. Whatever diseases, maladies, distempers, scourges, germs, bubonic plagues, filth, pus, muck, putrescence deposited there since the Lincoln Tunnel stretched its claws towards his buns. The false teeth leered at him and chattered. The engine grinded as in pain. A sickly, unshaven face glared at him from the mirror. It was definitely not his own. 'You bastard!' he said to it, shaking his fist. 'I'll get you yet!' Knock knock knock, swivel swivel swivel, the lock on the door rattled.

'Hey, Abraham – you OK in there?' The dulcet voice of Dominique.

'Coming!' He pulled his trousers up and fastened his belt, flushing the silver paper down the drain. The face in the mirror sneered at him, baring sharp, pointed teeth. Horns protruded above the ears. 'Ho ho ho!' it said. 'Asshole!' He opened the door and staggered out, with the lurch of the bus, into the raven damosel's arms.

GO! GO! GO!

Iowa City to Des Moines, Des Moines towards Omaha . . . Interstate 80, hombres! The flying billboards:

HE WHO SAYS THE MOST USUALLY
MEANS THE LEAST!

BEST WEENIES IN POWESHIEK – 80 CENTS!

HEBREW NATIONAL – COAST TO COAST!

THE PLATTER – IT'S THE WAY TO GO!

Giant hamburgers revolve in mid-air. Pyramids, topped with Colonel Sanders dimples. Platoons of doomed chickens crossing the road, migrating to safer climes (in an old *New Yorker* cartoon, Blok remembers, sez the fowl: 'He may be Colonel Sanders to you, but he's Adolf Eichmann to me . . .')

JESUS SAVES – NEXT EXIT

They pass it by. A tear falls from the sky and splatters on the windscreen, followed by another, and another. The giant Greyhound wipers turn on. The sky goes grey, then black. The ocean swishes, swirls by. Blok can sense Asher's malevolent eye. Having woken to his unexpected desertion Asher had surlily accepted an invitation to join the back seat group. But he had turned down the cocaine offer. 'No way, for God's sake.' Carl shrugged. 'I respect a man who keeps his independence,' he said, excluding him with his eyebrows. 'You're crazy,' Asher told Blok, between clenched teeth. 'This is mid-America, man. They give people life for drinking sarsaparilla. The driver always checks up on people who hang out in the john: a Greyhound driver is a man who has seen it all, and knows the depths of the soul . . .'

But the driver keeps his Eye on the road and on the instruments of his cockpit. The silver canine flying through stillness, on into the blackest hours. Omaha, Nebraska, at midnight, high on white powdered enthusiasm, pining for a Kentucky Fried. 'This is a one hour an' twenty minute rest stawp!' Asargelusha! Staggering about the abandoned thruways, under the eyeless glass towers, no sign of SAC bombers launched in the bleak night sky to Russia. Just a cruising Sheriff's police car outside the Greyhound Terminal. The fatigued pilgrims slumped over plastic tables as ancient blues drip from the walls. ♪ 'Never leave me . . . doodle doo . . .' ♪ A little wizened old man with a face like Popeye, a red cardboard hat and a red-and-white striped apron, coughs phlegm on to his grilled burger pats. Cellophane-wrapped comestibles repose in transparent compartments in automatic vending machines.

'America! The heart of darkness!'

'OK, Avram, pipe down.'

Night, and the smallest hours. Crossing the Mississippi. An immense swathe of black water, as if crossing the sea . . . into the depths of Nebraska. Blok feels the hum of the engine in his bowels, in his guts and in his brain. Internal combustion of cells. Induction, compression, power, exhaust, sparks leaping from nerve to nerve. Memory shards dancing in his arteries, riding the red corpuscles like bucking broncos, or like Raquel Welch in *Fantastic Voyage*: Lt.-Colonel Tswingli, editor-commander of the Israel Defence Forces Magazine *BABASIS*, banging his table in the midst of a pyramid of Egyptian skulls and burnt out tanks; Adam, the Dorian Gray of Jerusalem, sitting unaged in the T--n Café from 1951 till the Lebanon War; Yissachar Pri-On and his jellybodied mentor, the movie mogul Adir Kokashvili; red haired Esther and Thin, née Fat, Avi, old comrades waving from beneath a sea of banners proclaiming, 'NEVER ANOTHER WAR LIKE THIS . . .' Nurse Nili-Honey, and the peels of love thrown out of the window; the reincarnated Friedrich Nietzsche, stalking the wards in striped pyjamas . . . the ex-Prime Minister of Israel, with ten thousand o'clock shadow, waving a white flag from under his bed . . .

Ghosts and gremlins, shading into his dreams. Blok, with raven-haired Dominique curled in his lap like a lost domestic kitten – both drawn along a great conveyor belt into a long endless tunnel. Great celestial orbs light the shining black walls sporadically with blinding arcs, then fade. Mountains glimmer whitely at the end of the tunnel. Tiny figures, which he knows to be his father and mother, ski up and down their slopes. A white figure looms startlingly, jerked on a set of strings. He recognises the skeleton of the Almighty, the toothless, gaping skull. A gibbering moan drips from the mouth with saliva, as a bony hand spreads benediction. A neon-lit cinema glides past, its queue wrapped around the block. From the front of the queue red-haired Esther beckons, shouting: 'Come on in, I've saved you a seat!' But he is jerked by. The darkness falls again. He feels the age-old need to piss and presses his way as if through putty down the aisle of the bus. The inert forms of the passengers are sprawled in his way, a cat's cradle of legs, limp arms, snoring faces. He tries to squeeze past them, but becomes trapped. He presses down with his socked feet upon faces, noses, eyes, chins, popping them like ripe balloons. Sticky liquid soaks his feet to the calves. The skeleton of God is in the back seat, smoking, the black stetson on its skull. It leers at him and opens the door to the toilet. The horned beast is seated within. '*Occupé! Occupé!*' it croaks. He turns back up the aisle to the driver. 'I have to piss,' he informs the stern face of his father, who pulls the door open with a hydraulic hiss. He falls out of the bus, on to the open road. Typhoons and cyclones roil above him. A young girl, with a doll, approaches ahead. He shakes his head and she passes him by, disappearing down converging parallel lines. He pisses at the side of the road, but cannot stop, his intestines, his liver, lungs, spilling out. He tries to gather them with his hands and push them back into his abdominal cavity, but they plop and leap out of his grasp. Croaking like toads, they hop away into the horizonless fields, squelching into stagnant ponds, brek-kek-kekking into the dawn . . . The haze clears, and he is back seated at Art Mattock's kitchen table, gazing into the blurred faces of Asher, The Jesuit, Aladdin, Art Mattock and Van, switching memories . . .

'. . .The story of the Hunza Water of Kashmir, comrades! The weirdest journey Van and I ever made . . .' (Bessarabian nights, the swirl of shaggy dog lives.) 'We were on the road between Gilgit and the Karakorum Mountains, in the 'Northern Areas' of the subcontinent, disputed between India and Pakistan. We had joined a caravan of smugglers, headed for the hidden city of Ishkhabad, said to have the most erotic sculptures to have escaped the wrath of Islam. The old inhabitants were according to legend the original descendants of Noah's son, Japheth, who had intermarried with the elusive Yeti. The smugglers, who were all eight-foot-high Gilgits, with jet black beards made of wire mesh and fifty carat eyes which could spot a penny in a snowdrift at five miles, wanted to diverge towards a kiosk at Mir Khalf, below the Hispar Glacier, where they had heard the only remaining bottle of the local booze, the incredible Hunza Water, was on sale. As devout Moslems they could not buy the booze themselves, but Van and I, the foreigners, could procure it, and thereby gain their favour, which would protect us from the threat of being raped and skinned to make pocket books of our scrotums, which was the favourite local craft. Each one of our companions had at least two of these wallets, souvenirs of an attempted Indian Army raid, a couple of years before.'

'This man is telling you the truth,' Van declared to the kitchen table. 'He is embroidering nothing.'

'Mile after mile on foot we trudged towards this outpost,' Art continued, 'the Gilgits assuring me all the time: "Just a little further, then it's downhill all the way to the Himalayas." The leader, Kaboos, who spent rest stops tattooing his own eyelids with his eating knife, had to carry me, slung like a sack of potatoes, for most of the last twenty miles, on his left shoulder, his right being reserved for a Saprovyets Flamethrower. Van, more experienced, kept up on his own. The blinding snow made us see mirages: flying saucers landing and taking off on the glacier, strange convoys of hairy, waving giants. But the Gilgits only shrugged when I pointed this out, and twiddled their ammunition belts through their beards. We went up mountain peaks and down crevasses and eventually reached this remote village, which consisted of three huts and the hooch shop. I went in alone and bought the Hunza Water. It cost me thirteen dollars. The shop-owner wanted to sell me shrunken Yeti heads, but I was far too exhausted. The Gilgits seized the precious bottle and we hightailed it back, across the glacier, five days' march, to Gilgit town. We repaired to my hotel and locked ourselves in, the seven massive bandits and Van and me, in a room the size of my water closet. Giant cockroaches came through the walls, and the Gilgits caught and ate them, picking their teeth with bullets. Then they turned to the bottle. But when they opened it it had all turned to vinegar in the long haul from the shop. Kaboos vomited it all over my head. The others wanted to kill us and gain two pocket books, but Kaboos declared it was the punishment of Allah for their sin and not the fault of the foreigners. They wrote oaths, in their blood, on my Flatbush College notepaper, to abstain completely from that day on. I had the document until it was taken off me, a couple of years later, on an Air India internal flight, which was hijacked by Punjabi terrorists.'

Ah! C'est le narcotique, monsieur!!!

Breakfast, at North Platte, Nebraska. Blok savours the true West for the first time, as a buxom angel in a cream short-sleeved waitress uniform serves him a double dose of coffee, and a double egg and hash browns. The genuwyne Western smile. Two baby-faced law enforcement officers drape their behinds on adjacent stools and gossip about their first-born sons. 'He sure is a cute little son of a bitch.' So weren't we all, weren't we all . . . ? The sun outside is a glory, despite early November. The flat landscape ripe and not unpleasing. The giant billboards seem to hold genuine promise, a true larger than life pride in their offers. Asher, Carl and the two girls hop about by the side of the bus, trying to restore circulation, not least to the brain.

'I once did this sort of journey on a bus to Athens,' said Asher, trying to impress May away from Carl, struggling in the lee of the bus to light the first cheroot of the day. 'Three days and nights with no inside toilet, and the drivers could only speak Greek. They didn't know the roads and got lost in Yugoslavia, the wilds of Montenegro. We were stopped at the Albanian border by peasants who had never seen a motor vehicle before. They confiscated our supply of Italian Donald Duck comics and gave us the complete speeches of Enver Hoxha in Serbo-Croat before allowing us to withdraw. Middle-aged women had to defecate at the side of the road. The drivers played Hadjidakis cassettes all the way to Omoniya.'

'I spent thirteen days on a bus, from Turkey to India,' said Carl, hurrying up to make his play. 'We had to drive on railroad tracks most of the way. Water buffaloes sat down in front of us and we had to stop for days and sleep in the bush. The schedule before us had been ambushed by dacoits. Several passengers had their fingers cut off for their rings. The driver had been beheaded and raped.'

Out of North Platte, climbing higher, by Sutherland, Paxton, Ogallala, Julesburg, Lodgepole, Dix, Kimball (elevation 4700), Pine Bluffs, closin' in on Cheyenne . . .

'England,' Asher told May, 'the United Kingdom . . . it's not as ordinary as you think. Do you know there are people there who dance in wooden clogs, in broad daylight? Not to speak of those who dream of Free Estonia in Shepherd's Bush . . . some people never give up . . .'

'The Pyramids at Giza . . .' Carl related, rolling his cigar round his tongue, 'have you ever done Peyote on a Pyramid? The strangest things can be seen, at midnight, on any Egyptian or Aztec Temple . . . The CIA keep a twenty-four-hour, three-hundred-and-sixty-five-day surveillance on every ancient site. They collect information, on the Pole Star position, for the Masonic Grandmaster in the White House . . .'

Groping in the dark, devoid of any keys of ingress to the body and soul of the two travelling girls. All that could be gleaned was they had been at some eastern college, then lived in Greenwich Village, waiting on tables. Dominique told Blok her parents were both expatriate French marine biologists. They lived in a tank, at Riverdale Park. Dominique said she had developed a deep under-standing of fish and other aquatic creatures. May's parents, she mentioned in an aside, were dead. There was some job waiting, in Los Angeles . . . Blok merely tightened his grip on the softness of her shoulder, past Cheyenne, as the bus rolled on up the Laramie Range, the snow-capped Medicine Bow Mountains, up up, into the Rockies. At the Laramie rest stop Asher purchased for May a copy of the *Laramie Daily Boomerang*, once edited by Mark Twain in person, and Carl bought her a cellophane wrapped old flyer of

'Rules of This Tavern: No Boots To Be Worn in Bed; No More Than Five To Sleep in One Bed; Organ Grinders To Sleep in the Wash-house; No Razor Grinders or Tinkers Taken In'. Blok bought Dominique a few sepia coloured postcards of Wild Bill Hickock and Sitting Bull. Up, on into the snow-flecked mountains . . .

'We pay a heavy price,' Carl droned on, 'for our ignorance of the real forces controlling the world. See this dollar bill – President George Washington. A slave dealer, dope grower and Eighteenth Degree Mason. Now look at the back – the Eye above the Pyramid. The Great Seal of the United States and of Masonry. The words: "Novus Ordo Seculorum" – A New Secular Order, the Masonic dream . . .'

'On a ten thousand shekel note,' said Asher, 'Golda Meir cries Let My People Go. Has anyone seen a note for fifty ngwee?'

At Rawlins he bearded Blok alone in the toilet.

'We have a decision to make comrade,' he said firmly, as Blok strained at the bowl.

'Oh, God, God, God!'

'These girls have a Travel Lodge Hotel advance booking at Salt Lake City. That cunt Carl is going to stop off as well. They have no connection to Los Angeles until seven forty-five the next morning. Are we going to throw the race to this bastard? Or do we seize the time, and stop over too? What we do afterwards will depend completely on the state of our bodily fluids.'

'Oh God! God! God!'

Night again, over the Continental Divide. Stolen kisses are sweetest. The driver sonorously forewarns: 'There is no smoking in any part of the bus in the State of Utah.' Put your fires out, hombres! Past Wahsatch, Castle Rock, the Devil's Slide, Echo, towards the rest stop of the ox waggon trail, the Mormon's haven, Salt Lake City . . .

SALT LAKE CITY! The new Zion, the end of the Great Migration, the great trek of the persecuted believers dreaming of God's Kingdom on earth . . . Tall glass towers lining wide streets around the Cinderella Palace of the Mormon Tabernacle, glowing in lights in the Greyhound evening like a massive hologram. Upon its spire the Angel Moroni blows his trumpet to announce the Second Coming. Below, hugging the adobe, sandstone walls of the Latter Day Saints' Compound, Blok, Asher, Carl, May and Dominique lug their baggage towards the Travel Lodge. But at the hotel reception the two outsiders discover there is no room for them at the inn, although Carl and the girls had reserved their rooms ahead of time by credit card, over the phone. All other Travel Lodge venues are full too, the impeccable crew-cut clerk informs them. 'There is a Choir Convention at the Tabernacle.'

Thousands of sweet voices, raised in praise of the everlasting and the recurrent. They ended up in the YMCA, but even that was full of yodelling hopefuls, trying their lungs in their cells. Young and old, dressed in identical grey suits and black ties, wearing smiles which appeared to be nailed upon the corporeal cross of their souls. The spartan cells each had two bunk beds and one chair and one table, with one Book of Mormon in the drawer:

> *America's history foretold 2,500 years ago – 1st Nephi, Chapter 13 . . . Columbus, Fate of Indians, The Puritans, The Revolutionary War, Verses 12, 14, 16, 17 . . . Why the Fall and the Atonement? Read 2nd Nephi . . . The last days foretold by the Prophets . . . Where does the spirit go after death? Read Alma, Chapter 40, page 294 . . .*
>
> *Read of the happenings on this hemisphere at Christ's crucifixion and His visits here, 3rd Nephi . . . Christ told the Jews of other sheep. Who? . . . Are Christ and God one without form or was man made in the image of the Only Begotten? Ether 3, 3–16 . . . Are unbaptized infants damned or even deprived of their eternal glory? Read Moroni, Chapter 8, page 515 . . .*

They braved the shower room, unrobed men wagging their organs in attitudes unsuggestive of holiness. Laryngitic gargling from cubicles. Desperate moans from unlocked booths. Moans and creaks from the thin walls, perhaps deriving from termites forming new churches in the stones (the House of God, the bowls, the basons, the tongs of pure gold, the censers. None impure in either thought or deed. Stop that rubbing in thar!) . . . Lying down, exhaustion and Greyhound withdrawal seeping through, Blok feels his liver, pancreas and spleen crawling up back into his abdomen. Penises, oozing through the walls. The Angel Moroni, with a brace of gold tablets, rocking on an easy chair by the door, blew soap bubbles from his trumpet. The bubbles rose, tiny homunculi within them straining against the thin skins. Their minuscule mouths worked, silently.

'Wake up, Avram, this will not do!'

Asher, tugging his arm sternly, standing on the lower bunk.

'That ratbag Carl is fucking his prick off, I know it! We are being played for suckers, schmendrick! That nice French chick you cradled in your bosom, Avram, are you going to let that fuck hatch his seed in her vital orifices? Are we men or are we mice?'

As Groucho said: put a piece of cheese down and you'll find out. But Asher dragged Blok awake, into his clothes, babbling incoherently: 'I knew I recognised that man. The Cuban. Ernesto Che, in his new guise. Killed by the CIA, my eye! O.D.'d on Revolution and took the withdrawal cure in Paris. No wonder he babbles on on conspiracies. The spirit of May Days past, Goddammit, Saint Bartholomews of the future . . .'

'What on earth are you talking about, Asher?' asked Blok.

'An exorcism, comrade!' They scuttled along the deserted streets, reminding Blok of Art Mattock's admonition: 'Salt Lake City? It's the pits, friends. Nothing to do but drag Main Street.' The air was cold and crisp, the sky clear and star studded. They staggered along the walls of the Temple. Twenty-five hundred hours. Asher danced on embers, up South Temple Street, past Brigham Young's Grave, by the Eagle Gate and the base of the compound, quickening his step, towards the forbidden Travel Lodge, across the exclusion zone of the car park, up the side of the reception area, past the postcards and maps and Books of Mormon for sale, $1.00 only: *This Book Can Change Your Life* . . . The poster:

WELCOME TO THE HOME TOWN
OF THE MORMON TABERNACLE CHOIR!

. . . O O Say Can You See,
In the Dawn's Early Light . . .

Climbing up the stairways to the upper floors. A Coca Cola machine at a junction trembles and vibrates on its own. A faint burst of late night television from behind one closed door. The tinny cackle of a laughter track. The hum and click of heating systems. Elsewhere, not a dog nor man howls. No traffic. The Great Salt Lake, like the Dead Sea, lies dormant, fishless and indifferent. By its shores, under the desert moon, the ox–cart pioneers of Brigham Young, 143 men, three women and two children, arrived after unimaginable hardships of drought, oppression and famine into their new Promised Land, three years after the lynching of their Prophet, Joseph Smith, in Missouri. 'Give my love to my children and all my friends,' said the Prophet, before the mob hung him from the nearest tree. Missouri was blessed with woodlands. But the New Land was a bare Canaan, watered by Faith and Solidarity . . . By the waters of Babylon we sat down and wept . . . And from acorns – forests grow! Tall towers and tabernacles of cash and carry and supply. . . Righteousness and Prosperity! Wisdom through Obedience! Freedom of Choice and the Reality of Satan! Prepare Now to Meet God . . .

'This is the door. Number 43 . . .' whispered Asher, remembering the girls collecting their key. He put his ear to it, gesturing Blok forward. Blok added his eardrum to the panel. There were definite human sounds within. Strange intakes of breath, and indefinable choked–off cries.

'Goddammit!' said Asher. He slid a credit card in the lock. 'Should have used this earlier, to book a room,' he hissed. 'We learn too late to use our Access . . . our Mastercharge . . . our Diners Club . . . our American Express . . . our Visa . . .'

The door flipped open. They stood in the doorway, looking in upon, without a doubt, an odd sight: Carl bent, dressed only in his undershirt and scarlet socks, over the room's armchair. His hands handcuffed to a chain wound round the double bed's foot. His face thrust into the groin of Dominique, whose thighs were astride his bound arms, herself unclothed apart from black leather gloves and calf-length black shining boots. Behind Carl, May, in matching black leather, stood, gliding a thonged switch upon the captive's bare buttocks. The usurper's tongue lapping at the raven-haired girl's pubic hair. He looked up with a sly expectation.

'Oh shit,' Dominique said. May swung her arm and drew blood.

'Fuck off,' she said, 'or come in and close the door.'

★ ★ ★ ★
★

'Aaaarghh!'

Sitting on a bench was impossible. They dragged their carcasses along the barren tourist trails of the Tabernacle Tour: 'A True Monument to the Tenacity of an Oppressed People . . . How the Oxen Teams Dragged These Granite Blocks from the Quarries in the Mountains . . . The Pioneers, a Typical Mormon Family with their Ox-cart, Crossing the Inhospitable Lands . . . How Brigham Young chose the Great Salt Lake as the Site of the New Zion . . . The Sea Gull Monument, Marking the Miracle of the Gulls, Who Swooped Down to Save the First Mormon Crop from Swarms of Voracious Crickets . . .' Crick, crick, crick, crick, crick . . . 'the Tabernacle Organ, with its 11,000 Pipes, is said to be the Finest in the World . . .' Olé, olé to the Lord!

Slumped at the gates of the YMCA at five hundred hours (a.m.), they had rushed back to the Travel Lodge at seven thirty to be told (by the impeccable clerk): 'The two ladies checked out early this morning. So did Mister, ah, Gabriel. One o' the ladies left this here for – are you Mister Abrahams?'

> Tough shit, baby [May had written]. Dominique wants to move on, she says she's embarrassed. A girl's gotta live. That's for sure. Just to let you know, what you got as a freebie Carl paid two hundred dollars for. Love and kisses,
>
> May

PS. Here's an address in LA where they'll know where we are. But my advice is – give it a rest for a while.   M.

Aaaargh! They rushed to the Greyhound depot, just missing the schedule, 7.45, to the Angelic City. Stops at Provo, Cedar City Utah, Las Vegas Nevada, Barstow California, San Bernardino and Riverside. Alices escaped down the rabbit hole, with the Hispanic usurper . . .

'And here we have the statue of one of Brigham Young's fifty-seven wives, a typical homey frontier woman . . . and this is the Founder, Brigham Young hisself . . .'

'He looks like Emil Jannings in *Oom Kruger*, Avram,' said Asher bitterly. 'What a farce, Goddammit. The vibrations have got to me, Avram. Yea, verily, the voice of one's brain has e'en now broken through the mush to visit truth upon one's gonads: Goest we to resume our interrupted journey, until we come unto our own Promised Land. San Francisco, verily, Avram, let us not follow the Great Whores of Babylon unto the Gomorrah of our sins! For behold, it shall come to pass, and thine ass will be healed, even unto the lashes thereof, and temptation shall be postponed unto another day, selah, for we have its zip code. And we shall come unto a high place, with many mountains, overlooking the Bay Area, and we shall rest thereby, yea, and wash our feet, and wrap our corns and bunions with plasters, and find a haven with my good friend and Samaritan Joe Silver who dwelleth in the Twin Peaks district. And we shall look upon Fisherman's Wharf and be saved, and walk upon the Embarcadero. And we shall dwell in the House of the Lord, or in the vague neighbourhood, unto the end of our days, or at least until Christmas, whereupon we might set forth once again in our oxen farts towards the city of Dis-Ney . . . Yay. What sayeth thou, Blok?'

Leaving Salt Lake at 1.45 p.m., rumbling west, across Utah. The Great Salt Lake Desert, Skull Valley, the Bonneville Salt Flats, the Lake Wendover Nuclear Testing Grounds, Nevada (no mushroom clouds), desert scrub and brush, a monumental Negev, up through the Pequop Mountains. The desert sunset reddening dry cacti, the travellers twisting and turning in their seats, desperate to avoid bum contact, sliding down to lie leaning

144

on their shoulderblades, unshod feet thrust up and over the top of the seats ahead, with at least the advantage of reversing the flow of blood to already swollen piano ankles –

'Aaaaaahhh!'

'What a view, Avram! What a view!'

Night on Winnemucca, Nevada. Dunes, gliding in the dark. Tungsten, Imlay, the Seven Troughs, the Lava Beds of Pershing County, Ragged Top Peak, Two Tips, Reno. A brief stopover with a couple of halfhearted tugs at the gambling machines. Blok loses fifty cents, Asher two dollars. An apple, a pomegranate, and a pear. 'These fucking things are fixed, Goddammit!' Is there no balm in Gilead? Down, by dead of night and rush of tyres and thrum of eternal combustion, into Californy-ay . . . ! Floriston, Boca, Truckee, Soda Springs, Cisco, Emigrant Gap, Gold Run, Weimar . . . Ah! the bite of the lash, the unsheathed organ (with its 11,000 pipes) . . . the vaginal flower beckoning above, the tongue unrolling to gather pollen (is there a sting in the tale?) . . . in space, no one can hear you cream . . . who needs orgone boxes, comrades???

Sacramento, 3.40 a.m., glazed donuts under transparent plastic covers . . . postcards of a dead frontier . . . Richmond, Oakland, San Francisco . . . a low hush among the exhausted pilgrims, as dawn echoes over the last gasp of Interstate 80, the miracle of the Oakland Bay Bridge – Treasure Island! Yerba Buena! Alcatraz! The white fog rolls majestically across the tangled girders, and the stack of downtown towers, red in the sun, the white pyramid dominating the concrete palaces, with the rising hills, the forest hills, piercing the mists beyond –

And so Blok enters Wonderland, with Asher, who, making a phone booth call from the Bus Terminal, plucks him out of the Greyhound womb, by caesarian section, into a taxi ride to Valhalla: to Diamond Street, up vertical roads, plunging down the other side, the urban roller coaster of bucking asphalt flanked by lifesize dolls' houses, the landscape disappearing and then bursting into view at the crest of a junction, Ooh, Aaah, Goddammit, Avram, have you ever seen anything like it in your life?! The welcoming grin of Joe Silver, Asher's local friend of many moons past, a jovial bearded Orson Wellesian giant, ex-cinematographer and now proprietor of the Roxie Hart Cinema, as he showed them to into their quarters in the basement of his house on the hillside, in fact a ground floor by the time the hill dipped sharply down the back yard, from which they climbed a steel ladder up to the french windowed kitchen, overlooking the full city panorama across Mission and downtown, past the Bay Bridge nestling through its islands, to Alameda, Oakland, Berkeley, as far as the eye can glow . . . 'Did you have an unbelievable journey? You must be absolutely whipped . . .' 'Ah, Joe, the all seeing eye . . .' And the collapse upon twin mattresses set out below, beneath bird sounds . . . 'If you feel a cold nose nuzzling your neck, it's the raccoons. There's a family around. They don't bite, but they might slobber . . .'

Verily, the New Zion! the toytown charm outside time: the fog rolling by the suspension bridges, the foghorn warnings, the climbing and descending buses and streetcars, the cable cars and Chinatown, Nob Hill and Russian Hill and Telegraph Hill and North Beach and Japantown, long walks down 24th Street, past Castro and Noe and Sanchez and Church and Dolores and Guerrero to Mission and the bustle of Latino streetlife, and vast naive murals depicting the people in all their multicoloured splendour, the Mission Gift Shop and Smile BBQ, Botanica Yoruba, Grand Cinema, the Tower (Hoy: Julio Aleman en *Vacaciones de Terror*), La Quinta Mexican Food and Los Andes Supermarket and the Don Quijote Restaurant, the blue and red tiled squares of the pavement and down the wide red pavement of Market with its streetcars preserved from another age, past the Chun Kung Fu Academy of Self-Defense and Ben Frank's Classic American Hot Dog, and up and down the Haight-Ashbury with its hazy memories of unwashed psychedelic glory, and ersatz head shops and beggars and monologuists of the streets recounting the meaning of life to stray dogs and shops selling junk and occult goods, run by survivors of lost chemical battles vending mummy dust and rattlesnake saliva and love potions and jinx oil and dead homunculi in bottles. And down the Tenderloin with its Live Shows and Hard Core offers, See And Talk To A Nude Girl for $1, *Born To Raise Hell, Lube Job, Oriental Blue, The Infidel* . . . At the Market

146

Street Thoroughfare, at 5th, by the jazz band, panhandlers and chess players, a dour and unkempt girl tried to puncture his bubble by pressing into his paw a photostatted handwritten message:

There is death in jail!
 Keep yourself free —
 no matter what frequency you on!
Move East!
 The bomb will drop on the West
 Portland Oregon — danger spot —
Police department are destroying people!
Robots working as cops
 Are too many —
 Move East
 Never prove — be yourself
 you have been warned

But even this failed to damp his spirits as he wandered on up to Chinatown with its Buddhist temple shaped banks and miracle restaurants and Sam Wo's and X-rated fortune cookies and Chinese kites and Ronald Reagan dolls and the cinemas showing unsubtitled Hong Kong films in Shawscope: 'LOVERS' DESTINY: Chiao Yi is the proprietor of a curio shop in Macao and Ah Kuei has a second hand clothes shop; Chiao Yi has an eye for Ah Kuei, although he has an attractive wife, Ah Lan; meanwhile Ho Ta, a clever gambler, has won the love of the charming

147

Gerry, a gamester in a Macao casino whom he takes to his bedroom . . .' But Blok does not require exegesis. He has at last found True Love with the city of his dreams . . . Basking daily and nightly in its peacock preening, the eternal grooming of its scarlet and turquoise and jade and topaz feathers, e'en unto the down and outs, befurred prostitutes, the gay swathe of Castro, moustached musclemen clones, camaraderie and easy come easy go, despite the first glimmers in the winter of disasters yet to strike home . . . 'This is the City of the Sixties, friends, what can I tell you,' Joe Silver rolls a slice of raw yellowfish towards his smacking lips, 'Ah! Tokyo! Who needs it, when we can have it all here!' Kimono-clad waitresses offering boards of fresh sushi with the most exquisite of bows, while he reviews his planned programme for the Roxie Hart Cinema's Christmas Season: All Night Laurel and Hardy shorts, Chaplin's *Limelight* (Bring Your Own Kleenex), *Johnny Guitar*, Marx Brothers Marathon (*Coconuts*, *Animal Crackers*, *Horse Feathers*, *Duck Soup*, *Monkey Business*), *Kind Hearts and Coronets*, *The Ladykillers*, and a Robert Mitchum retrospective: 'The best girls come to Robert Mitchum retrospectives. You'll have to pardon me if I skulk off more often than not upstairs afterwards. You don't know what it is to be an available hetero-sexual male in the Bay Area . . .' Joe Silver was divorced, and had a teenage son, whom he met occasionally in the Golden Gate Park, for discussions on astro-engineering, baseball and available posts at Francis Coppola's Zoetrope Company. 'Yes, this is where its all happening . . .' Christmas looming a few days away, and the sun still shining brightly on tinsel bedecked streets and strange figures in red and cotton wool beards clanging bells and going Ho, Ho, Ho. Noel, Noel, Jingle All The Way, the temperature stopping around 68 fahrenheit, 20 degrees centigrade, and Blok and Asher performing marathon walks about town, playing Wac-The-Mole on Fisherman's Wharf and watching the jugglers, the one-wheeled bike rider, the man who snatches bananas out of thin air, ogling the girls in the cafés but with no obligation, then proceeding, along the harbour, spurning Alcatraz through a telescope, past the massed tinkling fishing boats, through the Marina, to the vast Presidio Park, climbing past Fort Point and goggling at the Golden Gate (no sign of a vertiginous James Stewart or a

148

transformed Kim Novak), round to the cliff forest of pines and cypresses thrust back towards the cliff by the winds, the Pacific Ocean pounding at the beach and the rocks and islets thrusting out of the sea, taking out their thermos flask and sandwiches below the sign declaring:

CAUTION! CLIFF AND SURF AREA EXTREMELY DANGEROUS. PEOPLE HAVE BEEN SWEPT FROM THE ROCKS AND DROWNED.

Death, where is thy sting?

Small wooden tables and benches hammered into the slopes. White foam cascading over the jagged rocks two hundred yards below. On a black drenched outcrop a seal rears up and barks. Blok barks back.

'Avram, you seem to be happy,' said Asher.

'Yes,' said Blok. 'I want to sit, and grow old, and die on this spot.'

No past, and no future, and outside of all history, and cut away from all umbilical cords. The remaining Ameripass vouchers put away. No return to Salt Lake City, Brooklyn, London, or further East, despite the direst warnings. Let the Bomb fall where it may. Let the City of the Angels wait too, with its fulfilled wet dreams. Let me be jest an' ole beachcomber, shufflin' along, pickin' seashells among the pebbles an' mutterin' to meself. Me skull'n'crossbones whitenin' here, me hearties. Me timbers shivered, in Popeyeland. No spinach, please, shipmates.

But this, too, was not to be . . .

THE SECOND FALL

The Vortex (III):

The Gods gathered, at the Holiday Inn, Memphis, determined to deny Blok his sanctuary. Everybody who was anybody was there. Ptah and Atum occupied the George Washington and the Thomas Jefferson Suites, while the rest of the Egyptian contingent, Horus, Isis, Nephhthys, Hiqait, Amun, Thoth, Shu, Tefnut, Nut, Geb, Osiris and Set, accompanied by their butler, Khnum, took over the seventeenth floor 'Grandstand' complex. The Sumerians Nannar, Enki, Enlil, Ninkhursag and An, and the Assyrians, Apsu, Tiamat and their son Mummu, shared the sixteenth and fifteenth floors with the Babylonians Ea and Marduk and the ubiquitous Tammuz, who had locked himself in with the latest copy of *The Hollywood Reporter*. The Indian contingent had the fourteenth to the tenth floors, and the Greeks lazily strummed their bouzouki on the ninth and eighth storeys. Odin, Wotan and Thor, in the gymnasium, worked out with a Soft Drinks group from Winston-Salem, North Carolina, who were en route to a Seltzer Convention in Oklahoma City. A great deal of confusion was rife at the front desk due to the large numbers of double identities: Horus doubling as Apollo in a room on the Greek floor, Shiva dashing between floors to become Dionysus, Zeus maintaining a room in the 'Grandstand' as Amun, Varuna being Mithra and vice versa, Krishna slipping his mask to double as Heracles, and the lady Ninkhursag keeping a vast array of suites as Astarte, Artemis, Demeter, Aphrodite, Isis, Inanna, Venus, and so on. Her dazzling costumes turned the heads of every bellboy and maid, as they struggled to glean the nature of the conclave from the large banner strung up in the Marinette Hall:

153

WELCOME, MASTERS AND MISTRESSES
OF THE UNIVERSE!

Whispered gossip in corridors and basements: Was it a convention of toy makers, leisure marketing strategists, or did the wan and waxed look of many of the participants call for a sleazier explanation? 'Didja see that dame with the snakes in her hair? Man, that sure did look fucking real.' 'Weird stuff, bro.' 'You said it, man. An' cats flying about on the roof?' 'Those ugly mean little mother fuckers with forked tails an' horns?' 'Weird, man. An' that sweet lookin' dude who checked in an' asked for the stables.' 'What will they think of next?'

The Central Politburo met in Ptah's quarters, having ordered the Valley Forge breakfast, skillet eggs, grilled rye bread and bacon, communal coffee pot, no cream. Present were Vishnu, Varuna/Mithra, Marduk, Isis/Demeter, Shiva, Adonis, Zeus, Gaia, and the Monster Eel of Polynesia, Te Tuna, otherwise known as the Phallus Which Does Not Wither. Jehovah, crying off with a migraine, sent his regrets. No one had seen him since the gathering began, anyway.

'I hope you have all slept well,' said Ptah, ever courteous, flicking rye crumbs from his knee.

'Those fucking Greeks kept up an infernal din till the small hours,' said Marduk, massaging the rings round his eyes. 'Can't they squabble quietly? *Malakas* this, *malakas* that, all the bloody night long. And do they have to break every plate in the place?'

'It's our love of life, baby,' said Zeus, winking. 'We have our reputation to think of.'

'And then someone turned on the swimming pool muzak,' said Vishnu, 'just as we were getting settled. Five thirty a.m., Goddammit! I rang the management, but they were no help at all.'

Te Tuna did not reveal that he had eaten the General Manager, at three a.m., followed as dessert by the Chaplain on Call, the Reverend James C. Abernathy. His eyes looked beadily on the minuscule Elvis Presley, slumped in a bottle at Ptah's side, but the Creator-Deity was massaging his toy with his obsidian taloned claws.

'Boys! Girls! Let's not quibble on details. We have a number of

154

reports to produce. We have a great many terms to define and redefine, and several languages and belief systems to review and debug before we can come to grips with the zeitgeist, poor mangled creature that it may be. Market research. Redirecting Input and Output. Changing Directories. Filtering. Piping. Making sure no mortal escapes his fate. That's our task, like it or lump it, comrades. Not all eternity can be fun.'

The Reverend Abernathy hammered in vain at the inner lining of Te Tuna's stomach. The minuscule Elvis jerked on invisible strings, strumming a selection on his tiny guitar. I ain't nothin' but a hauwnd dawg. Sighs reverbrated about the George Washington Suite, spreading a sombre mood throughout the Inn, afflicting even the Jains who had smoked themselves into the Ocean of Clarified Butter, and the Incarnations of Whirlwinds, the Jungle Sprites, the Rakshasas and Fire Deities, the copulating Vedic couples, the Buddha, startled out of parinirvana, the Nipponese Spirit Master of the August Center of Heaven, who had thought he was way past mere neurotic depression, and even the Sun God Ra, whose human disciple, Nathan Bloom, alias Adonai the Avatar, was at that moment licking the webs between his toes and adoring every spot on his golden, burning skin. The ruling class cannot evade its responsibilities. A God's gotta do what a God's gotta do.

'OK,' said Ptah, 'let's discuss Avram Blok.'

He passed round copies of the file.

*

Dear A & A,

Hey there, folks! glad to hear you're grooving on San Francisco. I once spent three weeks there non-stop in a bathhouse fifty feet underground, but that's another story. Not your tipple and a sadder prospect alas these days. Just when you think you've achieved something you're tipped back in the shit again. But no bad vibes, comrades! You've found your Promised Land! Don't overdo the sashimi. There's an Edward Hopper retrospective at the Museum of Art, but I expect that is not your bag either. Just cruise on! (If you see any strange behaviour on Strawberry Hill just don't say I didn't warn you!) Over here everything is as normal. I evicted Aladdin and he camped out in the street, accusing me of stealing his passport. Orlando and Clara eventually swept him off my sidewalk, so I now sleep a little better at nights. The Haitians suddenly returned while I was away and left again, leaving me an eight-foot-high Burmese pot plant. Shall I send it on by Greyhound Cargo? Only kidding, *mes enfants*. The Jesuit has left! Zounds! Sapristi! He says he has business in California, some new activity in Silicon Valley. Beware! He may be headed your way. And where he heads, headlines follow! He's dyed his false beard red, for a change. You made a great impression on him. He said you were the first beatnik Israelis he'd met. In fact you were the first beatniks of any kind he's met since at least 1960. How's it feel to be genuine fossils? I had a letter from Jacqueline. She is back at the Gates of Hell, née Cheetham. The charges against her were dropped by the Chief Constable whose foot she nearly crushed. Perhaps a dash of Christmas Goodwill in the heart of the Police State! But she says she may head back West in the spring to join a new locus of the war for peace, in New Mexico. A group in a place called Truth or Consequences (no kidding!), not far from the White Sands Missile Range. So maybe you two can detour later on and see the cacti and the amazing Indian caves. Keep hold of your senses! What with Ronnie Reagan announcing he's running again for Big Chief (Surprise! Surprise!) and pledging his commitment to East-West dialogue, you'd think the New Age has finally dawned. Me, I'll stay put for a while, teaching my frum Flatbush students useless knowledge about the Songhai Empire and the destruction of Timbuktu. At least I've got rid of Pedro too, back with his rightful owner! Wheee!

Yo-de-li, yo-de-lay! Love,

Art

P.S. Give my love to the Castro and all who cruise in her . . . ah, days of wine and roses . . . *a salaam aleikum.*

'Further options,' said Zervan Akarana (the Boundless Time), shaking his coiffured mane, extracting a new page from his folio, 'Dreams. Always an efficacious mechanism, though open to perverse responses. Sightings of Immigration Officials. Doorstep inquiries, that sort of thing. Ditto, random approaches in the streets by prophets of doom and homicidal maniacs. Threats of mutilation, castration, amputation of limbs, blinding with acid, gang rape. A sudden incomprehensible outbreak of Guilt, brought on by some further correspondence, a news broadcast concerning troubles at "home", newspaper headlines, grocery store rumours. A plague of domestic disasters: eviction from the sanctuary of Diamond Street, tetanus via raccoon bites, locusts, frogs, blood foaming from floorboards, pus from walls, an infestation of spiders, dry rot, jock rot, urinal infection, crabs, other STDs (various), fleas, lice, neighbours with new sixty-watt speakers and a collection of reggae discs, next-door loft conversion, major sewage works, a family with small children moving in, or a deaf Johnny Carson fan, major rifts developing with his travelling companion, over-use of toothbrush, other utensils, the playing of transistor radios or walkmans, or a relationship with a third party. Sudden public cataclysms, ethnic unrest, riots, income tax and immigration raids, serial murders, typhoons, floods, earthquakes, fires, rebellions, mass epidemics, invasion from enemy nations or outer space, demonic infestation, Armageddon, nuclear war, the Last Judgement.'

Moderate applause. There was a break, while the Queen of the Underworld, Persephone, performed an old Dean Martin number, 'Amore', accompanied by Krishna's Gopis on kazoos. The meeting then adjourned for lunch (southern clambake or chicken gumbo with pecan pie, the manna machine being broken again), buzzing with polite anticipation of the afternoon's offers, a paper to be delivered by Tezcatlipoca, the Dark Brother of Quetzalcoatl, the Plumed Serpent, on 'Hallucinatory Principles In the Blok Saga, Some Observations On Psychic Supply and Demand', another by Osiris, in his human form as King Men-Kau-Ra, on 'The Elders of Zion – Myth Or Myopia', and a keynote address by Dionysus (if sober) on 'Nietzsche, The Eternal Recurrence As Manifested in Situation Comedy'. In the lobby, a scuffle erupts

157

between Beelzebub, the Canaanite deity, and Jehovah, just emerged from his long sulk to try and fix the manna machine. Held back by the mighty sinews of Thor, Jehovah spits abuse at his rival: 'Turd! Vermin! Fink! Arsehole! Just wait till I get you alone!' 'Wanna step outside? Wanna step outside? Let's do it.' Wotan restrains Beelzebub with a half nelson . . . It was going to be a tiring millennial decennium, even if it did not last, in cosmic time, the thirty-five billion years the Vedic divines had cheerfully forecast . . .

★

'I need the house,' Joe Silver informed them, with an expansive shrug. 'Mary, my wife and I, are having another go at the matrimonial tombola. We are going to require space around us. At least two thousand versts, with fitted minefields. I have to give you one week to vacate, before ah start blastin'. Sorry folks, but that's the law of the West . . .'

They had been watching Tex Avery revivals, in a season of the Golden Age of Forties' Hollywood mounted by Joe at the Roxie Hart Cinema. MGM and Warner Brothers Cartoons, black and white Hitchcock, 'film noir': Dmytryk, Farrow, Tournier, Val Lewton, *I Walked With a Zombie*, Welles, *Kane* and *The Lady From Shanghai*, *The Postman Always Knocks Twice*, *Double Indemnity*, John Ford's *The Grapes of Wrath*. And a special late night show: the selected work of Irving Klotskashes, king of the Z-movie feature . . . *SLIME! (Invasion of the Giant Snails)*, *The Martian Bolsheviks*, *Blood! Blood Blood!*, *Beast of Bataan*, and *Bebopaloola From Beyond the Stars* . . .

'Ah, yes, Irving Klotskashes . . .' Blok was thrown back to Jerusalem of one decade before. 'That must be the same man I met in the madhouse: The unfinished Judas Pig movie . . .' Shades of Christmas past at the Klander Asylum's cinematherapy programme, the coming of Klotskashes and his erratic film crew, and the fire which cut short the first week of filming, gutting the asylum in the Great Judas Pig Cataclysm of 1974 . . . Ah, those old calcified days . . .

'The unfinished film, about the asylum ghost – yes, we've heard of that,' said Joe Silver. 'The man is said to have some surviving cans locked in his safe at his Big Sur retreat. He lives in a house on the cliff, overlooking the Pacific breakers and the migrating whales . . . the Moby Dick of shlock . . . I tried to get him out of his retirement once, to speak at a late-night triple bill, but no way. A disappointment to his fans, but what can you do? Why don't you go there, Avram, up the coast, to Big Sur, with your harpoon, and tease the beast out for our show?'

'No, thanking you,' Blok said. He did not wish to stir the past, the present being a potent enough brew, given their imminent eviction from Eden. 'Maybe we can get a job in town . . . get some cash, so we can afford to rent an apartment . . .' Hold on, somehow, by the skin of their teeth . . .

But Asher received, out of the blue, a letter from Jane Springs in London:

Hey there, you bastards, got away from the cold and the rain, eh? You've probably done the right thing. The weather is absolutely pissing and frozen, you wouldn't even put a dog out. Lucky I'm trapped in my cell. Negative cutting does sound like the perfect metaphor for the brave new Thatcher world. Well. The poor old Film College hasn't reopened. Henry Gibson is still hanging on, hoping for a last-minute reprieve or at least a stay of execution. He says he hopes to get the ball rolling in April. Meanwhile you should fry on in hell. It can't be any worse than this hole. I'm seriously thinking of calling it a day and taking the assisted passage back to the koala bears. The enclosed letter arrived for you from Los Angeles, from the friend that you wrote to some months ago. It must have crossed yours. At any rate, he seems to have changed his address, so this should help you find him, if you still want to. You don't know how pissed off I am that you're there and I'm here, but what the hell. The world's wanderers. See you boys sometime, somewhere.

Jane

'Can you interpret this?' Asher shoved it in Blok's face. 'Nothing about love and romance. Nothing about the nuclear war. No

159

politics. No sociology. Gurnischt. Go understand these antipodeans. That's what comes of being born upside down . . .' But
the enclosed letter seemed to give him food for thought, which he
consumed, crumb by crumb, in the basement, a wicker fly swatter
at hand, to guard, unnecessarily due to winter hibernation, against
the slobbering raccoon. The early March mist, rolling in the
Golden Gate Bridge, creeping across Marin County, Sausalito and
the redwoods. The cheerful clanging cable cars. The happy going
unlucky cruisers of Castro. How time flies when you are just
marking it, allowing your nest egg to dwindle slowly on Biaggi's
Pizza and Herb's Fine Foods and take-away enchiladas, living on
the kindness of strangers, a dead Christmas long slipped by . . .

'My old friend Doron, in LA,' explained Asher, 'another colleague from Neanderthal times, having succesfully crawled
through the Palaeozoic to the New Age, karma remounted. He
has been camera operating on several Independent projects. He
lives at the north end of Fairfax, not a bad part of the town. Offers
of temporary housing, job opportunities to be explored . . .
Wha'd'you say, Avram? We've overstayed our welcome in this
pretty pretty town, and there are no brethren here to teach
Hebrew when the chips are finally down. So what can we do? The
nest egg is dwindling. We can't sell Redwood Dreidles on Market
or third-hand pseudo-religions, or be waiters at leather gay discos,
now, can we?'

'I suppose not,' said Blok.

'Time to move on,' Asher declared. 'Who knows, we might
even run into the whiplash ladies out there . . . Not to speak of
getting close to Truth or Consequences. Play, Avram, play upon
the dreams . . .'

The Gods, working their mischief. The siren call of Klotskashes
Land . . . There did not seem to be any choice, for the moment,
apart from a retreat to the East. Blok wandered out towards the
beach, on his own, treading the wide swathe of sand stretching
south from the Cliff House, below Sutro Heights, parallel lines
converging in the far distance, a vast emptiness hanging above
him like a grey vulture's wing, a sense of freedom, which
had touched him for a brief interval, fading. He wandered again
down the Hispanic realm of Mission, watching the strange

cloaked figures with their dogs, the ebullient housewives, the dry cleaning emporiums and taco bars, the garish colouring of life's eccentricities – but he had become a tourist again.

Go, man, go!

They took the 6.00 a.m. schedule, which would allow for maximum daytime travel and arrival in daylight, a night arrival judged too lethal to survive without an armoured pick-up car. Joe Silver, making the sign of the cross over them as he ushered them on board the bus, remaining in paradise while they were driven away, back across the San Francisco Bay Bridge in the spring fog, down the trail of unwaked Oakland, past Fruitvale and San Leandro Bay, up on to Highway 580, across the Altamont Pass . . . Asher studiously ignoring the view as he settled down with the *Archeologie du Savoir* (his earlier expressed ambition, to read Wittgenstein's *Tractatus Logico-Philosophicus* on the bus, having been dropped in favour of completing Foucault): '*Do you think that I would keep so persistently to my task were I not preparing – with a rather shaky hand – a labyrinth into which I can venture, in which I can move my discourse, opening up underground passages, forcing it to go far from itself . . . I am no doubt not the only one who writes in order to have no face. Do not ask who I am and do not ask me to remain the same: leave it to our bureaucrats and our police to see that our papers are in order . . .*'

Yea! Past Modesto, Turlock, Livingston, Merced, Chowchilla, Madera, Herndon, Fresno, Bakersfield, San Fernando, North Hollywood . . . the contours of round, familiar hills, shadows of a true déjà vu from a thousand and one visual sittings, sunflowerseed mornings at forgotten, fan cooled, creaky seated, flickery projection Levantine halls . . . a knowledge that has no archaeology, a connaissance with no savoir –

'This is it, Avram! This is it!'

The Dream! The Dream! Enter Klotskashes Land, the true minotaur's cave, leave your strings at the door – Los Angeles, man! Can you believe it? The Source, Avram, the Source! The elevation of the bizarre into the commonplace which pervades the entire world. The true motherlode of abundance and plenty: plenty o' money, plenty o' sun, plenty o' suntan, plenty o' space, plenty o' wheels, plenty o' asphalt, plenty o' signs, plenty o'

161

billboards, plenty o' hopes, plenty o' despair, plenty o' bullshit, dogshit, poodle parlours, pooch halls an' petoramas, nightlife, crime, law enforcement, personal defence and armed response, plenty o' rich an' plenty o' poor, nosh houses, lounges, saloons, hofbraus an' taco stalls, burger joints, steak'n'chop house grills, rib rooms, pubs, doggie diners, gardens, casas 'n' inns, mama gruber's 'n' pumpernickel cellars 'n' mrs knott's chicken dinner 'n' little joe's 'n' homes o' the stars 'n' the Universal City Studio Tour, yea, check yore baby strollers at the Courtesy Desk, tour Natalie Wood's dressing room 'n' visit at Womphopper's Wagon Works, the West's most famous wagon wheeler-dealer, we got burgers, steaks, chicken, ribs, salads, fish, sandwiches an' the world's best chili, plus the West's widest saloon selections an' the wompinest, stompinest country-western sounds **an'** footshakin' entertainment – bring yore family, friends 'n' neighbours, an' if anyone leaves hawngry, ah'll kiss a rattlesnake! Not to speak of Disneyland! Plastic dinosaurs in a papier-mâché prehistory, plastic hippopotami baring plastic teeth in ersatz swamps, plastic bears strum and yodel, hologram ghosts gibber, plastic polynesian birds and totem poles sing, a plastic Abe Lincoln recurs eternally, in a Nietzschean time trap, and plastic pirates lean from the riggings of ersatz ships firing blanks at plastic trippers, Blok and Asher among them, squealing in childlike abandonment, fixed in the new mould –

'Yo ho! Yo ho! A pirate's life for me . . .'

'Fucking A, Avram! Fucking A!'

Tomorrowland belongs to us . . .

(Ze process iss bekinnink to vork, Igor! Increase ze power zu Level Acht!)

Rescuing them from the Los Angeles Greyhound Terminal, Asher's compatriot, Doron Kolchak, whisked them out of the lethal quadrangle of Downtown, up the Harbour Freeway and on towards Santa Monica Boulevard and the human face of West Hollywood, off the Jewish luxo-ghetto of Fairfax Avenue, where, in the garden of a small, cloned, two-storey bungalow, they were welcomed by Doron's wife, Nehama, with cold papaya juice and cheese pops, while their two offspring, Eli and Anat, squabbled within over Action Man SWAT teams in a mixture of Hebrew and

English, with half an eye for some ubiquitous glove puppets desperately leaping about to get their attention from the television screen . . .

. . . Good to see you, man! . . . It's been a long time . . . Had a good trip? Yes, the Greyhound is murder . . . We got the spare room ready . . . hope the kids won't drive you mad . . . It'll be good to have familiar faces around, Nehama feels isolated sometimes . . . this certainly isn't Tel Aviv . . . Do you remember . . . ? And how's so and so . . . ? Herzliya Studios . . . ? And what happened to Adir Kokashvili . . . ? And those documentaries of yours, Asher . . . The way we were, the way we were . . . but I'm more optimistic now . . . we've progressed here . . . although Nehama . . . it's a problem . . . but there are some projects that we can discuss . . . I've made a few good contacts so far . . . of course, you have to watch your step . . . too many Israelis have tried to conquer Hollywood, they think it's run by Jewish money . . . but, as you know, money has no religion . . . everybody sells, everybody buys . . . so they end up running shawarma concessions . . . living on the aromas of home . . . of course there's always hard core . . . it seems the king of that here now is a strange Christian Palestinian with an Irish Arab name: Liam O'Habash . . . does that ring any bells?

Ding, ding, ding. 'Wasn't that the man who used to sell dirty postcards in Jaffa Road . . . ?' Another time, another place again. Who can remember all those false starts, those pastoramas, dud realities? 'In America,' said Doron, 'every shmuck can be a king.' His two offspring ran onto the lawn, screaming, Eli having grabbed a toy flamethrower from his little sister's hand.

'Snatch, snatch, snatch, take, take, take,' said Nehama. 'We might as well have stayed in Bat Yam.'

'The Homeland,' Doron reminisced bitterly. 'Running on the hills with khaki and pouches, killing and being killed. Not for me.'

'At least there you get killed for something,' said Nehama, 'even if you don't believe in it. Here you can just get killed for nothing, if a kid high on some rubbish doesn't happen to like your face, or just if a policeman panics . . .'

'Well, that's more cost effective,' said Doron.

'What's life, anyway?' said Asher. 'We give birth astride of a

163

grave, the light gleams for an instant, then it's night once more. Samuel Beckett,' he explained.

'No one waits for Godot here,' said Doron. 'If he don't show, that's his problem. The party goes on without him.'

'What happened to your ex-wife,' Nehama asked Asher, trying another tack, 'the Scots girl?'

'Janet? She is still in the media.'

'I liked her, she was very nice.'

'Everyone liked Janet. Including me. But you can't build your life on affection.'

'What can you build it on?' Nehama asked.

'Quicksand. That way you have no illusions.'

'Asher, you're as cynical as ever,' said Nehama, sighing. 'Don't you believe in anything at all?'

'The Second Coming of Trotsky,' said Asher. 'I have seen it written in the stars, in fortune cookies and on Bazooka Bubble Gum wrappers.'

'We have already done that in this town,' said Doron. 'It was called *Reds*, with Warren Beatty. We saw that at Grauman's Chinese, remember, honey? Bad direction, good editing.'

'Here everything gets swallowed up,' said Nehama. 'They would make a movie of our garbage, if they thought it would make money.'

Nehama was not happy in Los Angeles. It was not her idea of a haven. The bare, pedestrianless labyrinthine streets stretching for miles and miles. Infinite lines on a grid with no beginning and no end. The car ride to the grocery store, the newspaper stand or the automatic laundry. The vast, dangerous car parks of the shopping malls. The legless kingdom of wheels.

'But what can I do?' she confided in Blok one evening, as he helped her with the washing up, while Asher and Doron rolled joints in the front room, with the offspring (hopefully) in bed. 'We couldn't face the thought of the kids growing up only to go into the armed forces, breeding cannon fodder for the Jewish Wars. And this was long before Lebanon. Doron came out of the October War by just this margin. He had been a cameraman and his jeep hit a mine. I sat there by his hospital bed watching him and myself becoming icons in someone else's warped creed. The wounded soldier and the caring, grieving wife . . . But it's true, I miss it more than he . . .' While Doron moved about the State of California, taking moving pictures, she did some part-time work in the nearby Fairfax Senior Citizens' Leisure Center, in which elderly Jews played chess and backgammon and practised yoga and satori, attended by foot-massage specialists and signing up for bi-weekly Talmud lessons. Nehama had obtained an unofficial degree in homoeopathic therapy. 'Natural things. I know it's a cliché in this city, but wherever one can do something . . . Still, it's a strain, praying I won't find stashes of pills hidden under my kids' pillows. Only the other day the police caught a gang of eight-year-olds robbing a bank in Pasadena. They had four pistols and an Uzzi submachine gun. Madness, Avram, everywhere . . .'

Family life. The lure of domesticity, even under this harsh/ benign familiar/unfamiliar sun, this lush flipped Western mirror of the parched East from whence he came (or was that someone else entirely, platzing on the scorched levantine earth?). The warm attractions of normality, of mundane worries and cares: taking the kids to and from school and fixing the meals and arranging the home help and driving to and from work and juggling the weekly budget and going to or entertaining friends. The rent, the payments on the car, pensions, income tax, insurance. All that had always seemed to him a living death. But he had nothing to offer.

He travelled with Asher to search for the address left him on May's Salt Lake City note. But they could not locate the two wandering women. Taking the staggeringly misnamed Rapid Transit bus down Venice Boulevard, mile upon mile past low, flat buildings and tall, wide billboards and revolving petrol station signs to Muscle Beach, Venice, with its ersatz canals, its murals of itself in imagined snow, its body cult men and women, black kids breakdancing to their ghettoblasters, winos trading bottles in brown paper, would-be writers capturing it all in notebooks, they trekked up to a small house off Cabrillo Avenue, where a pair of muscle-bound gay clones, preening on the lawn, informed them the girls had had an apartment there but had moved to a hotel off Hollywood Boulevard, they did not know which. They offered to take the two boys' address to pass on in case of contact and 'come up an' see us sometime'. Their shining brown pectorals winked, nudged. Another place, another world . . .

Blok began examining the Personal Classified Ads in the Los Angeles X-rated press, poring over **'Punishment Miss: Foxy w/f loves to strap and tan your naked ass red hot. Obey Miss Stephanie',** or **'I am for real, no ripoff, I am your fantasy girl, I will wrestle you to the floor with my luscious body B & D or I will step all over you with my 5" black spiked heels'** or **'We Give Good Phone – two freaky ladies, leather mistresses seek obedient slaves for verbal service, 213–677– 60---'** . . . **'Hustlers – Outcall Massage: Young girls who really hurry to your home, office, motel room. They're pretty, but who cares? Turn 'em upside down, they all look the same. Fun lovin' broads out to make a couple of bucks by making you feel good!'** Taking in **'Doped Chewing Gum Nuggets: FRANTIC POTION works instantly on younger women, makes them frantic to suck and they will LOVE IT! 12 for $5. (Not aphrodisiac) Mexican Joe, 256 South Robertson, Beverly Hills . . .'**

'Brek-kek-kek-kek, kek-kek . . .'

'Forget it, Avram,' Asher said. 'Your brain will turn to mush, your eyes will fall out and your marrow will begin to leak. They're probably with that freak, Carl, whoever he may be . . .'

Another soul vanished in the gargantuan maw of the city of fallen angels and mobile succubi. Lost in the mess of oblique legends and phantasms of fake nirvanas on offer twenty-four hours: The Living Ek, the Maharishi, the Unification Church of Sung Yung Moon, the Scientologists of L. Ron Hubbard, the Sons of David, the Sons of Ra (and was Henry Gibson's poor lost son devouring his mealie meal somewhere in one of those ersatz pagodas, stupas, ashrams, ziggurats, shrines?). **I Am Guru – Who Are You?** (Who, indeed?) **I Am The Living Truth In Yourself, Beneath The Confusion And Anxieties Of The Troublesome Person You Mistakenly Call I . . .**

Second Comings!! 'Yes,' said Doron. 'You name it, we have it here. The joy of simple prejudices without the accompanying need to test 'em in revolutions and wars. Do you know the Elders of Zion live right here in Fairfax, or at least nine out of the ten? A

166

sweet hippie chick I met at the laundromat told me that the other day. Apparently they've retired from active service, given up on the Messiah and the world. One runs a fish shop on the corner of Drexel. Another has a car hire firm on Wilshire Boulevard. One does astrology, another acupuncture, another shampoos and clips pet poodles. One sells pineapples in Farmer's Market. Three of them play in the local klezmer. I've also heard they run the mortuary business. So perhaps they're not doing too bad.'

'And the tenth?' asked Blok, holding his exotic beverage, which Nehama had fixed in her cocktail shaker, for the Sunday garden pow-wow, relaxing in the glorious spring sun, end of a week spent not only fruitlessly chasing bondage, but visiting Disneyland and Universal City Studios, not to speak of Asher's incursions with Doron into the Public Broadcasting Services, in search of more concrete deliverance, a hope of daily bread to come . . . But Blok, leaving the two technicians to it, had walked about the unwalkable streets, up Laurel Avenue towards Santa Monica Boulevard, and further north, to the startled, even outraged gaze of the native motorists zooming by, perambulating up Sunset Boulevard, an ant which has lost its column, below the giant billboards of the Strip, the palm trees and hanging gardens, immense electric hamburgers and gargantuan lingerie, the fifty-foot woman ever poised to attack, the amazing colossal man, the stars and starlets of the silver screen, the invitations to live shows, dead shows, light shows, amateur nude contests (male and female), topless bars, close encounters of the nerd kind, trudging hour after hour, as through quicksand, towards the tat of Hollywood proper, the paving stone stars polished by volunteer fans, the cinema palaces and make-believe towers, the foot and hand-prints of the great in cement, and shawarma bars and comic book and fan mag emporiums, ten cent Donald Ducks for fifteen dollars, gosh, how time flies . . . and the grim Hispanics waiting round corners, under the iconic mountain sign . . . Who loves ya, baby? The sun, beating down on his bare head, scrambling already scrambled brains, the sheer confusion and fatigue of signs and wonders, ersatz miracles and dead ends . . .

'The tenth what?' asked Nehama.

'The tenth Elder of Zion,' said Blok. 'Irving Klotskashes, your famous shlock director now retired in Big Sur. Everybody knew about it in the Asylum.'*

The three Israelis looked at him anxiously.

'You're blending too well with the city, Avram,' said Asher. 'As your astrologer, I advise caution.' He raised his glass with its purplish blue liquid, pleased with the previous Friday's meeting of minds over possible film projects with Doron, primarily, a PBS documentary on the Indians of the San Manuel Reservation (Then and Now), and a latent project on the anti-nuke movement's planned protest at the New Mexico testing sites, a possible link-up with the Jesuit and Jacqueline, later in the year . . . A genuine potential Return for Asher from the pit of has-beenhood . . .

'Down the hatch!'

Blok falls, clutching at straws. Sliding down the rabbit hole of his lost ghosts, fatigue, moral exhaustion, lassitude, the weariness of a purposeless quest, the snapped, writhing umbilical cords . . . While Eli and Anat, behind their parents' backs, pop their blue and red pills and, up above, in their post-convention satellite orbiting the earth, the Gods (Ptah, Osiris, Jehovah and all the gang) peer jaggedly through the countless shards of space debris and cosmonaut skeletons, cocking their thumbs up at Blok's turmoil and the inexorable progress of their Plan:

Increase ze fluence zu Level Elf!

---

*The Elders of Zion, according to the inmates of the Klander Asylum in Jerusalem, were not the all-powerful bogeymen of anti-semitic legend, but a committee of ten wise men formed by the Rabbis of Lodz to counter the schismatic claims of the Jewish False Messiahs, Shabetai Tsvi and Jacob Frank, by computing the precise date of the Coming of the True Messiah. Over the centuries they met in various lands, fleeing from war, pestilence and persecution, the present incumbents meeting in New York's Lower East Side, at Mottel's Delicatessen. Their names were: Yankel Tillimzoyger, of Brooklyn Heights; Zev 'Meshuggener' Weitz, of Greensboro, South Carolina; Eliezer Conforti, of Bnei Brak, Israel; Nathan 'Jacque' Hadayah, of Rehovoth; Zunz, the Ba'al Shem of Vienna, Azaniah, of Azaniah Carpets & Tapestries, Petah Tikva; Reb Zvi Kook Zweischaften (The Monk), of Jerusalem; Berl Eibeschutz, of no fixed abode; Heimie Goldschlaeger of Manhattan; and Irving Klotskashes, of Hollywood, California. According to the inmates, it was the Elders who formed Klotskashes' film crew in the abortive Judas Pig project at the asylum. Their aim was to exorcise the old asylum ghost, the Judas Pig, and gain valuable brownie points in the long march towards the Divine Computation. But circumstances forced their retreat, and Jerusalem sunk back into its millennial torpor.

Down the hatch!
'Read him his rites,' said Ptah.

Omphalos (The Vortex, IV):
Elelelelelelelelelelelelelelelllllllllll . . .
Alalalalalalalalalalalalalalalllllllllllllll . . .
Illillillillillillillillillillillillillillill . . . . .
Oliolioliolioliolioliolioliolioliolioxenfree . . . . . .

– He slides, down the chute, past jungle drums and glowing incense and shofars tooting in the distance, down, into the yawning, grinning mouth of audioanimatronic spong–

Braaaaaaaaaa . . . LET THERE BE LIGHT!

– Main Street, ploughed by Biblical oxcarts. Marching men in chain mail and spears. Two youths in loincloths carrying an immense cluster of giant plastic grapes. Children rushing shrilly in the dusty wake of an Ark of the Covenant. An audioanimatronic youth casts a recurring catapult stone at the forehead of a giant figure, ringing a bell. Bunting-decked tanks trundle by. At various entrances, neon signs beckon: SHEKEL ARCADE. THE BURNING BUSH. THE GOLDEN CALF. SEE THE WALLS OF JERICHO FALL. WRESTLE THE LIONS WITH SAMSON. EXORCISE DYBBUKS. TEAR THE BABE IN HALF WITH KING SOLOMON.

Blok follows a phalanx of audioanimatronic worshippers, wrapped in prayer shawls, carrying a blank scroll of the Torah, through a turnstile manned by a youth in High Priest robes (the breastplate, the *ephod*, the mitre, the Urim and Thummim). An 'E' Attraction (Only 85 Cents or 1 voucher!). He emerges into a dark vestibule, with arrows pointing in all directions. Hollow laughter booms from concealed loudspeakers. Martial music echoes from accordions. Four entrances resolve dimly in the gloaming, each signposted by a playing card: The Jew of Hearts. The Jew of Diamonds. The Jew of Clubs. The Jew of Spades.

He enters the Jew of Hearts. A large saloon bar littered with debris fashioned into post-modern sculptures: a smashed refrigerator, a cracked bathtub, with broomstick, a rusty, abandoned immigrant ship, a downed Spitfire, still smoking. The lounge is empty, except for Carl/Guevara, polishing glasses behind the bar. He waves to Blok. Blok steps forward. A jeep crashes down, out of the sky. His old commanding officer from *BABASIS* Magazine, Lt.-Colonel Tswingli, steps out of it, dressed in battle fatigues. He claps Blok on his back. 'What's your poison?'

'Potassium cyanide,' Blok answers. Carl/Guevara pours them two glasses. Tswingli drinks, turns black and expires. Carl claps a hand over Blok's glass and shakes his head, motioning him towards the back of the bar, through a door into a dark vestibule. A circle of shadowy robed kibitzers in booths gaze through eyeslats which open and close, choking off dusty shafts of red light and the cries of pleasure and pain coming from beyond the peepholes. Blok hands an 'A' ticket to the sullen young Guide, dressed in 2000 BC chain mail. His chosen slat opens to reveal, in the room beyond, a man he recognises as the False Messiah, Shabetai Tsvi, stretched naked upon his stomach on a medieval rack, ministered to by Dominique and May in full domination regalia, wielding the tools of their trade: the police slugger, the five finger paddle, the English switch, the kat o'nine tails, the leg spreader, the flat nickle-studded paddle and the five gates of hell. Gasps burst beyond false teeth biting down on a Travel Lodge towel: 'I have been a Bad Messiah! I have misled My People! Beat me!' The two girls proceeding to oblige. Blood spurts from the scars on his back.

'CUT!' cries Irving Klotskashes. 'We'll have to take it from the top again.' He rises, the mogul in the flesh, with the inevitable cigar glowing in his mouth like a spacecraft poised for take-off in moon craters, its ash littering the room. Upon a divan behind him Adir Kokashvili, the Tel Aviv film magnate, breathes stentoriously, an immense human tub of lard, clicking its worry beads. Pok, pok, pok.

'Take five. Where is my fucking assistant?' Blok's old friend Yissachar emerges, in a white dressing gown, from a side door, carrying a golden jar which emits a thick white steam. The Great Director drinks the potion. His face grows, like a Melies moon. Blok lies upon the rack, stretching his nude body upon the False Messiah's drying blood. Dominique gently straps him into the clamps and shackles. She strokes his hair, and passes her gloved fingers across his testicles and penis. He experiences a massive erection. His organ grows, brushing the ceiling. Everyone in the room backs away, pressing uneasily against the walls, which fade. The moon of Irving Klotskashes winks at him from a jet black sky. Fireworks erupt from the Sleeping Beauty Castle. Blok rolls up his organ, placing it in a yellow plastic wheelbarrow which he pushes on down the hill. The Jew of Clubs flashes on and off by the drawbridge. He trundles his cargo across the bridge. Art Mattock, the Armenian Van, Jacqueline Happenstance-Moore and the Jesuit are waiting on the other side.

Ordering Club Falafels at the Jewburger Galley, they sit eating them around a green plastic table. A waitress dressed in a Moroccan festive costume takes away Blok's wheelbarrow and penis and presents him with a punched 'B' voucher.

'Did I tell you how we four first met?' Art asked Blok. 'It was in the course of a conspiracy which we were supposed to have hatched to kidnap the Secretary of State, Metternich . . . We were indicted, in 1841, along with six more Jacobite comrades, in a case which became known as the Austerlitz Nine . . . We had all gone up to Vienna to camp outside the Hofburg, smoke dope and picket King Ferdinand, who came down at dawn to remonstrate with us. Jackie told him to go boil his head . . .'

'What a sad face that man had . . .' recalled the Jesuit.

'Was that the year we had the Magic Mushrooms?' Van asked, musing, 'The Illyrian Commune, remember?'

The three old comrades sat back, heads inclined, mouths open, emitting thousand-cycle hums. Jacqueline winked at Blok, taking him by the hand towards the exit, shovelling their empty Jewburger cartons into the plastic refuse bins. Dominique and May beckoned from the swing doors of the Galley. Jacqueline joined them, leaving Blok alone in the café. He followed the sign pointing towards the Jew of Diamonds and exited, finding himself on the corner of La Cienega and Santa Monica Boulevards, carrying a laundry bag with his soiled clothing, at the entrance to the West Hollywood Washomat. The automatic laundry was full of tanned young men and women tending their Maytag top loaders. Two older figures in shorts and T-shirts rose to greet him. He recognised Friedrich Nietzsche by his iconic

171

whiskers and the Frenchman Michel Foucault by his shining bald pate.

'Do you have any conditioner?' they asked him. He shook his head. But they appeared unabashed.

'Let's go back down to Fairfax,' they said, in unison, 'the Elders of Zion might have some.'

'OK,' said Blok.

They walked together along the wide motorway, startled drivers casting suspicious and outraged looks at them as they wandered under the great billboards:

DISCOUNT BARKING

HERTZ RENT A STAR

DO NOT BLOK INTERSECTION!

'The repeatable materiality that characterises the enunciative function,' said Foucault, 'reveals the statement as a specific and paradoxical object, but also as one of those objects that men produce, manipulate, use, transform, exchange, combine, decompose and recompose, and possibly destroy. The statement circulates, is used, disappears, allows or prevents the realisation of a desire, serves or resists various interests, participates in challenge and struggle, and becomes a theme of appropriation or rivalry.'

'You don't say,' said Nietzsche.

'Precisely. You got the point,' Foucault nodded.

But Blok suddenly remembered that he had left his penis at the Jewburger Galley. He left the two philosophers to argue down the breadth of Santa Monica Boulevard, and returned to the Washomat, to find it transformed into a vast Drive-In Massage Parlour, with a revolving sign which said:

THIS WEEK ONLY: FREE STAY HARD LOTION. RUB A LITTLE ON THE PENIS AND IT TICKLES AND THRILLS DEEP DOWN IN THE VAGINAL REGION AND SHE WILL NEVER KNOW YOUR SECRET AND SHE WILL SAY: 'THANKS, I NEEDED THAT, I WANT MORE OF THE DICK.'

The neon sign of the Jew of Spades beckoned him into the reception lounge, where Carl/Guevara looked up from a video colour monitor displaying blinking rainbow shapes. 'What can we do you for today, man?'

'I want to see the manager,' said Blok, not wishing to admit to Carl that he had left his penis in the building.

'I'll take you to him,' said Carl, leading him to a lift which ascends to the thirty-fifth floor, to a plush padded office in which, behind an immense, empty desk, the diminutive, vaguely-recalled figure of Liam O'Habash sits curled in a giant black armchair. The myopic mice eyes scurrying behind the old tortoiseshell pince nez. Behind him the panorama of Los Angeles pokes lazily through a blanket of smog. Blok places his 'B' voucher on the glass-topped table, beneath which he notes snapshots of his childhood trapped under the dirty glass: Blok and his childhood friends Fat Avi and Square Gideon and Muki the Mutt sailing woodplank pirate ships in the neighbourhood cesspool; Blok spitting into the ultra-orthodox matzohs; the gang searching for aliens and spies in the hills and terraces of Jerusalem; the prepubertal notes passed round in class:

'Did you know Moses was never found in the bulrushes? Bela Bira saw him, at the Veterans' Association, boning up on his pedigree . . .'

'Did you know Abraham never intended to sacrifice Isaac? He was just playing chicken on the Mount. Daddy told Mummy all about it, when they thought I wasn't listening . . .'

'Our dreams, eh?' said the homely pornographer, smoothing out the ochre coupon. 'All our fantasies and secret desires. What are yours, truly, Mister Blok? You never told me, all those years ago . . . I remember – the magnificent nurse and the Hungarian lunatic. Yes, those were surely the days. Scrabbling for a living, with black and white postcards, selling shrink-wrapped mags in alleys. And now I just sit up here and it all comes to me. I press buttons and frustrations are satisfied. I nod my head and fantasies

173

become real. I twirl my finger and dreams come true. It's amazing what you can achieve if you just persevere.'

'I would just like to collect my penis and leave,' said Blok.

'I have it here.' The achiever pulled open a desk drawer. He held it up, between forefinger and thumb, an unprepossessing wrinkled flesh peanut. Blok tucked it with relief into his pants.

'Anything else I can offer you?' asked the persistent porno-grapher. 'Free spoonfuls of my resurrective elixirs? Beautiful girls? Boys? Donkeys? Alsatians? Chimpanzees? Trained Sumat-ran eels? Finger fucking? Half and half? Trip around the world? Golden showers? Enemas? Toilet training? Verbal abuse? Anal worship? Coffee or cream? Infibulation? Scatophilia? Necrophilia? Sadism? Bestiality? Or am I flogging a dead horse?'

'What is the way out?' asked Blok.

'Ah! that would be telling!' O'Habash and Carl/Guevara both laughed, beckoning Blok over to a medieval embrasure in the wall of the office. He looked out, down upon a vast castle court-yard, in which a great fleet of Greyhound buses was drawn up, disgorging a multitude of small, hunched figures, leaping out with flaming pitch torches, some clad as monks, others in prayer shawls, or the ill-fitting khaki of Reserves Duty, dinner jackets, praks, smokeengs, women in haute-couture gowns, and multi-tudes dressed casually, in summer shirts, slacks, jeans, T-shirts, all flowing in a determined stream across a drawbridge, mumbling and waving their lamps.

'Kill! Kill! Kill! Burn the bastard!'

Art Mattock and the Jesuit stand beside him, sweating in their false beards.

'This way!' They sweep Blok through a side door into the waiting seats of a capsule, resting on metal rails in pitch darkness. 'Sit! Sit! Sit!' The Jesuit hands an 'E' coupon to an audioanimatronic guide. A metal bar pins them to their seats and the capsule lurches, accelerates, up an increasing, invisible slope.

'Not a rollercoaster, for God's sake!' cries Asher, who is pinioned beside him. 'I swore never to ride one of these!'

'Is there a loop?' asked Blok, white with terror.

'Sure,' said Art. 'What's the use of a rollercoaster without a loop?'

174

'AAAAAAAARRRRGGGGGGGHHHHHHHHHH ! ! ! ! !'
Blok's howl, flung back in his face. Shrieks and screams of un-
seen riders in the cars preceding and following, echoing in the
blackness.

'They ought to have a new category after the "E" Ride,' says
Carl, crouched on the front bar, cradling a Kalashnikov and
festooned with ammunition belts and grenades, while Doron
Kolchak, perched on his shoulders, films Blok's face with a
hand-held Arriflex BL. 'The "F", "G", "H" and even "I" Ride.
There is an infinite capacity for the increase of divertissement,
don't you think? People will pay good cash to be entertained
properly, to be taken out of themselves. The humdrum run of life,
who needs it? We all want something else than what is. The drive
to terrorise the world, hijack aeroplanes and sow revolution is the
same, when all's said and done, as that to be fucked in the ass by a
giant nigger, or to ravish Marilyn Monroe, or ride the Matterhorn
Bobsleds, eh? Don't you think so, Blok man?'

'EEEEEEEEEEEEEEEEEEEEHHHHHHHHHHHH...'Blok
felt his flesh drawn tight over his bones, his eyes sucked into
the back of his head. The faces of other riders shooting up and
down in their capsules glowed at him like multiple moons:
Yissachar, Jacqueline Happenstance, Shabetai Tsvi, Foucault,
Nietzsche, Henry Gibson, Bill Flint, Esther, Shuli, Nili, Thin
Avi, a grinning pig, a drooling sheep and a disgusted black cat
blowing cigar smoke rings.

They paused at a crest, then shot down again, the rails leading
the capsules at breakneck speed into the yawning open mouth of a
giant face, dripping perspiration, which was, of course, Blok's
own. Red flames flickered deep in the gullet. 'I'm going to be sick!'
he shouted in Art's ear. The Professor passed him a vomit bag.
They crashed forward into the mouth, the flames rising all about
them. The heat was intense. He could see the preceding riders
combusting, their capsules calcinating into black shells. He could
feel his clothes shredding around him, his flesh melting on his
bones.

'It is fucking hot, isn't it?' Asher commented, passing him the
suntan lotion.

They trudged on, along the Venice Beach. Tanned, fit and

beautiful bodies lay in relaxed positions all about them. Muscle-builders chinned up firmly on bars. Surfers rode the waves. Ice-cream vendors pedalled by on tricycles, leaving their triadic marks in the sand. The helicopters of the Los Angeles Police Department hovered above them, official ears and eyes strained for signs of misdemeanours and crimes.

'I like it here,' said Asher. 'There is an inner uncertainty and vulnerability that I can really appreciate. The climate reminds me of home but the people don't. This surely is my definition of paradise.'

'Not mine,' said Blok. 'The ersatz smiles. The fake enthusiasm. The ephemerality of life. The metropolis of putty. Everything is an image or a representation of something else. And the wide open spaces. Oh dear. But I don't want to go "home" either, to life as a prisoner in a mezuzah, the rebuilt ghetto, war, manifest destiny. Agoraphobia or claustrophobia . . . There must be a golden mean . . .'

'We should be so lucky, comrade. And the whiplashes of Love?'
? ? ? ? ? ? ? ? ? ? ? ?

*

Indeed. The true, parched nightmare, as Los Angeles March gives way to April, rolling on towards dusty May, the continued barrenness of the Los Angeles small ads, the postponed plans and dwindling nest egg again, as another letter arrived from Art Mattock:

Hi there, Sun Worshippers!

Found your nirvana yet, in La La Land? You people do move about, don't you? We gentiles are slower to budge, despite appearances. I'm still here, but not for long. Jacqueline is still in England. Apparently there is going to be (or already has been by the time you get this) a big Easter 'Embrace The Base' exercise. Perhaps they are going to nail the whole thing to a cross, then elevate it to the sky! We will just have to imagine it. I myself am taking the term off, and am about to vanish, for six to eight weeks, upstate, to shoot bears in the Adirondacks. You didn't know this aspect of my secret life, did you? It's the old frontier bloodlust, boys! I shall be with Van in a shack up by Loon Lake (appropriate, *non*?). Bliss! No risk of knife-wielding Tunisians! Just us, Bageerah and Baloo. And Pedro. We have him again. He is cross with you, Avram, for failing to take him out enough walkies. We shall sick him on the wild hares and opossums. I shall probably have to bring back his pelt! So it's Davy Crockett's life for me this spring! Raccoon hat and Natty Bumppo. If you're in dire need, enclosed P.O. Box number. Pony Express delivery once a year. Ever been stung by a dead bee? So lawng, pardners!

Art A

'I am definitely going to stay,' Asher told Blok, driving him down the freeway in a battered third-hand Chevette, plighting his troth ever more confidently with the metropolis of wheels. 'This is the end of my rainbow, Avram, for the time being at least. Doron thinks he can tie up the San Manuel project. The Noble Red Man's Fall, et cetera. Wounded knees and sitting bullshit. Humane, progressive, ecological. Everything the discerning radical cineaste needs to turn himself into a true Liberal, even unto the guild-approved salaries. What is there for me elsewhere? The Jane Springs era is over. What else do I have in Gottstrafengland? The climate? Spare me, soul brother. Los Angeles, Avram, who would have believed it? To become another cliché . . . Or do you think I'm just mellowing into mush? Fading away like the Cheshire Cat's smile? The Grin Without a Cat? That was the title, wasn't it, of a documentary by Chris Marker . . . the revolutionary aspirations of man . . . Is this what we're all coming to? Fade into the Sunset Strip, with greenbacks . . . Is this your spitting Asher speaking? The man who penetrated Boss Security, disguised as a sans culotte? The man who chased George Papadopoulos's prime ministerial limousine with a hand-held Beaulieu 16? The man who was denounced by his national press as an agent of the Popular Front for the Liberation of Palestine? The man who crawled down the two-foot seam at Fryston Colliery, with chortling coalminers pulling his trouser legs? The man who stole La Lotta Continua's fairest flower off the hands of Mao Tse Kraut? Am I, too, doomed to prosperity? Don't bother to wipe the tear from my eye . . . How about that gorgeous redhead, Avram, the one coming up in our right lane? Hey there, honey, how about a good aerobics session? Ah, she gives us the two-finger fade! Freeway flirting, who can resist it? And what about you, Avram? Knock, knock, who's there? Opportunity! Is it come in or fuck off?'

? ? ?

Alone, the sun, the surf, the sea palling, travellers' cheques depleting by the minute, with only the small nest egg left un-hatched in the National Westminster Bank in London beckoning as the final reserve . . . Options evaporating in the Los Angelene smog: PSI (Pollutant Standard Index): 0–100 Good, 100–200 Unhealthful, 200–300 Very Unhealthful, 300–500 Hazardous. Blok County – 600. Humidity – 2000 per cent. Highs in the Upper Ten Thousands Fahrenheit. Lows −50 Centigrade. Extreme haziness throughout . . .

– What am I doing here? What am I looking for? What is the point of all this energy wasted pursuing a goal denied me by definition? Or is this just an incorrect escape route from that other desert, far away? America is spitting me out, he thought suddenly, as he stood, on the Venice Beach, looking out towards Japan. Squeezing me out, in the run-up to a barren summer, like the last drop of a defunct toothpaste, to make way for new, shining products . . .

(The Gods, having done their work well [they have all the time in the world]: 'We'll get him on general dissatisfaction,' Ptah had urged, 'let's keep the fire and brimstone for a later date. Draw out the angst, the fear, the tension. Give him the slow burn in the gonads. In the long run, it toughens up the soul. Anyone for another hand of gin?' The pitter-patter of retreating claws . . .)

Wandering down the wilderness of downtown, the grimy, neglected towers, the grid of death, the jingle-jangle morning of Latin American pop, the hurrying office workers, the perturbed tourists, the hustlers, the bustlers, the rustlers of souls . . . sinking into the boiling concrete of the proto-summer heat . . . pondering the contours of another disappearing act, to replace the Greyhound run . . . A rent to open out in the great papier-mâché

178

backdrop, to clamber through to new realms . . . to lose his way completely, and never be brought to account – yea!

The Vortex, V (The Great Escape):

So Blok descends into the underworld of the city, entering a low bar on Hope Street and Ninth and ordering a tequila sunrise, surrounded by the unemployed and the unwashed, who adopt him as their favourite gringo. They offer him a ride, down the reverse route of the illegal immigrant trail, to Mejico and the Peyote wonderlands. He accepts, and travels for five days in a concealed compartment inside the petrol tank of a chicken truck, emerging in a bare cantina in Zacatecas, at an elevation of 9000 feet. He slumps, exhausted, in a wicker chair, but looks up as an eight-foot tall Indian enters and offers to sell him an empty Coca Cola bottle containing the essence of Zaplotocl, the Guatemalan Maize Spirit. The only problem is he must sell the bottle at a lower price than he bought it, or be cursed with the curse of Montezuma for the rest of his life. Blok can only dredge up from his pocket an old Israeli ten agorot coin, now worth 0.0000000000001 of a cent on the international financial markets. The Indian seizes the coin and exits, laughing raucously. A gaunt, withered American walks over to Blok's table and introduces himself as William Burroughs, the famous literary junkie aesthete. He informs Blok that in Lima, Peru, the local currency, the sole, is depreciating at the rate of 3000 per cent per hour, offering him a phial of the dreaded hallucinogenic mind-bending drug, Yage, which he has procured from the local guerrilleros. Blok takes the drug, and is transported immediately to the Cathedral Café in downtown Lima, in which several novelists are discussing their advances over steaming mugs of maté. He discovers that a financial recovery has taken place due to the imposition of a State of Emergency, and the sole has rocketed to an unheard of value of 7,000,000 to the dollar. Appalled, he throws the bottle of Zaplotocl into the nearest garbage can and stows away aboard a tramp steamer, the *Ayahuasca*, headed for Yokohama . . .

Walking the streets of the alien port city, without a yen in his pocket, Blok stumbles timorously into a small noodle parlour in an alley off a neon-lit strip club. American sailors and their geisha

179

girls stagger outside, laughing and urinating into the street. The proprietor, a wrinkled old man with a long white beard, notes his air of melancholy. He addresses him in Hebrew, something in his eyes having revealed the chagrined burden of his genes. Introducing himself as Yasujiro Ben Gurion, the old man leads Blok into the back of the shop, where his fellow converts to the Mosaic Faith are just commencing an Israel Bonds meeting. Blok flees in terror, fetching up at the Czechoslovakian Consulate. A suave, well-dressed teutonic man with a cigarette holder, a monocle and a wooden leg, looks him over and introduces himself as Klaus Barbikan, an agent of the East German Abwehr. He offers Blok an assignment, on behalf of world socialism, which would involve an immediate departure to China.

Arriving in Beijing, Blok regrets he has never learnt properly the art of daily transport on a bicycle. But he rendezvous with the local Revisionist agent, a Eurasian named Iskander Ho, in the grounds of the ancient Forbidden City, buzzing with the activity of seventeen separate film crews recreating feudal China with the enthusiastic support of the Chinese Government. Mingling among the hordes of ersatz eunuchs, earnestly discussing their demands for union approved salaries, Ho passes him a train ticket and new false papers, enabling him to travel in the identity of one Eponymous Bosch, a Greek-Alsatian trader in rubber goods, bound for Huang Yuang, in the remote mountainous region of Tsinghai, formerly known as Sinkiang. There he is to rendezvous with a secret group of fundamentalist Maoists, fanatic followers of the discredited Gang of Four, who are to be assisted in their goal of reviving Mao Tse Tung's Cultural Revolution and reducing China to chaos, so that the Tibetan Nationalists, backed by the CIA and the KGB, can achieve their long-hoped-for independence and the dismemberment of the People's Republic.

Travelling seven days and seven nights on the train, whose toilets have ceased to function, drinking in the fumes of lysol and Chinese piss and turds around the clock, men beside him playing endless games of checkers, women stuffing chickens, children solving Rubik's cubes, Blok finally breaks and confesses the plot to a dry goods merchant named Han Tse Ban, who is travelling in the seat opposite. Han Tse Ban promises him the protection of the

People's Republic and urges him to continue his mission as a double agent, promising him free vouchers for Peking and Hunan Restaurants for life throughout the known globe.

In Huang Yuang Blok walks into the Green Poppy, the address he had been given by Iskander Ho in Beijing, only to find the eight-foot Indian waiting for him with the bottle of Zaplotocl beside a steaming bowl of won tons. He pulls the yet unempty phial of Yage from his pocket, upending the dregs onto his tongue. In a trice he finds himself in the majestic snow of the Himalayas, upon an icy summit overlooking the forbidding Kangshung Glacier, not a stone's throw from Mount Everest (otherwise known as Qomolangma Feng). He trudges on through the snow, clutching round him the remnants of his RAF flying jacket, failing to acknowledge the waves of several bands of sherpas, who pass him in the company of their Western TV crews, heading for the pyrrhic peak. Hunkering down, he unfolds the crumpled pages of the Bardo Thodol, the *Tibetan Book of The Dead*, given to him as a code by Iskander, and reads the contents gloomily:

> *And then the Lord of Death will place round thy neck a rope and drag thee along. He will cut off thy head, tear out thy heart, pull out thy intestines, lick up thy brain, drink thy blood, eat thy flesh and gnaw thy bones. But thou wilt be incapable of dying. Even when thy body is hacked to pieces, causing intense torture, it will revive again.*

Unreassured, he puts up the pocket tent and prepares to pass the night. Strange moans, groans and creaks punctuate the frozen silence, the static of radio messages, sent by Nazi scientists hiding in glacier caves, to Mars. The low hum of flying saucers, the flip, flip, flop of NATO drones. A sound of squelchy footsteps echoes without the tent. A hairy paw pulls the tarpaulin flap aside, gesturing him to come outside. He puts his old Palmach sock cap on and steps out, to be immediately surrounded by a baker's dozen of grey hirsute creatures, ten feet tall and naked apart from leather hide codpieces concealing their private parts. They carry him on their shoulders, grunting mournfully, to their encampment in a fog-hidden crevasse, where the Chief Yeti hands him an opened

181

tin of US surplus ham and proceeds to tell him their story, accompanied by sad, dissonant chants which cause the snow to melt into crystal tears, flowing down the craggy mountains, down deep fissures, crevasses and flowering valleys, to the rivers and the seas, towards which Blok flows, navigating his yak-hide canoe, beached on the Ganges banks, captured as a suspected Sikh terrorist, imprisoned in Patna jail, excaped across the sub-continent, riding the purple Yage, the Punjab purge, the Khyber pass, the Ayatollah's toupee, the kif of Baghdad, Ararat Mon Amour . . . all the further stages of Blok's global journey, until, one night in Turkestan . . .

★

But, instead of all this, Blok found himself on a routine flight from Kennedy Airport to London . . . A stand-by schedule from Los Angeles Airport, Klotskashes Land left behind, for the moment, Asher's wave and turning back fading, the mundane drone above the cloud-covered continent, the harsh rasp of true rapid transit. A bucking taxicab ride to Art Mattock's Brooklyn sanctuary, now occupied only by the Salvadorian couple, Orlando and Clara, tending the burglar alarm in the Professor's absence. But romance seemed dead in Avenue L. The Hassidim still ambled about the stores and fishmarkets, the D train still hurled its human flotsam in and out of Manhattan, the skyscrapers scraped the sky nonchalant-ly in a pall of early summer heatwave. The populace mere blobs of dripping flesh squelching along the molten pavements, the water hydrants opened, spraying the streets, the balm of air-conditioned shops and arcades, but the heavy weight of ninety degrees centi-grade squashing thought, killing joy. He sent a postcard to Art's Pony Express box number, by Loon Lake, but no reply. Ending up in the plush lounge of the Pan American building, on Park Avenue, to endorse a date on his return ticket. A pretty girl in a blue uniform confirmed his booking.

He took the train to the plane.

UNIGHTED KINGDOM

The Yeti's Tale:

Our ancestors came from a dying planet, which had filed for global euthanasia with the Intergalactic Medical Board. Being the only few families optimistic enough to face the horrors of an uncertain future, they chartered a space vessel from the nearest trade planet and proceeded on a voyage of salvation. Through the known and unknown galaxies they travelled, parking illegally, kibitzing on strange species, cultures and customs which froze the blood in their veins. Having chanced on earth by mistake during a routine misdirection, they found it wholly covered in water, apart from a tall mountain on which a large but frail wooden boat appeared to have been shipwrecked, disgorging a small family of homo sapiens and a mixed bag of other mammals, reptiles, amphibians, birds and things that creepeth upon the earth. The Chief Yeti (or Eloeem, as we called ourselves in our language), made himself known to the humanoids, who abased themselves before him and offered him an immediate mixed grill. The Eloeem were not keen to remain on the watery orb, but soon discovered their vessel was permanently disabled, and that the Earth was their forced destination. They hung their harps upon the willows thereof, and wept. Eventually the waters receded, but not before the close proximity resulted in unions between our celestial ancestors and the humanoids, resulting in the hirsute race that we have now become, driven out, later, by the grandsons and granddaughters of the Boat people, to wander in the high places of the earth, shunning the humanoids, who, consumed by an atavistic fear of their alien in-laws, hunted us down for our pelts. Today, twelve and a half thousand years later, only this rag-tag band of optimists you see before you survives, living off mountain scrub, bamboo shoots, and cans looted from fallen US spy aircraft and British Himalayan Climbing Teams, our hopes lost, and living on old, faded glories . . .

★

Again the dull grey, the misty Heathrow morning. A strange muffled quiet in the concourse, as if another pace of life ruled here, a scaling down of ambitions. The immigration officer perfunctorily stamped Blok's visa, hardly glancing at his passport. The white-shirted customs inspectors gazed past him as he toted his bag down Nothing To Declare. The relatives and friends waiting for their loved ones beyond the swing doors peered at him without recognition.

Rumbling down in the bus past the dull pastel green peeking beyond the motorway, the lazy flyovers and terraced homes of Metropolitan Londoners, the slow quotidian motion of pedestrians, the dullness of landscape and psyche . . .

He had been away for nine months. The familiarity of the place appeared to him like a jaded family ghost. He tried from a booth to telephone Jane Springs at Inglenook Road and at her own Ladbroke Grove flat but neither call was answered. He phoned Walter and Annie's number in Willesden Green but got an unobtainable tone. Taking the Number 38 bus from Victoria Station, he walked from Holborn to his first Bed and Breakfast base at Russell Square, merging with the anonymous Greeks, Venezuelans, Japanese trippers tasting the edge of the City. Lucky enough to find a vacancy, he left his holdall behind and emerged into the streets, walking down the wide swathe of Southampton Row and Kingsway to the arc of Aldwych and the ancient monument of BBC Bush House (External Services), and up the Strand, the Law Courts, up Fleet Street, the icon of Saint Paul's, down to the Victoria Embankment and the muddy slow roll of the Thames. Past the old tourist trap ships and under the bridge by Cleopatra's Needle, opposite the concrete prison of the South Bank Arts Centre, to Charing Cross, past the cardboard boxes of tramps and misfortunates sunning their rags in the haze. 'Cupo-coffee, mate'. Blok handed over ten pee. Then back north to Trafalgar Square, buying a London *Standard* on the way to update himself on current affairs:

BANK RATE SOARS TO 10 % AS POUND SLIDES. The country's coalminers were on general strike. WHOOPING COUGH BABIES TO SUE. GLC AXE AMENDMENT; WHAT *YOU* THINK: PAGE 6. A former Transport Minister of

Nigeria has been found bound and gagged in a crate at Stansted Airport in the company of an Israeli anaesthetist. Two other Israelis were found in an adjoining crate. Why are they surprised, thought Blok. The image of his parents flickered for a brief second. Do Not Return To Sender . . .

THE NEWS IN BRIEF: Does Ronald Reagan Believe in Armageddon? Poison Toads On the March. Killer Grizzly Bears Stoned On Drugs. Peril of LSD Flavoured Charity Stamps. Cockroaches Removed From *Both* Ears. Cat That Swallowed Engagement Ring. Naked Man Attacks Victim No. 4:

> A man naked except for a string vest and a white plastic bag over his head with holes cut out for eyes and mouth has made a fourth attack in the Berkshire village of Stoke Poges, snatching a handbag containing £30 from Professor Toshiko Oshio, who is holiday from Japan. A detective said: 'This man is sick and needs to be caught before he is responsible for something more serious.'

Blok thought: Perhaps this *is* the place for me. Where anything goes, with minimum harm. Solicitousness does survive, even in the hinterland of Nanny's 'Free' Market forces, one for one and all for none. Despite it all they recognise one is in need of attention, even if only of the police.

He thought of Jacqueline, as he idly took the turning up Long Acre to Drury Lane. The Film College was shut, its yellow peeling door bolted, with an aerosol arrow pointing at its defunct sign with a one-word message: 'PRATS'. The Covent Garden Club was empty of anyone who looked familiar. He thought of Jacqueline, as he walked back to Russell Square, trying Walter and Annie's number again. Still apparently disconnected. He could imagine Walter's tirade: 'British Telecom? They can wait for their cash.' Plop, the plug left dangling. He took the tube to Willesden Green. There was a For Sale sign up in front of the exiled couple's home. The windows looked into empty rooms, with painters' ladders and benches, and broken furniture, builders' junk and a frigidaire upon the front porch. The basement at Inglenook Road was occupied, and the doorbell to the ground floor rang unanswered. He rang the bell of the flat above, of the computer couple, whose female half came to the door, monitor eyed. He tapped out his question on her keyboard. She flashed error messages at him. Jane Springs had left, as threatened, for Australia. A forwarding address was available, but not of much use to him. The flat was temporarily unoccupied, but Hayim Lubovici had already sold it to a Naval Intelligence researcher, who worked at a top secret office block on Lillie Road, at Earl's Court.

Blok returned to Russell Square, counting his reserves, which he estimated would last him two weeks. There was, in his holdall, an out-of-date return ticket to the abandoned Holy Land. He put it in his pocket and walked down again, past Holborn, and on to the British Museum. It was full, as museums are, of ancient artefacts: Greek bronzes, Mycenaean pots, grinning harpies beaming the souls of the dead up to heaven, Elgin marbles, caryatids, Egyptian sarcophagi, the Rosetta Stone, the Dead Sea Scrolls, Indian and Chinese shrapnel, Roman blasts from the past, shekels, papyri, cuneiform squiggles. The stamp room, which would have made Baruch Blok's eyes water. The room of famous persons' handwriting: Nietzsche, Bach, Lewis Carroll. Alice in immaculate hand crafted lettering, an obsessive work of strange love. He walked down Great Russell Street and across Tottenham Court Road to the mess of small streets beyond. A metropolis of nondescript wonders. An anonymity which could not fail. He remembered Asher's dinosaurs and their open hospitality of the lost and the arcane. He took the defunct airline ticket out of his pocket, tore it in half and threw it in a dustbin.

The result was immediate. A black London taxicab drew up beside him with a screech of brakes, its For Hire sign switched off, its dishevelled driver gesticulating wildly to him to 'Get in, for God's sake!' He hesitated, recalling vague warnings against terrorism by Arab Jewnappers. 'Get in, you shmuck!' the familiar voice cried again. He got in and the taxi shot off, up Great Titchfield Street, towards Regents Park. The driver twisted his head round to bare his teeth at him.

'Wotcher, mate!' gurgled Henry Gibson.

Wot?

Watt?

What?

A rescue mission? The seventh calvary? In this day and age? Do us a favour, guv'nor. Predestination, Goddammit! Man is born to sorrow and grief . . .

'Hoisha! Hoisha! Hoisha!' cried Henry Gibson, urging his rattletrap forward, leaning into the non-existent wind, urging the windscreen wipers to scrape dry gunge off his front view, turning into the Marylebone Road, past Madame Tussauds and Baker Street. 'Where to, guv? Right you are, squire. Garn! Shiver me timbers! Wot's up your end? Aaase the wife? I should coco! I 'ad that Menachem Baygin in the back o' the cab once.' Blok slumped, buffeted, in the black leather seat, hanging on to the strap.

'I don't really drive a cab,' Gibson told him, as they soared on to the Westway flyover, above Edgware Road and the ABC Three-plex. 'This is a complete illusion. Actually we are both sitting at home, watching *Coronation Street* on magic mushrooms. No, seriously, mate, I bought this thing second-hand for private use. It can be a pain in the neck whenever I stop at traffic lights but it does have its moments. But it's good to see you, Avram! Hallelujah! What has happened to the great Asher Katzman?'

'He has stayed behind in Hollywood,' said Blok. 'He's going to make a film about Red Indians.'

'Hoka heyyy . . .' They shot past Paddington, heading for the turn to Shepherd's Bush. Gibson was staying there, apparently, emulating Blok's previous domicile, in a basement flatlet below his ex-receptionist, the diminutive Belinda Kenneth. Over a hot toddy, whisky and boiled water, amid the expected chaos of his one bedroom, its two single beds piled with files, books and jumbles of clothes, the rescued flotsam of the four-storey house in Belsize Park, Gibson explained to Blok the loss of those six packed rooms, which had been mortgaged, without the knowledge of his staff colleagues, to the future of the Film College. 'I had to sell the house to pay the debts,' Gibson said, nonchalantly, tripping over the rusty movieola. 'Sic transit gloria mundi. And on Tuesday she was even sicker. On Thursday I buried her, with full military honours. Toot toot! *Allahu akbar.* Do you know Omar Khayyam? —

189

"Then said another with a long drawn Sigh,
My Clay with long oblivion is gone dry:
But, fill me with the old familiar Juice,
Methinks I might recover by-and-bye!"'

They drank a toast to the long dead Persian boozer and Gibson insisted on hearing Blok's tale, the Brooklyn Sanctuary, the Greyhound Express, the Paradise of San Francisco and the Purgatory of Los Angeles.

'So welcome to l'Inferno!' said Gibson. 'You do the Divina Commedia in reverse. That'll show that wop Dante he can't screw us up with false optimism! "Midway this way of life we're bound upon, I woke to find myself in a dark wood, where the right road was wholly lost and gone!" I have that fucking copy some-where . . .' He dived under the right-hand bed, his voice boom-ing sepulchrally from its pit ('Goddammit! *Sadie's Dungeon Frolics!* So that's where the fucking thing went to . . .') – straightening up to follow Blok's puzzled gaze at the plastic female shop's model stuck in the garden outside the basement's french windows, festooned with climbing ivy. 'Ah!' he exclaimed, 'you are seeing mine latest perversion, *nicht wahr*? Plestic lov, is ziss a zign of ze times?' But it had been placed there, he explained, by the house landlord, Mister Policek, a retired Estonian seaman, who had dreamed, upon each wave of all the seven seas he had sailed, of a small house in a civilised country where he could cultivate his own garden. Estonia, of course, did not exist, having been subsumed into the Soviet Union in AD 1940. Now Mr Policek lived upon the top floor of Number 8, Stockton Road, London W6, looking out from his crow's nest over his make-believe figurehead and his crew of long-term tenants, Belinda on the ground floor and a phalange of Japanese Seventh Day Adventists between his memories and hers. Gibson had been taken on as a short-term tenant, en route to his sister, who lived out in the English countryside, not far from the small Cheethamshire hamlet of Mucus-On-The-Pond.

'Maybe you can have the flat after me,' Gibson clapped Blok on the back. 'All you have to do is look meek and gentle, like *moi*. No loud music and no girls. And no Jews. And no Blacks. And no

Communists. And definitely no black Jewish Communists. Now it's just me and my pet mouse, Algernon. He lives somewhere in the walls.'

'I don't know if I can afford the rent,' said Blok.

'Ah!' Gibson said, throwing his arms up in horror. 'Ah! *aber* zat iss *unmöglich* . . . !'

Money! The inevitable pratfall. Nations collapse, kingdoms fall. Samuel Beckett bums transferring pebbles from one pocket to another. Cash flow liquidity crisis. The buck never stops here. Blok reflects on his dwindling prospects, as he walks about this new area of the city, like a dog sniffing out territorial claims which will never be accepted *de jure*: the square of the hypotenuse of Shepherd's Bush Green, west of the gibbet which hung there in quieter times when yokels drove flocks towards the market, past the Central Line underground station, clothes and travelling goods shops, Dry Cleaners, Macdonalds, Rumbelows, Kentucky Fried, Superdrug, Mecca Bookmakers, the Starburger with its moustachioed Turkish waiters, the Wellington Pub, Yogi Smurti's International Newsagent: 'EBU NIDAL TEROR TIMI TÜRKIYE'DE, NUN WINS £20,000 IN BET WITH MILLIONAIRE, SPIES TRAPPED BY RANDY BEETLES, PRINCE BATHED VICE GIRLS IN BUBBLY, past the BBC offices and the Metropolitan Line into the cosmopolitan market, the rainbow crowd, rags and hardware, eels and pies, kids' togs, crockery, foam, second-hand books, travel agents with free maps of the Caribbean, electrical goods, a real snip on Saisho midi-systems today, guv. Here today and here tomorrow. But Blok is a mere wisp in the wind . . .

Under the wrathful eye of Mister Policek, he transferred thither from Russell Square, Belinda Kenneth sweet-talking the old salt into accepting a guest in transit, although the tar did not like Blok, smelling out, like the Good Lutheran he was, his deicidal heritage. 'I donna like his face. He is a hippy.' 'No, no,' Belinda said to him soothingly, 'he worked with us at the Film College. There are no hippies any more.' The landlord sniffed, dredging up his painful memories of eternal Red mendacity. 'I trust Meester Geebson. He is a gentleman.' Estonia *über Alles*. Belinda had adopted Gibson as a mother hen might adopt a stray chick, keeping him at a wary distance, as she knew he still secretly pined for her, though she was still keeping up the weekly visits, now on alternate Mondays and Fridays, with occasional special Sundays, of her boy friend Brian, now a Sergeant of Constabulary and Fellow Craft Mason of the Second Degree, having taken the oath at his North Wessex Lodge, kneeling upon his bare right knee, his left forming a square, his right hand upon the Holy Bible, affirming his Lodge's dedication to Saint John the Essene, though he seemed a little subdued on his visits, and appeared to have something on his mind. 'Not a brain,' Henry Gibson commented unkindly, to Blok. 'That is not allowed in the Force.' But Belinda brushed these unkind thoughts off, sitting ofttimes with Gibson and Blok in her kitchen, listening to Henry's perorations of the glowing plans he had had for the Film College, which came to nought due to the lack of faith of certain unnamed staff. 'Shertain people who ushed to work fer John Ford. You know what ah mean, shucks, honey. Now that was one mean hombre, ah mean, son of a bitch, Goddammit!' Or he would lean back, working his lips round his nostrils, lowering his voice to a hoarse whine: 'Ah could have bin a contender, Johnny, but what did ah get? A one-way ticket to Palookaville . . .'

For the College had remained closed since Blok left, and, after several months of uncertainty, its death knell had finally sounded. No one, apart from Bursar Duguid, Melancholy Jove, knew until the funeral that Gibson had double mortgaged his house to pay its earlier debts, which alas, were too heavy. Loyal veterans like Bill Flint, Orde Clapper, Frank Gaines and Nobbie Marx, had offered similar sacrifices, but too late. In fact, even Del Rushforth offered some nest egg he had stashed away from his creditors, but the axe had already fallen. Sonia Prang returned to children's television. Klaus Lager to Deutsche Rundfunk. The ex-students had sadly departed to their respective countries and even 'Blind Lech', the projectionist, had left, though he had climbed aboard a Japan Airlines flight to Rangoon, by mistake, in lieu of Lot, the Polish carrier. Belinda Kenneth now worked for a cutting room in Wardour Street. And Gibson was due soon to escape the glare of Estonia inland. But there was one possibility that might give Blok another option, a possible handhold in the crumbling cliff face:

the ex-scheduler, Sheila Ratchett, had apparently formed a squat in an empty building in Westbourne Park, together with members of her Party and a few other orphans of the storm such as Mahmud the Iranian Prison buff and Christos Trikeratopoulos, the sound assistant with the smallest ears in London . . .

And Jacqueline Happenstance? No one seemed to know her location. He scoured the newspapers for news of further arrests at Cheetham Common, but that Western front appeared quiet. He inquired about bus and train schedules to Little Cheetham but made no move towards the relevant stations. Eventually, Walter and Annie's next-door neighbours at Willesden Green informed him the South African couple had gone to Sweden, to live with their son in Uppsala. 'I think that's where it was, where they give out the Nobbly prizes . . .' No forwarding address was offered. He lay awake, shoehorned into the Stockton Road basement's spare bed, listening reluctantly to the snits and snores of Henry Gibson's wet dreams, the scamperings of the mouse, Algernon, in the walls and the ceiling, behind the plasterwork, gnawing the insides of doors. It must be nice, to be able to live in the interstices of people's lives, concerned only with the sudden dash across the kitchen floor to the breadcrumbs. Of course, unless a cat is near . . . Squeak, squeak, squeak. Pok, thok, tok, go Henry Gibson's breath bubbles. Wheeeeee, thlop. Wheeeeee, thlop. The creaking of old springs. The muffled clomp of Seventh Day Adventist Japanese arriving home late after their menial chores as waiters or croupiers . . . the literal and bodily ascent of Christ into Heaven, both the just and the unjust will be reborn, although the unjust will have to wait a millennium. The physical Second Coming, no less. But still the grunts and moans of the Shepherd's Bush Road, the late denizens of its cheap guest houses, Hotel Athens, Hotel Paradise, Hotel Bad Breath and Greasy Eggs . . . the cries of Scots vagrant anguish: 'Ah, ye fek! ye fekin fek! ye fek! fek ye fek! fek! fek!' Stricken albatrosses, dragging the surface, incapable of flight . . . Memories of pain and exile, do they fade? The scattering of the Fear into small shards, shrieks of wounded neighbours, financial gripes, loneliness, gnawing the insides of doors . . . Wondering again about about the purposes of his purposelessness. The shield necessary in a locked zealot house

193

crumples like dry putty in the open field . . . It bends and droops, like the soft watches of Salvador Dali's *Persistence of Memory*. *The Invisible Man, The Phantom Wagon, Autumn Cannibalism*. Something being cooked that would never be done. The soufflé of self doomed to fail. But were there not out there persons chasing after Success? Lassoing it with the force of their personality and devouring it with loud howls? Even Asher, bent with the Old Che on his shoulders, ersatz ammunition belts wrapped round his neck, the siren cries of the oppressed, but nevertheless, when the chips were down, seizing the Angelic dream . . . Is man not a natural carnivore? But wasn't Hitler a vegetarian? Impasse. And Jacqueline and the hopes of the feminine, the Matriarchal Return? Who knows. Do only false memories persist? And how can one tell the difference? Is self-knowledge too important to be left to the self? Come back Gestapo, all is forgiven.

Wheeeeee, thlop. Wheeeeee, thlop. Blok, unable to find a solution. In the morning, setting his face in the general direction of Cheetham Common, he ventured north only as far as Westbourne Park, in vague search of Sheila Ratchett's squatters. He found them in a dilapidated terraced property off the Western Road, in the shadow of the motorway and traffic fumes, the hacking coughs of the tubercular city shaking the patched-up windows, the outside walls of the block covered with half done murals and graffiti bravely proclaiming lost causes – HOMES FOR PEOPLE NOT BALANCE SHEETS – THIS IS A NUCLEAR FREE ZONE – BREAD, LAND, PEACE! – and inside a cheerful mess of peeling and chipped plaster, broken staircases, worm-eaten banisters, old mattresses and bric-à-brac, young men and women grappling with alarmingly rusty wires protruding from cracks and ceilings like some monstrous hallucinogenic growth, wielding tools in modern exorcisms, an immense kitchen-dining-room looking as if it had been hit by a bomb which only affected comestible goods – cereal packets blasted to smithereens, vegetables strewn everywhere, pastas, piles of onions, burst sacks of rice, curry powders lining chairs and tables, crockery in the sink in excess mounds like an old Popeye cartoon. Posters covering the worst damage in the walls, proclaiming the creed of the Proletarian Party of Power (PPP): Preparing for the Proletarian Praxis:

194

Margaret Thatcher as a slavering wolf in SS uniform with a Union Jack sash. Sheila Ratchett came down the stairs, preceded by her free-flowing bosom, dodging his embrace but offering him some cold porridge, which he turned down for the moment, as she told him: 'Welcome to the real face of Thatcher's Britain! Are you stuck? Mahmud has a spare bed in his room.'

Ah! So.

But Henry Gibson said to him: 'Don't do it. You'll go blind, but that's a minor matter. Fleas, bedbugs, mice, *c'est rien*. But do you really want to live in the past? Marmalade sandwiches and non-existent plumbing and Rizla papers and roaches and unrequited sexual angst? *Ce n'est qu'un début* and off the pigs and mantra chanting and yabyum? Tibetan headbanging and cross-legged hernias and Oh Money Pad Me Bum and Oh the Jew in the Lotus? Not to speak of Revolutionary Marxist-Leninism (Seventh International) – now that's quite another matter. She will drag you out to their summer school, somewhere in Devon, and make you dance round maypoles, waving the portrait of Enver Hoxha, and burning effigies of Ronald Reagan. Give us this day our daily head. I understand they drink the blood of Labour Party moderates, whom they abduct in Liverpool shebeens and sacrifice by the light of the full moon. Did you know there is a secret cabal, in Highgate, who have Lenin's brain, preserved in a glass tank, which is zealously guarded around the clock? They are called mysteriously "The Aquarium". I know about all these horrors because my son, who is a disciple of Adonai the Avatar, alias Nathan Bloom of North Finchley, keeps me informed of the latest twists of the International Communist Plot.'

Gibson's son, in fact, had, along with the other seventy-five paid-up members of the British Branch of the Worship of the Sun God Ra, received new instructions to go forth and spread the Faith following Nathan Bloom's return from the conference of Gods at Memphis, Tennessee, although the Avatar did not reveal that his role at the conference had been strictly to be prostrate at his Master's feet, licking the webs between his toes and taking down the Sun God's tetchy complaints to his recalcitrant worshippers, concerning the merchandising of his various products at point of sale, Ra Ra Mugs, Ra T-Shirts and the Ra Ma Dan Ginseng

Extract, not to speak of the four-volume Avatar Saga, i.e. *The Path of Ra, Return of the Sun, Warriors of the Last Heatwave* and *The Pulse of Ra-Mageddon,* which were not selling well despite enthusiastic notices such as 'Star smashing antics in the classic tradition' (*Ra Times*) and 'Best S-F Middle Earth has yet produced' (*The Silmaril Epitaph*) . . . Thus the sudden appearance of Gibson's errant son, Jonathan, with a vanload of boxed trinkets and shrink-wrapped hardbacks, which Gibson, shorn of the Belsize Park haven, had to deflect to storage at his sister's country home in Urr-Hovis land, to which he was about to retire, inviting Blok too to 'take a berth' thither, if bounced by the Estonian matelot. But this could not, as yet, resolve the issue of manna, financial sustenance to keep Blok afloat, the subject of fruitless queries after gainful employment at Belinda's place of work and other film editing holes-in-the-wall in Wardour and Dean Street, Soho, as Gibson explained: 'There are still people around in the business who will talk to me. They say Fuck off. But I have such thick ears . . .'

So Blok wandered on about the city, waiting for his hopes to gel, riding the Central Line in to the West End, politely grasping the leaflets handed him on streetcorners offering formal dress for all occasions, the Eton jacket, the Cavendish style, the Prince of Wales, offers of English tuition, calls to picket the Kuwait Embassy ('The Iraqi masses will protest at 1 p.m., August 16th . . .'), offers of personality tests to bring out his hidden and dormant abilities, discount hairdressing, two hamburgers for the price of one, previews of eternal life after death in the Islamic heaven, sitting upon benches in small parks watching the young girls toasting their pale midriffs in the muggy metropolitan sun, youths sunning their pimples, idly turning the pages of the progressive listing magazines, the lonely hearts club band:

AHIMASA LIFESTYLE MALE (27 LIBRA) SEEKS INTELLIGENT RADIANT PRO-ACTIVE FEMALE TO HELP SAVE THE WORLD. LOOKS UNIMPORTANT BUT AWARENESS ESSENTIAL. BOX XXX –

SOCIALIST WOMAN, 30, INTO MUSIC, DANCING, ARTS, NATURE, SEEKS MALE WITH SOCIALIST CONSCIENCE, WELL ENDOWED, WITH FEMINIST SYMPATHIES. (ooooh . . . ooooh . . . oooohhhh . . .)

BLACK, CREATIVE, TRENDYISH LESBIAN, INTELLIGENT MATURE, SEEKS SAME . . .

SUBMISSIVE BOOTBOY WANTED. PLEASURE AND PAIN CAN GO HAND IN HAND. I'M UNPRETENTIOUS, UNCONVENTIONAL, GAY, GOT MY ACT TOGETHER. HOW ABOUT YOU? (No.)

CONTINENTAL WOMAN, 30s CREATIVE, ATTRACTIVE, SENSUAL, SEEKS LOVING MAN (ah!!) PREFERABLY GOOD LATIN-AFRICAN DANCER (drat!) COMMITTED TO STRUGGLE FOR AN ANTI-OPPRESSIVE WORLD EVEN WITHIN PERSONAL RELATIONSHIPS. (Sigh, sigh, sigh.)

THE MAN WHO FELL TO EARTH SEEKS THE WOMAN WHO FELL TO EARTH . . .

INTELLIGENT, ATTRACTIVE, DARK, TALL, BEARDED, LEATHER, COLOURED, BISEXUAL, SINCERE, PASSIONATE, LEFTY, ORIENTAL, SLIM, AMAZING, PSYCHOTHERAPIST, FILM PRODUCER, FRECKLED, DOMINANT, WORKAHOLIC, CREATIVE, HANDSOME, CARING, UNORTHODOX, SOLVENT, MASTERFUL, BEAUTIFUL, WARM, FRIENDLY, GOOD-LOOKING, GRADUATE, PROFESSIONAL, SCORPIO, ARIES, PISCES, AQUARIUS, MATURE, SENSITIVE, OPTIMISTIC, TENTATIVE, DECLOSETED, NICE, INTERESTING, PISSED-OFF, EDUCATED, BRIGHT, MASOCHISTIC, SHY, FUN-LOVING, SUFFERING TERMINAL ENNUI, SEMI-VEGETARIAN, MAVERICK, OPEN, LIKES TO LAUGH, HEARTBROKEN, ATTENTIVE, DEPENDABLE, GENTLE, LIVELY, CHARISMATIC, INTERESTED IN MEETING GENUINE, UNATTACHED, TO REKINDLE FAITH IN MANKIND . . .

Aaaaaaaaaahhhhhhh! Only to return 'home' to *la maison* Policek to find Henry Gibson grappling with a can opener and a sealed container of peas. 'Asher Katzman had a good recipe for spaghetti bolognese, but where is the man now that we need him??' 'Never mind that, read this,' said Blok, passing him the book section of the progressive magazine:

> Desire in Language, a Semiotic Approach to Literature and Art − Kristeva holds that linguistics, be it generative or structural, has tended to disregard prosody. It has in general ignored suprasegmental features and then argues that these features, being chronologically prior to the infant's mastery of the phoneme, are irreducible to the language of the unconscious.

197

'Hola!' Gibson stabbed the page with the can opener and threw it across the room. 'Them's fightin' words, pardner, but we ain't beaten yet. Have you seen this?' He passed Blok a pamphlet which had been slid under the door surreptitiously, a directory of medical advice which could be obtained by telephone calls. They spent the evening breathing heavily down the line at tape-recorded messages explaining masturbation, baby care, cancer, haemophilia, impetigo, vasectomy, nappy rash, nose bleeds, drug abuse, gall stones, incontinence, scarlet fever, shingles, manic depression, puerperal depression ('the blues'), skin grafting, premature ejaculation, sex during pregnancy, athlete's foot, child abuse, incest and a variety of sexually transmitted diseases. By the end of this session Gibson was on the floor, licking accumulated fluff off the carpet. Blok had to shovel him into his bed, calm his twitching, and place a bottle of Bells in his hand . . .

Again walking the late night streets of an unusually warm English July. Along the Shepherd's Bush Green, through the underpass of the Holland Park roundabout, up Holland Park Avenue, past Notting Hill Gate and Queensway, along the railings of the dark, empty mass of Kensington and Hyde Park. Marlborough Gate, Peter Pan Pond and the Long Water. Round Marble Arch and the Tyburn echoes into post-midnight Oxford Street. A smattering of night owls peering into shop windows, eyeballs up against the reinforced transparency between them and the consumer society, the almost latest fashions, personal computers, rags, shoes. A row of plastic legs without torsos rise and fall spasmodically in an animatronic cancan. Videos play soundlessly. The mock Imperial splendour of Selfridges, the gawky bulk of the department stores. A few young men stagger by with beer cans. An old man with a cane stands aside wistfully. A bundle of rags stirs in a locked entrance. A bottle waves from the murk. A night bus whooshes by. A police car wails past. All is transitory and unavailable. Blok considered the many options which appeared to have foreclosed about him in the foregoing. No Asher, no Jane Springs, no Walter'n'Annie, no Art Mattock, out after bear . . . And Jacqueline, *toujours* Jacqueline, the unattainable, still out there in the shadow of Armageddon or even perhaps back over the sea by now, laughing in the Professor's kitchen. He

198

had set out again, early that morning, to Victoria Coach Station, determined to plough north towards Cheetham Common, but the queue to the ticket office stretched to the exit, many travellers being undecided about their destinations, and some seemed to wish to reach towns and villages that appeared to be completely unknown. Blok's feet dragged, his will wilting: even if he could find her, parting the warp and weft and weave of the Peace Women, splashing with his galoshes among their ideals, what might such a meeting gain? Further embarrassment and humiliation. No Good News to impart on The Struggle. There is a limit to what one can inflict on others. Some vestiges of pride remain, even in the full blast of one's redundancy. He turned away, again, ticketless. *Moribundi te salutant* . . . A shambling yeti, holding out a cracked US mug towards him at the closed gates of Tottenham Court Road tube, shrugged, snuffled and withdrew . . .

Blok thought: if I were a Czech student or a Buddhist monk I could end it all with a can of petrol. Goodbye, cruel world. One might then at least have the accolade of a footnote at the close of the Six O'Clock News. Between Prince Charles and the Singing Baboon. And now tomorrow's weather, hot and sticky. So where do we go from here? Perhaps, after all, the Squat? Yesterday's brave new world, in curdled yoghourt. The ratchetting sheila and Mahmud's gibbering ghosts of SAVAK victims gnawing gloomily at his ear. Oozing dreams. Squashed eyeballs running along the floor. The infinite niches of the underground catacomb. The High Priests' fingers seizing his larynx. The Jew of Hearts transplanted in a brick wall. (And not even a drop of Amontillado!) Or, the dewy joys of the Gibson sod, the Avatar's dribble, cold comfort farm, the pudgy hand of the footsmashed Chief Constable waving his pot and rod of office . . .

The Pot of Manna, asargelusha!!! He turned down the abandoned Charing Cross Road. Gaunt, poorly dressed figures looming out of the darkness, mumbling their 'Ten pence for a cupocoffee, mate', not that a cupocofee could be had for love or money, as far as Blok could see, but the hand was withdrawn, the plea stifled, as Blok was allowed to proceed with a shrug, bringing himself up short before a neon-lit window in which he could examine himself: the stooped stagger, the straggling hair, the

199

unshaven uncouth gape above the unkempt, wrinkled clothes which clearly showed their wear and tear. In short, one of us, brother. He preened in his newfound belonging. I have always dreaded this, he thought, the reductio ad infinitum, the plunge into the true lower depths, remembering the bums of New York, the staggering madness of Total Fear, Total Fall, Total Loss and Total Dislocation. Gimme a quarter, man. Fuck your ass, mother-fucker. Vomit staining the stairs of the subway. Down, down, down. The Gates of Dis. The River Phlegethon. The Downtown Local. The Inner Rings. MIND THE GAP!!!!! Zombies in buried sidings, eating rats and slugs and beetles. Basement of basements. Everybody Out.

He crossed Trafalgar Square. The dead fountains. The pigeon-shat blind stone Admiral. South Africa House. The National Gallery. Whitehall and the great Ministries of bygone Empire. 10 Downing Street and Big Ben. On impulse he turned towards the Embankment and the night-time barrio of old blankets and cardboard boxes under the blackened railway bridge. The gates of the underground station closed for the night, the dragging men huddled against the walls across the way from the closed fish and chip shop and postage stamp emporiums. A red-haired, wart-faced, ruddy-nosed young man with a ginger moustache approached him.

'Got a fag, mate?'

As it happened, Blok had purchased a pack of ten Benson & Hedges only a few days before, on impulse, so he could appear to be taking his time serenely on his idle park bench watch, though he did not, in fact, smoke. His saliva had uselessly shredded five of them.

'Ta, mate. Stranger in town?'

'You could say that.'

'Well, at least it's not cold. You should be here in the winter. Stalingrad ain't in it. Separates the men from the boys.'

'You've been here long?' Blok asked, indicating the massed blankets.

'Long enough. Every week here is ten years. Look at 'em. Used to be old timers, gentlemen an' ladies of the road. Now it's Tebbit boys, nearly all. Got on their bikes, from up North. Chasing jobs gone with the wind of Maggie Thatcher's arse. My name is Bradbury.' Blok shook a calloused hand. 'I had a house and a job and a family, in Ilford. And now, as you can see, I'm a free man. Free to shit in the street, at the end of the twentieth century. Don't you like that word: Progress?'

'It does have a hollow ring,' Blok agreed.

'Why don't you come visit my home?' the man waved a hand, towards the hidden river, beyond the double gates of the station. 'I have my own box by the Festival Hall. Luxury accommodation. All mod cons. The Sally Ann soup van is due here any time. Stick around. Free tea and a bun. It beats scrabbling in dustbins for sandwiches the tourists gob up. In fact, mate, that's it coming.'

'I couldn't . . .' Blok demurred. 'It's your food . . .'

'God's gift, son,' said the homeless redhead. 'Thou shalt not look it in the cold sores of its mouth . . .'

He stood in line with the other streetdwellers, as they climbed out of their boxes and emerged from piles of rags, passing cigarette butts from one to the other, clearing their throats, spitting nervously. A young man and a young woman opened the back of the van and began spooning forth thick steaming vegetable soup, handing out wrapped rolls and paper cups.

'Ta luv.'

'Ta.'

'Ta, me luvly.'

'Think you very much.'

'This is a damn sight better than the Sanctuary,' Bradbury told Blok. 'You have to stand about there an' sing 'ims. The Lord is my shepherd I shall not want. Well, I want it all the bloody time, but I can't get it. Pardon my French,' he nodded his head to the mousy girl who gave him his tea. 'It's all fine for them what has it to say it all don't mean a thing.'

They walked across the railway bridge, two lone figures against the cold Victorian girders, the lit dome of Saint Paul's gleaming like a picture postcard up the dark ooze of the Thames. The concrete South Bank concert halls, art galleries and national theatres coming closer with every step.

'Fall in here and you'll die of the pollution, mate,' said Bradbury. 'Forget drowning, you'd never get that far. The city is

201

poison. Only the rats survive. In the summer it's not too bad, actually. Later on, that's another story . . .' They stepped down on to the esplanade graced day and evening by thousands of proper citizens and trippers imbibing the joys of Art: English Romanesque at the Hayward, Vaughan Gryll's multi-image photomural at the Festival Hall, Wagner's *Meistersingers*, Honegger, Tippett and Franck (numbered deckchairs £2.50, sitting on the grass £1.20), Offenbach: *Orpheus in the Underworld*, Gounod: *Faust*, Bernard Shaw's *Saint Joan*. At the National Film Theatre: *We of the Never Never, Sleep My Love, Without Reservations, Imitation of Life, Doctor Strangelove, Nightly Dreams, Street Without End.*

They approached the huddle of boxes beneath the curved arch of the edge of Waterloo Bridge. 'A businessman in San Francisco,' said Bradbury, 'is going to build and sell plywood shelters for us lot at five hundred dollars US the piece. He calls 'em "city sleepers". No kidding. I read it in a bin by County Hall. I hope Mrs Thatcher doesn't hear of that. My dollar account is rather low. Old fridge boxes are the best, I find. But washing machine crates are a can-do option, though a little cramped at times.' They drew nearer the clumped piles of cardboard, with feet and tops of heads protruding. 'Personal computer boxes are more prevalent now, but they are becoming too compact.' A couple of lazy hands waved at Bradbury as his familiar voice echoed. He stopped at a rather large furniture box with up-ended This Way Up signs. Rapping with his knuckles on the near panel.

'Here y'are, luv. I brought you a sandwich.'

'Does it 'av termaaaters?' rasped a hoarse voice with the texture of blunt chainsaws. 'Blood o' th' maarters, that's them termaaters . . . Give me terrible wind, them legumes . . .' A vast bulk arose, like a tattered whale, from the depths of the cardboard container. Flowing wispy hair, a rubberlike, wattled hand, a head like a drowned papier-mâché Minerva aged in seaweed and encrusted with barnacles. Two sharp eyes gazed out of the mess at Blok as the rubbery hand seized the sandwich.

''Ow's yer father, dahlin'? Give us a fag!'

Blok knew he had met his match.

★

Meanwhile, in Los Angeles . . .
Meanwhile, at Loon Lake . . .
Meanwhile, at Alamogordo, New Mexico . . .
Meanwhile, in Havana, Cuba . . .
Meanwhile, in the Himalayas . . .
Et cetera, et cetera, et cetera . . .

★

The Imperial ministries of Whitehall loomed in the clear August night. A police barricade lay across the silent entrance to Downing Street, seemingly without further protection. But the mighty bag lady wiggled her spattered Sainsbury's plastic carrier at the maw of ultimate power.

'She 'as vicious dogs, 'er in there! Doberman Panzers, Great Dames. They is trained to sniff aat the poor. Yer need a shotgun fer that lot. Ar! she's evil! She must be destroyed!' Spit sprayed the empty asphalt, the feet of the toy soldier guarding the Horse Guards Parade. 'Blor's a kiss, Sarge!' But the toy soldier stayed stum. Big Ben, behind them, struck three. Bong! Bong! Bong!

They waddled on, up towards The Mall. It had not taken long for Blok to be introduced to his neighbours in the cardboard city of Westminster: Bradbury he had already met, and the White Whale, alias the one and only Katharine Weale. His other immediate companions in the adjacent boxes were, according to Bradbury, Smeg, Bob-a-Job, Dishcloth, Larry the Limb, Moka Java, Lydia the Tattooed Lady, Chuck'n'Di the transvestite, Arsehole, who claimed his true name was Rasul, Young Fish and El Alamein. Young Fish, Larry the Limb, Bob-a-Job and Dishcloth were teenagers, drawn to the Big City by the lure of jobs but trapped in the unemployment spiral. Moka Java was a coffee-coloured man who unconvincingly claimed immigrant status in a broad Cockney twang. Arsehole was a cheerful middle-aged Indian. Lydia was a red mohicaned walking modern graffito. Chuck'n'Di was said to offer himself in Soho, to a decreasing band of punters. El Alamein and Smeg were older vagrants, veterans of roads and gutters.

Katharine Weale had wandered the city for as long as anyone

203

could remember, carrying her shopping bags of flotsam, clinking bottles and odd sods. Some said she had been a famous madame, brought down by the Profumo scandal. Others said she had been a civil servant, the Parliamentary Private Secretary to the Minister of Commerce and Trade. Smeg said she was the femine incarnation of Beelzebub, but offered no unmethylated proof. She herself revealed nothing, emitting only the usual cacophony of nods, winks and blasts of spatulant sound, spraying the street and pavements. Her strange patois seemed to derive from ersatz entertainers' views of the cockney tongue. 'Maybe she's a German spy,' said Bradbury, 'dropped 'ere by Zeppelin and ain't been told the fucking war is over.'

'Ar! 'at's good, sweetie! Gi'rs a kiss!'

On towards Trafalgar Square. Katharine knew everything there was to know about the hidden undergirth of the city, and spat it all out to Blok in the shadows of closed shops and locked arcades, sharing a half eaten ham roll redeemed from the nearest garbage bin. The London legends of tube stations which were not on the map and which only appeared now and then, Venus flytraps of the underground, with names like Hobbs Lane, Iggulden Common, Mugwort Hill, Chilblain Road, Earwig Court, Smudge Green and Spooning Bec. People who got off at them were never seen or heard of again, and those who boarded the trains there, with strange looks and saucer eyes, disappeared into the crowd, to the detriment of future generations. There were the phantom pubs, which lured the unwary to experimental penal colonies in Wales. The hordes of supporters of football clubs which did not exist, vanishing through open sewers. The rats in City offices, who were in league with a revolutionary network of cleaning ladies, gnawing their way into computer systems to disrupt the world's finances. The dead who answered operator calls dialled from telephone booths in the small hours. And the infamous Bingley, who ordered various takeaways from booths, and then murdered the delivery girls. Blok told her, in return, of Lenin's brain in Highgate, attested to by Adonai the Avatar. She nodded her large head sagely, saying: 'They ought ter get a foo more songs aart o' the blighter. Ah liked that one abart the werkin' class 'ero . . . lovely Riter meter maid . . .'

Blok had abandoned Mister Policek's shipwreck. Leaving most of his belongings in the one suitcase, he had written a note to Henry Gibson: 'No agriculture please, I am Jewish. No more Avatars, I am an atheist. No more dependence on the kindness of friends. Love has developed glaucoma. I have your address, I might send you a postcard.' Leaving himself that merest thread of contact, he had taken one holdall on to the District Line and got off at the Embankment station.

Why?

The question ceased to have any meaning, as he dragged The Mall, past Saint James's Park, gawping up at Buckingham Palace, gobbling leftovers at the bronze feet of the Queen who had said she was not amused. 'Windsers an' Plantaargenits, bunch o' bleedin' cut-throats! Chop ther bleedin' 'eads off, aar say! That Oliver Cromwell, 'e 'ad the raat idea. Make 'em clean aart the doubleyer cees, laak in Chiner.'

String 'em up, it's the only language they understand. A police car drove up, a white slug in the gloaming. Blok hid behind the gilded monument. A gruff voice shouted something out the window to the bulk of the White Whale, who shook her mitt angrily. 'Up th'revolooshern! Kill th'pigs!' They waved her on, Blok creeping in the shadow of her billowing rags, down Birdcage Walk to Westminster. 'Nothink in this bleedin' paartr th'werld 'cept Em Pees an' beggars,' she croaked, wagging her jib, dragging her shopping bags on the road. Blok had offered to carry some of them for her, but they appeared physically attached, an unremovable tumour.

'You get yerself aart a'here, Eh-Bram,' she said. 'This ain't the life you should be aarter. You should marry a good solid gel, what looks aarter yer. Unless yer one of them noofangled jolly chappies.'

'I don't think so,' he said. 'I adore women. But I can't seem to supply what they want, excitement, dependability, support, a defence against predators and tax inspectors.'

'Can yer get it up?'

'Usually.'

'Then yer ain't got nothink to worry abaat. Ah wus wiv a Jooish feller once, 'e 'ad a stick the size o' a perlicemern's trunchern. But

205

'e were no bloody good at makin' money, couldn'sell a fireside
stove ter'n Eskimo. Wot bloody good areyer, I aksed 'im, wot
'appened ter all yer peeple's tradisherns? But he had them great big
bollocks, arrr . . .' Katharine's narratives usually petered out in a
glottal spray of slobber. 'Bollocks! Bollocks! Bollocks!' she cried,
waddling over Westminster Bridge, towards the huge sign over
County Hall, proclaiming:

GLC–WORKING FOR LONDON
353,567 PEOPLE
ARE UNEMPLOYED IN LONDON TODAY

'A perlicemern's trunchern!!'
The great bridge over the dark turgid scum of the Thames.
Houses of Parliament on one side and the Anglican Church on the
other. Neo-classical serpents wound about the ornate lamps on the
riverwalk, watching the staggering shards of the Free Market
forces passing in the small hours.
'Bow-locks! Bow-locks!'
Closing down the top flaps of the Hotpoint KR432 refrigerator
box which he had inherited from a denizen who had moved on,
whether to higher or lower things no one could tell, Blok settled
down for the rest of the night on a blanket kindly provided by
Bradbury, clutching the only part of his past he had dragged along
from Shepherd's Bush, the final annexe volume of his age-old
scrapbook, with the latest jetsam of the spews of the world:
SECRET PLAN TO MAKE AIRBASES INVISIBLE;
IRELAND OUTLAWS SUCKING TOBACCO; TYRAN-
NOSAURUS REX: SCIENTISTS UNCOVER THE FACTS;
IRAN TO FINGER THIEVES.

> Iranian authorities are using a new machine for cutting off
> thieves' fingers in accordance with Islamic law, the Teheran
> newspaper *Kayhan* reported yesterday. A member of the
> Supreme Judicial Council also said recently that Iran had
> invented an electric machine for cutting off hands.
>
> Reuter

To make love, a dinosaur had to get his leg over. Even if he happened to be a 160 ton brontosaurus, the female could only bear his weight if he followed the golden rule – always keep one foot on the ground, Dr B. H––, of the University of Reading, said of the creatures' sex lives: 'It must have been utterly charming to watch. They were at it for 140 million years with great joy, delicacy and decorum. If you weigh 100 tons you can't just go bouncing around.'

Too true. One remains, panting, chained down to terra firma. The dawn opening up yet one more day of shadow boxing. Trudging the streets, a walking begging bowl, trying to interrupt safe trajectories – 'Cupo'coffee, mate?' – the eyes, desperate to avoid contact, the quick change of pace, the sideways shuffle, the twist of mouths, pursing of lips, sagging of long-suffering shoulders, the odour of guilt left trailing like a snail's slime in the road . . .

VICTIMS OF THE WORK ETHIC

Tokyo: Psychiatrists report an upsurge of psychosomatic disorders among Japanese men in their forties who are unable to cope with the introduction of a five-day working week. Taught to give their all to the employers in the post-war boom, they failed to develop any outside interests, say the psychiatrists, 'and their families treat them as big pieces of rubbish'. Many victims were found stealing back to their offices on Sundays. Psychosomatic symptoms included intestinal pains, insomnia and eye sores.

Observer, 7 October, 1984

Invisible men, invisible women, in the cracks in the walls . . . Beetling in the tunnels of the underground system, among the buskers desperate to entertain the crowd, madding down and up the escalators, flowing in and out of rabbit holes. Bob-a-Job, a grim youth from Durham, played the flute and tap-danced erratically. El Alamein had once sung First World War songs at Leicester Square. Hang Out Your Washing on the Piccadilly Line. It's a

Long Way to Ticks and Rabies . . . His original name was Jeremiah Scareburn, and he had served in the Western Desert with Monty. Later he slept in Charing Cross Station for several years, taking time out for destitution in Glasgow, Liverpool, Manchester and Leeds. Then he had written a book, in piles of grimy notebooks, about his travels in the gutter, which had eventually been published by an eminent house in Bloomsbury and sold above twelve thousand hardback copies. 'Those were the good days,' he told Blok. 'Supermac, Retail Price Maintenance, You Never Had it So Good. Before Profumo. I was wined and dined by all the nobs of London. I wore a bib and sat down with lobster pickers at the Savoy, with ladies whose hair curled to the ceiling as I talked about giant fleas and chamber pots and buggery in gaol and vomiting and skin diseases known only to the most professional circles. The *Daily Telegraph* serialised me, and Ken Tynan wrote the play, which was banned by the Lord Chamberlain.'

'So what happened?' Blok asked. El Alamein told him his cautionary tale:

The Author's Revenge (Jeremiah Scareburn's Warning):
'My problems began when I was commissioned to go back on the road and write the sequel, Volume Two. I should have realised one should not tempt fate. But I plunged into the pit again. I wandered all over this fucking island, from Land's End to John O'Groats, tasting ashes in Plymouth and Bath, Birmingham, Sheffield and Edinburgh . . . I drank rotgut from rocket fuel of abandoned missile systems . . . I slept in municipal garbage dumps, empty mine shafts, telephone booths, sewer works, air-raid shelters filled with freezing water . . . I was beaten up by policemen in every county in the realm. I offered my body for medical experiments, which left me with these permanent shakes. I even took part in an illegal human sacrifice, and had parts of my left leg eaten. I plumbed the depths, writing down every experience faithfully and sending off instalments to my publisher. And then, after two years of hell, I returned to London, to the eminent house in Bloomsbury, to find my publisher had flown the coop, with my manuscripts, my royalties, a hundred thousand quid of the eminent house's money and his Spanish tottie, to the

Mediterranean. No one knew me from Adam. My fame was long forgotten. I was thrown out on the street like a dog.

'Anyone else would have given way to despair. But we saw off Rommel, didn't we? Blood, sweat and tears . . . I followed the bastard, across the Continent, walking, cadging lifts off truckers, stowing away on trains. I followed my publisher's slime, across the Riviera, through Northern Italy, down to Rome and Sicily, and across the Ionian Sea to Corfu. Hopping after him from island to island, Paxoi to Levkas, to Cephalonia, Zakynthos and then across the straits into the wildest Peloponnese. I joined up with a band of gypsies, who performed magic tricks and cut-price sexual intercourse, the Pubic Wars . . . finally caught up with my nemesis in a remote cottage on the summit of a barren mountain. The gypsy kids raided his Buick in the night, stripping it to its chassis. I had the bastard where I wanted him.

'I crept up, after midnight, to the stone walls, listening to the sounds of joy and intercourse. The stars were blazing bright in the sky. The gypsies left me an axe and withdrew. I looked in at the window. They were both naked, on a sheepskin on the stone floor, with my manuscript, I recognised the pile of notebooks, on a table just beside them. They looked up and screamed as I entered – a ghastly sight, I must have been, torn and stinking, bearded and battered, with the moon at my back . . .

'He began offering me deals: imminent publication, within twenty-four months, unless prevented by strikes, lock-outs or other circumstances beyond corporate control, indemnification against liability for costs, fifteen per cent royalties on all hardback copies, eighty per cent of Book Club rights, Digest condensations and ninety-five per cent of US sales. But I decapitated them both with the axe. Still his head continued to gabble at me, offering to up the hardback royalties to twenty per cent, the US sales to a hundred, and no deficit on returns. I pursued the skunk's skull round and round the shack, hacking it to a pulp. Then I piled the lot, manuscripts and carcasses on the floor, dowsing 'em with petrol I siphoned from the stripped Buick, and added my own blood-soaked clothes on the pyre. Lit it with a match I found in his pocket and walked down the hill naked and pure. The gypsies asked no questions. They clothed me and took me to Corinth, and

209

I hitched on from there. Three months later I stood on the white cliffs of Dover. I have never since then sought a life of prominence. Modesty, that's the word, my boys. One should never aspire above one's station. Still, I had a good war. It's the peace that's the bloody trouble, *mes enfants*. Does anyone have another fag?'

'MIND THE GAP!'

Blok got up from the bench at the Bakerloo northbound platform of the Embankment Underground Station. The sepulchral tape-recorded voice punctuating each train's arrival. Art lovers embark, disembark. Severed heads, slashed larynxes still gabbling. Severed limbs twitching from waste bins. Human intestines and old bones flowing out of Katharine Weale's shopping bags . . .

'MIND THE GAP!'

What? Those homunculi again? Those little people, spilled from their bottles? Time passing, with hob-nailed boots. You should have listened to your mother. Or anyone, apart from the demon of extinction. But he seemed to have the only tune. The days getting shorter, the nights brisker, then cold. The street people icing up at sunset, hoping to thaw out in the dawn. But the dawn is a mere bleat of grey from a sky which leans closer, pushing its fog as if stuffing its human pâté de foie gras . . .

He had caught a glimpse, late in September, of Henry Gibson, promenading the South Bank walkways, peeking at the cardboard flotsam. Asking questions, receiving no answers. He had the look of a retired bailiff. The thick glasses, the hunched shoulders, the tentative waddle, the suspicious crawling approach. No one volunteered information, and Blok hid behind a concrete pillar, in the lee of the cafeteria of the Festival Hall. Behind him lovers of Bach spooned down the soup du jour, twirled spinach quiche down their gullets. He had not long before eaten one pork pie, earned by two hours' trudge for ten-pee handouts. Henry Gibson turned away, looking glum and perplexed. Blok moved his box far down the line.

Bradbury had introduced him to the non-welfare state, and to a National Insurance Number. He stood in line, at the Supplementary Benefits section of the Department of Health and Social

Security, being questioned about his future prospects. He told the harassed young Asian girl in the glass booth he wished to become a nuclear physicist. She told him there were said to be a number of vacancies at the cleaning end of the catering trade. Becoming bold, he asked her if she had a regular boy friend. She told him to make way for the next case.

'MIND THE GAP!'

He thought a few times of the Israeli dinosaurs, and one brisk day walked north to their area. Up to Baker Street, Park Road and up Wellington Road to Saint John's Wood and another mode of being. Acacia Road and Marlborough Hill and Swiss Cottage and gardens, bookshops and health food stores. West Hampstead, Brondesbury, Kilburn, more polyglot squares on the chessboard. Passing by the house of Asher's ex-friend, Dudik 'Big Daddy' Birenbaum, ground-floor windows open, pot plants yawning. The soft churn of multicultural music. A fat ginger cat baring its teeth. Remembering the early joys of his English discoveries – that one could befriend strange cats on fences, or tickle dogs on pavement walks. The strange idea that battlefields did not necessarily lurk behind each façade. But that all seemed irrelevant now. Bradbury had warned him: 'Don't stay with us long. Misery is addictive.' But he moved on, idly passing by his old abode in Inglenook Road, then turning back. Someone had discarded a half-eaten Macdonald's in a wastebin. He devoured it. It tasted the same as it would had it just slid off the assembly line.

MIND THE MAP!

Adrift, in topographical mindfields. THE FEAR! When all has already been lost, who cares? One rubs away against pavements. Skin unrolls down drains. The numbness of repetitive time.

MIND THE NAP!

The October, November nights are colder. A Salvation Army van brought blankets, contributed by jumble sales in Zambia. Katharine took Blok to a church hymn meeting, where she denounced Christ and all his pandering. They were evicted, gently but firmly, by black-uniformed men and women.

MIND THE RAP!

The police finally caught up with him, arresting him with Dishcloth and Smeg, outside Waterloo Station, cadging their ten pees off commuters bound for the Conservative constituencies of South England. Richmond. Woking. Esher. Staines. Weybridge. Money-on-Thames. Empty yer pockets, lads. Not a good night, is it? Avram Blok? Ain't seen you before, sonny. Wot are you? Some sort of Polish kike, eh? Well, keep out of my manor.

MIND THE SAP!

It rises, from the roots, then oozes, hardens, congeals in ice. December is even colder than November. They say it's a real snap coming . . . 'I use th' *Sunday Tarms*,' says Katharine. 'It's th'best insoolayshern. We used ter swear by de *Daily Telegraph*, but 'ats a real rag nowadays . . .' The colour supplements, in particular, made solid pulp for shoes . . .

MIND THE PAP!

The nights lengthening, marching on towards Christmas. The days, shorter and shorter straws. Eventually they would cease to dawn completely, the sky remaining black as pitch, the street-lights failing, the Christmas lights receding, the cries of Noel turning to frosted cubes, Father Christmases freezing to death at their posts, tolling their sepulchral bells. NO 'ELL! NO 'ELL! El Alamein died that way, with only five shopping days left to Yule. He was found, rigid as a glacier, eyes little frost balls, jacked in his box, come eight thirty a.m. by the stalactites of Big Ben. 'Poor sod,' said Bradbury. 'An' all them folks he murdered . . . every time it was someone else . . . Lords, ladies, tarts, coppers, lawyers, literary agents, social workers . . .' Mysterious council persons, dressed in black, with cardboard conical hats embroidered with strange zodiacal designs, came and took him away in a giant black garden bag and an unmarked van. The box dwellers stood around, in a tight knot, huddled, as the Thames moved languidly, like putty, towards the sea . . .

MIND THE TRAP!

And darkness was on the face of the deep. And nothing moved upon the face of the waters, not even the sightseeing tourist boats. And God said: LET THERE BE LIGHT!

Coins tinkle in disconnected meters . . . The charity workers swooped, with blankets and provisions, collecting the box dwellers and driving them, with cattle prods, towards the warmth of indoor sanctuaries. Christmas trees festooned with baubles and

212

little tinselly gifts: a bar of soap, a toothbrush, toenail clippers, a pair of eyebrow tweezers. Many luminaries came and fed them soup in person, by means of large wooden spoons: the Archbishop of Canterbury, the Moderator of the Kirk of Scotland, the Pope, the Prime Minister's consort, the Leader of the Opposition. Several members of the Royal Family recited hymns. Jesus Christ arrived, and signed autographs. Many people wept openly, on their knees. False teeth rattled into mouseholes. Upon a colour television screen, high above the multitude, the Queen spoke hope to Her Nation. Katharine Weale shook her fist at the apparition, dragging Blok and Bradbury out of the sanctuary.

'AAAR! STONE THE BLEEDIN' CROSS!'

The streets of the city were deserted. People were clustered inside their houses, in their nuclear or extended clans. Streamers of fake joke spaghetti wreathing round Dads and Mums. Many people imbibed cheap wine. Others, beer or stronger stuff. The South Bank walkway bare and desolate. Corpses floated down the setting concrete river. Dead fish played melancholy jazz airs on oboes and trombones.

'DARN WIV CARPETALISM!' Katharine shouted. 'Where is John Lenin now that we need 'im? Didn't yer say 'is brain was somewhere in 'Ighgate? Lead on, MacBlok! Arr, its tarm f'r straight answers!'

They turned north again, pickled and sizzling in methylated fluids. Staggering north across the Waterloo Bridge up Kingsway, Southampton Row and in the lee of Euston, passing by the few ladies of the night hanging forlornly about King's Cross, no turkeys in sight at all. Tramp, tramp, tramp. Snakes spilling out of Katharine's plastic shopping bags, escaping into nooks and gutters. Giant rats leaning up against corners, picking their teeth with finger bones. The empty junction of the Camden Town, splitting off to Hampstead, Highgate or Holloway. The women's penal facility, where many of the suffragettes of Cheetham Common saw service. Sisters of the earth in situ. But at the junction of Fortess and Highgate Road, just above Kentish Town, Katharine faltered, suddenly sitting down on the street.

'Ah can't go any farther, sweeties. It's me 'art, the old ticker!'

The beached whale. Thump, thump, thump. Bradbury put his

213

ear to the massive, rippling mess of rags merging with an encrusted abdomen. Kathump! Kathloomp! Kachunk!

'It's still there, Kat.'

'Ar, it's collectin' its cards. Nah 'ope, nah 'ope, comrades. Ah should 'ave one o'them noofangled transmutes. Git old Maggie's 'art put in. Ar! Made o' solid steel, that one.'

Kapoom! Kapoom! Kaploom!

'Ah'll just sit 'ere an' 'ave me Xmas dinner,' said Katharine, extracting from her laden bags a squashed steak-and-kidney pie and a shredded tomato sandwich repossessed from the Sanctuary binge, together with her battered thermos flask which, twisted open, gave off a heady odour of rancid space shuttle fuel.

'You go on an' find Lenin's brain fer us, Eh-Bram,' she swung her arm, 'ger forth and meet de orakul . . . be a real werkin'-class 'ero . . . aks 'im 'ow t'r'libate us from Maggie Thatcher, when do we stick ar knife in 'er gizzard? When do we avenge th'oppressed victims o' nearr-farsist Tory rule? Garn, Eh-Bram, yer blasted kike, show 'em yer perlicemern's trunchern! Get artofit! Shove off! An' don't come back wivaart wotchacallit – that gorlden disk, them old choons!'

'Better let her be, she means no harm,' said Bradbury. 'Meet yer later, when she's calmed down a bit . . .'

'Aart! Aart! Aart!' shouted Katharine, propelling Blok up the Fortess Road with the power of her sputum. He waved to Bradbury and tottered up, alone, towards Tufnell Park, Archway, and Highgate Cemetery.

That golden disk . . . them old choons . . . the wheel of being turning . . . Karl Marx mumbling in his tomb. ('Philosophers have only interpreted the world, the point is to change it, ba-bam, ba-bam . . .') Not a stone's throw from the cemetery, the glass vas containing the Great Leader's brain bubbled into the midnight of Christmas Eve, its elderly custodians slumped before television, tuned to a Channel Four late-night movie, in which a hired Santa Claus at Macy's Department Store in New York turns out to be the real thing. Seven sleeping old men, drooping in their settees and easy chairs, while little chow dogs wolfed down the remains of a Marks and Spencer's Plum Pudding. The seven members of the Aquarium, in descending order of seniority: Bream, Perch, Salmon, Trout, Halibut, Roe and MacFarlane. They had tended their secret and sacred task since the autumn of 1925, when the personal bodyguard of the late Great Leader, accompanied by the great surgeon Akhmat Akhmatsky, had brought the still pulsating organ in a camel's skin calabash to London to escape its certain destruction by Joseph Stalin, who had already suppressed his mentor's Will, and was preparing to crush all opposition to his creed of Socialism in One Person. The seven original members of the North London Branch of the Party had been selected by the Leader himself, in his last breath, as the most loyal and most discreet of trustees. Only one of them, Pilchard, had died in the interim, but the original six, having recruited MacFarlane, a trusted comrade of James Maclean (despite his non-aquatic moniker), held on stubbornly to their lives and their secret down the decades, keeping their solemn oath of total silence to such a degree they no longer spoke to each other, but communicated by means of hints and gestures, the lifting of eyebrows, the flicker of eyelashes, the twiddle of an index finger or the flaring of a red wrinkled nostril, codes honed over half a century of unstinting devotion . . .

Blop. Blap. Blop. Dials juddered, preserving fluids bubbled and gasped, recording Vladimir Ilyich Lenin's frozen dream: the world, covered with Socialist Electrification, a great network of pylons crisscrossing the globe, Technology! bringing power to the remotest African hut, Indian howdahs, Chinese kow-loons, Latin American ranchos. These electrons, buzzing around in people's heads, wanging through their ears, roused them to full democratic participation in their respective soviets: everywhere, people of all races, creeds, genders, in clean, pressed overalls, voted for the forward march. The earth was completely tamed, the bourgeoisie disappeared completely from the stage of history, infantile left-wing adventurists slid into oblivion and the globe revolved regularly and majestically in its orbit, sending off little shards of spaceships, bearing youthful and healthy pioneers to spread the word among the stars . . .

Blip. Bloop. Blup. Soft bubbles emerged from the trembling Aquarian lips, floating above the coloured card denoting the end

215

of transmission. Night owls could now switch to unregistered channels, tuning in to messages from outer space, often in thinly scrambled code. Neutrons, positrons and quarks zinged through prima materia. Souls swam desperately in the primordial soup, looking for the rim of the bowl. Awake! Awake! As Blok trudged on, up past Archway, turning into the steep suburban streets, looking for a warm dustbin. He regretted leaving the Sanctuary, and other, warmer memories flickered dully, though he could not quite place them. His brain was unused to pure alcohol, which he had managed till now to avoid. The only images he could dredge up were of crusts of bread, apple cores, Macdonald and Wimpy baps, chips wrapped in greasy paper. Even wasp grubs, fried in the comb, could not survive this fragility. A strange sound bubbled in his veins, circulating in his blood system. A low hum appeared to pervade the quiet streets, the leafy gardens. Puddles in the gutter had become frost. Frost dangled in the freeze of branches. He could see the evidence of extreme cold, and yet his body could not feel this. His feet, the torn shoes shod in Sunday supplements, were detached clumps, leading him nowhere. The hum enveloped him, vibrating his eyeballs. He emerged at the top of the hill by the Highgate tube. The road forked down in four directions. The sky was a steel dark grey. A sheet of ice lay over the road. A strange apparition appeared before him: seven aged men, dragging, over their shoulders by means of thick ropes, a cart with squeaking wheels on which, in a bell-shaped glass case, a great grey-white blob of matter pulsated, gasping asthmatically. On its flank, his legs dangling over the churning left wheel, Carl alias Che Guevara, his breast crossed with ammunition belts, rode shotgun, the girls Dominique and May hanging over his left and right shoulders, in form-fitting black and red rubber costumes, dangling whips down his bosom. Behind the cart, a stout, limping figure he recognised as the Chief Constable of Greater Cheetham tottered, dressed in an ermine and turquoise coat, festooned with the symbols of the compass, the level, the square, the beehive, the ark, the hourglass, the scythe, the all-seeing eye and the ineffable name, tolling a large, cracked bell. BONG! BONG! BONG! He heard the voice of Katharine Weale: 'AARRR, COMRADE! GI'R'S A KISS!'

216

He slipped and fell in the roadway, his face striking the freezing surface. The tip of his tongue, protruding, stuck to the ice. His feet scrabbled for purchase on the slope. His body began to slide. His tongue, its tip still rooted to the ground, unrolled from his mouth relentlessly as he slid down the Archway Road. Past Shepherds Hill, Cholmeley Park, Cromwell Avenue and Winchester Road, under the bridge of Hornsey Lane, past Waterlow and Despard Roads and down to the main Archway junction. He lay there like a shipwrecked starfish, his tongue fastened for three quarters of a mile to the asphalt of the highway.

Voices spoke.

'Avram Blok! Goddammit!'

'Blok, you bastard! Are you all right?'

How can one be all right with one's lips at Archway and the tip of one's tongue by Highgate tube? From the corner of an eye he saw wheels. A black London taxicab, its doors swung open and six persons climbing out to stand over him. Kneeling down with worried looks. The dredge of his memory naming them, despite their wrap in giant overcoats: Henry Gibson, the scheduler Sheila Ratchett, the black South Africans Walter and Annie and beside them a red-haired, solicitous face which he could only just place as Janet, Asher Katzman's ex-wife, from children's television. And, was that sixth figure, bending over, brushing his face with the unwinding threads of its scarf, the sweetest, unlikeliest apparition of all?

Jacqueline??

'Goddammit Avram! We nearly didn't make it!'

Helping hands pulled him off the ice.

217

III

Paradiso . . .

THE SECOND COMING

Berl, Cherl and Shmerl decide to emigrate from the Old Country, 'Mother' Russia, to the New World.

Berl says: 'Ven I get to Amerikeh, I vill immediately change my name to . . . Buck!'

Cherl says: 'Ven I get to Amerikeh, I vill immediately change my name to . . . Chuck!'

Shmerl ponders a bit and then shrugs: 'Me, I think I better stay the way I am.'

Cautionary Yiddish Tale

*Hatched from the egg, pushing the sharp edges of shells away, pecking
away the fluff and gunge, the potter Ptah, hands at the cosmic wheel,
shaking, breaks the hundred billionth clay pot, born of the bull's back
passage on an off night, a Friday afternoon sperm, rising from the ashcans
of rubble Europe, pushing aside the lid noisily, threshing among the spent
chicken bones, offal, orange peels and squashed apple-juice cartons,
sprung out like a fresh shoot from good Mother Earth, the zygote of
Buddha and Pest, budding all over, born of the unity of forced isolation,
Papa and Mama Blok hiding in their respective cupboards of courageous
Hungarian gentiles until freed by the Tatar battalions of the victorious
Red Army, the emergence in umbilical slime upon the illegal immigrant
ship* Irma Klein, *heading at less than full steam for the Promised Land,
hunted down by Royal Spitfires: Turn back! Turn back oven-fodder,
Jerusalem is not for thee! Slap! Maestro Plekhanov's hand on the new
born babe's bottom and the first wail of protest, certainly not the last . . .
But the hope, after all . . .*

★

Blok turned the final twist in the path, coming into full view of the
large wooden building cunningly painted to appear as an old
gothic Transylvanian castle circa 1805. The special FX pumped
through hidden loudspeakers had died away, and a hand–painted
sign now pointed towards the house, proclaiming in bold capitals:

DON'T LOOK NOW,
USE YOUR NOODLE,
THIS IS IRVING KLOTSKASHES'
PRIVATE CABOODLE!

Ersatz lightning flickered within the arched lattice windows of the castle. A low growling sound of Doberman Pinschers came from the grounds at the foot of the house but there were no signs of real life. Abandoned gondolas slapped melancholily at the quay of an artificial stream. A large metal 'K' revolved creakily on the highest turret, moved by the evening Big Sur breeze. Another flash of light from within the largest ground-floor window briefly revealed the silhouette of a massive form supine upon a four-poster bed. Then the window was dark again. Blok stepped up the pathway, spiralling up the flat bed of a neatly cut lawn. A stone statue of a silent film star's Quasimodo lurched pitiably from a pedestal. A lone raven with clipped wings waddled up to peck Blok's shoe. He stepped up to the great walnut front door, aged by Max Factor Number 55 ageing resins and, lifting the heavy rusted metal knocker, rapped three times upon its rough surface . . .

But, much earlier than all this –

*

'Psychotic episodes,' said Henry Gibson, 'the experience of total loss, or bereavement, or the fading away of one's personality. I found it a pretty frequent phenomenon, myself. One in five of the population of the British Isles will succumb at one time or another to a major mental disability. One in ten will have to be locked away for a while. One in twenty, for recurring periods. I was on Largactil for about three years. Just after my poor wife left me. She said living with a gibbering idiot who did not know his own mind was becoming too much of a good thing. It was the heyday of Swinging London. Everyone else was having such a good time, smoking dope and screaming at Beatle records. I was cold, miserable and repressed. I am still cold, miserable and repressed, but now society has caught up with me.'

Blok was silent, looking out through the kitchen window at the expanse of snow stretching forth, covering the rolling hills of Cheethamshire as far ahead as he could see. Little clumps of sheep stirred pathetically in the distance, marooned in drifts, with a lone farmer cutting a thin black path towards them from the skewed hulk of a stalled tractor. From this side of the house, and with the double glazing, one could not hear the staccato grunts of the pigs, clustered in their heated pens and weaneries. Henry's sister Charlene hustled through the kitchen, dressed like Scott of the Antarctic, with a hefty bag of tools.

'I'm going to check the insulation, Henry,' she rasped. 'Keep an ear open for any calls. They might airlift feed by chopper.'

'Eleven tons of pigswill, dropped by parachute,' Gibson reflected, as she stormed out, door banging. 'Did you ever think you would live to see the day?'

Blok shook his head, poured another coffee. There were no external sounds to disturb the hum of the fridge, the chunky clatter of the dishwasher, the thrum of the central heating boiler, the chink of cups, the wheeze of their breathing. Idly he turned the pages of the February issue of the *Pig Farmer's Monthly*, which had been the last penetration from the outside world since the storms cut the farmhouse and the village of Mucus-On-The-Pond off from the rest of the United Kingdom. Blok had not known the Gibson farm was a piggery until he had recovered from his frosted Christmas to a New Year of strange cadences and effluvia:

FEEDING THE PIG OF THE EIGHTIES: OFF-THE-SOW, by John Bacon:

> Controversy still rages over early creep feeding. The detractors believe the sow will do it all until her peak yield starts to topple three weeks from farrowing. While the trend towards earlier weaning has severely dented that argument a new one is emerging, exemplified by the 'start-em-low-and-gradual-and-bring-em-up-quickly' approach . . .

'There's nothing in this entire magazine that's not about pigs,' Blok complained to Gibson. 'Every advertisement, every reader's letter. Even the cartoon is a pig one.'

'That's the way it is,' said Henry Gibson. 'When you find a cause, it's sufficient. Other choices become an illusion.'

But certain memories did percolate, of other porcine visions, in a far off land, heavy with representation . . . failed exorcisms, futile quests of pre-Katharine Weale desires . . .

225

'Dreams,' Henry Gibson said, 'nightmares of decline and fall. I've had it all. I used to have the shakes, attacks of panic, when I realised I had no idea who I was, that I'd always relied on defining myself by what others expected me to be. Mister Goodhusband and Old Reliable. Mister Jack-of-all-trades. The creative artiste. But then my wife proved to me I was really nobody. This put a crimp in my style. The clichés of loneliness . . . When you begin talking to the bathtaps, that's when you know you're a goner. Or when you freak out at the mirror: Ach! I am so ugly! Ugly and withered and grey! That was at least the balm in teaching students. Their fresh faces, radiating hope. Their vim and vigour. The spring in the instep. Ah! Sucking the life's blood from those firm unyielding bodies – sharpening one's teeth on the application forms. Varm bloood! shlurrrrpppplllrrrp . . . But it never lasts, *mon vieux*. You just droop on and sag further. Blood is just a little thicker than water, and much thinner than cash money. So what can you expect? The accumulation of memories, sans advancement? You know what the medievals thought of that? They believed memory served to recall the realities of Heaven and Hell. *Verstehen?* The memory of Paradise, *liebling*, mit all the seraphim and cherubim, playing one's tune. The Inferno, with top hat'n'tails, where Satan and all his myrmidons are being tortured daily, with fire and brimstone and lectures on deconstructionism. Heaven and Hell, according to medieval thought, lie not in our future, but our past. Dante the Wop had his own variation: Hell in the past, Heaven ahead if we could make it, and the acquisition of penitenzia and wisdom in the present, as we all schlep up the spirals of Purgatory, reaching for the girly pates . . . Go make your self-determination out of that, baby.'

But Blok's most recent recollections were of neither heaven nor hell: Jacqueline, sitting over his bed in the chaos of the Westbourne Park squat. Unknown women and men having thawed him out with hot towels and compresses, Iranian Mahmud massaging his toes by a method which had saved a billion limbs throughout the Orient since the Flood, and Janet, blowing her cigarette fumes away from him in the background, proposing: 'Tea. It's the only withdrawal treatment. Apart from whisky, and rum.' Walter and Annie, sympathetic but unable to offer accommodation as they

226

were just visiting from their new perch at Uppsala to meet their daughter who had come up from Botswana. 'You wouldn't believe it, Avram, us warm-blooded blacks wandering in the snow in our duffels. People look at us as if we have a strange disease. But it will not last, O Lord, these wanderings, it is too fucking cold out there . . . If you have any chance of a home in at least a sub-tropical zone, mein boy,' said Walter, jabbing him with his pipe, 'you should seize it with both hands . . .'

Perhaps. But so far he has the grimy sparseness of a weekday Portobello Road, with Jacqueline holding his arm in lieu of a crutch. A temporary support. She had already told him she was not staying on. Her return to the United States had been delayed, she admitted to him, by her relationship with the Vest German, Frida, whose broken legs had taken a long time to mend, but then: 'Our relationship didn't survive after that. Lovers' tiffs. You know how it is, Avram. The blue blood, but what the hell, that's how the wind blows. I've done what I can, I think, for Cheetham Common. Now there's work for me back home . . .'

It was only good luck she had been present at all at his rescue, having come to London to meet Walter'n'Annie on their brief Christmas visit, and via queries on Asher interfacing with Janet, and then with Henry Gibson, who had coincidentally just that very hour received news of a Blok sighting at the Sanctuary. The mad drive up the frozen trail to Highgate, via Bradbury and the White Whale's bag droppings, and the stroke of fortune at Archway . . . Now she was smiling earnestly at Blok across the table of a small ethnic minority eatery in Notting Hill Gate, picking at vegetable samosas. An odd location to air the siren call of the Jesuit from the deserts of the White Sands Missile Range, the belly of Mutual Assured Destruction.

'Alamogordo, New Mexico, Avram, do you know the significance of that name? An obscure piece of nowhere chosen by the bright sparks to set off the first nuclear bomb. Now it's the country's second major testing ground. A real challenge for the movement . . . Heck, I suppose its ridiculous, trying to save the world when saving one person is so bloody hard. Will you promise me at least to stay alive, Avram, and not flush yourself again down the tubes?'

She squeezed his arm, holding on with strong, gentle fingers.

'I'm sorry you had to go to all that trouble,' he said.

She shrugged: 'We're the troublemaking generation. We've never been out of trouble, have we? My sister, Victoria, included. Nothing humanoid is alien to us. But you were nearly dead out there.'

He looked at the big blonde close-cropped girl smiling at him, broadcasting her support but nevertheless maintaining the firm, invisible barrier of their incompatibility.

'You might say you had the courage of your convictions,' she mused, 'if you could figure out what your convictions were . . . Hey, man, I'm no clearer about myself than you are. But I function by assumptions. A certain way of life feels right for me. Other ways just seem wrong. It's simply a matter of making a decision and sticking to it. As your conscience allows. There should be a little compass inside you.'

'I'm the crocodile who hasn't swallowed the clock,' said Blok. 'I don't know which ship to follow to Never-Never-Land.'

'Don't follow. Define your own way,' she said.

'OK,' he said. He gave her his parole. She packed and left for Heathrow Airport, shouldering her rucksack into the fog. A few days later red-haired Janet drove him in her battered Citroen 2-CV up in the January murk into the country, to Charlene Gibson's piggery at Mucus-On-The-Pond, conveying to him on the way Asher's latest best wishes from Los Angeles: 'He's still doing fine. Just come back from location, completing the San Manuel film. Still staying with his Fairfax friends . . .' She, too, broadcast a calm sympathy, and an offer: 'Why don't you come up to Edinburgh some time, Avram? I'll be there for Easter, at my parents' home. It's a small village twenty miles out, on the Firth of Forth – Craddock. You've never heard of it. A bit on the cold side, but you might like the change. It's not the big city grind.'

So many suggestions of redemption . . . the soul, purged by the wide open spaces . . . Snow drifted out of the light grey Cheethamshire sky. Blok trekked out alone in the heavy boots and sheepskin 'Biggles' jacket provided by Charlene Gibson, towards the white copse on the neighbouring hill. A sullen beauty to the landscape that he had not anticipated. The clichéd clean crispness of the elements. A silence broken only by the plaintive cry of the farmer to his trapped sheep: 'Here, peep, peep, peep, peep, peep, peep . . .' The animals did not respond. Perhaps they just wished to die quietly in this lush whiteness, embalmed in purity, frozen to salvation. And yet Blok felt entirely alive . . .

Succoured, who would believe it, by the piggery, amid the rubble of Henry Gibson's stored knick-knacks and the preserved past of his elder sister, who had escaped the boarding house life of Bournemouth in her own chosen path to a life of bachelor farming in the Country, Muck and Money, dragging with her the flotsam of their tender youth in turn of the Fifties' Great Britain, when a quarter of the world was pink, not punk, and Britannia ruled the knaves. *Tom Brown's Schooldays* and Bulldog Drummond and Biggles and *The Thirty-Nine Steps*. Gibson spent the first days of Blok's sojourn bending his bedside ear with gleeful readings from his sister's old fodder – Angela Brazil and *Little Women* by Louisa M. Alcott and *The Invisible Schoolgirl* and Enid Blyton and *The Bumper Book For Girls* and *Sally At School* and Shirley Flight, Air Hostess, in *The Great Bullion Mystery*: '"It was the tail end of the monsoon season and torrential rain was shadowing the wings of the stately Super Constellation L–10490 as she ploughed her way through vast, billowing clouds . . . Air hostess Shirley Flight moved smoothly along the soft-piled carpet extending the length of the passengers' saloon, to the accompaniment of an appetising aroma of prime turtle soup from six little silvery bowls upon the tray which she was carrying level with her right shoulder, on her outstretched hand . . ." I am not sure whether that is physically possible . . . hein? Blok? Are you paying attention? Are you listening, Jewish schwein?'

Oink. Oink. Oink. The little silvery bowls, the Lost Empire, the English monsoon battering its flakes against the farmhouse walls, relaxing into its white carpet, in which our hero gambolled, among the five pigmen and one girl, Rosalind, all stereotypically taciturn as they tended to the bloating porkers. There was also a veterinarian who came once a week to poke implements up the doomed beasts' orifices. Blok at first shunned them, repelled not only by their smell but by genetic rejections, but eventually found himself passing by the pens quite nonchalantly, mumbling greetings to the pink wiggled snouts, tucking in to their Lincocin Premix. Pork is just pork, after all. As Henry Gibson said: 'It's either them or us, pardner.'

A tiny figure appeared to be ploughing through the snow towards him from the direction of the main road. It looked like Omar Sharif in *Doctor Zhivago* but resolved itself into Sheila Ratchett, waving to him from the buried hedgerow, her warm breath preceding her on the glacial air. She took his arm, and they trudged back to the farmhouse, Gibson's eyes lighting up when he saw the sheaf of newspapers she drew from her holdall, but dimming back when they were revealed to be a week's supply of the Proletarian Party's organ, *Permanent Power*. 'No *Times*?' he squeaked. 'No *Telegraph*? No *Guardian*? No *Observer*? Not even a weeny smidge of *Newsweek*?' But Sheila was a stern catechist. She had hitched a lift on the Cheethamshire snow plough, to bring them the latest on the global resistance to imperialist crimes. 'Who needs the Tory and Social Fascist press?' she asked. 'Television feeds you enough garbage.' But the Gibsons' TV had been out of order for three weeks, and Charlene never watched it at all. 'But I *want* more garbage!' Henry protested. 'More swill, more crap, more Tory lies . . .' She gave him a peck on his cheek and tousled what was left of his hair. This strange relationship was unexplainable. It had begun sometime during Blok's sojourn in the boxes, when they had joined forces to try to find their disappeared friend, a truly odd union of opposites, square pegs in their respective round holes, for Sheila Ratchett was, despite appearances, not as totally immersed in Proletarian Power as party dogma demanded. She liked motion pictures, which, despite their iconic co-option into theoretical schemas, were still regarded by the Party Polit-buro as frivolous daubs of bourgeois 'art', since according to Executive Committee Chairman Clive Ogilby even Sergei Eisenstein had been a reactionary running dog stooge of state-capitalist repression. The official Party line was still that only the ten Chinese proletarian ballet productions authorised during the Great Cultural Revolution were truly kosher cinema. The Party had long denounced China's repudiation of the Gang of Four and was preparing a further denunciation of creeping revisionism in Albania. Its sole model was henceforth to be Kim Il Sung's North

Korea, a development even the long loyal Sheila thought a little extreme.

Henry sighed. 'It all sounds like my poor boy Jonathan, who sold his soul to Adonai the Avatar alias Nathan Bloom,' he said, reminding them: 'We have a barn here full of unsold copies of the Sun God's science fiction saga, including *Warriors of the Last Heatwave* and *The Pulse of Ra-Mageddon*. I am authorised to give a thirty-five per cent discount. I also have fifteen crates of enamel Ra Ra Mugs and Ra Ma Dan Ginseng Extract. We tried some on the pigs but there was no apparent consequence.'

'There's a fool born every minute,' said Sheila Ratchett, 'and I'm beginning to believe it's me. But shit, we still have to find some way through the mush in this banana republic . . .'

'We'll reopen the Film College, Sheila-Podge,' said Henry, 'and make them all stand at dawn by their moviolas, spick and span, and well brushed. You can inspect their ideals every morning, and send them to the semiotic cells if the bubelehs don't measure up.'

'Maybe I will bring you a *Newsweek* next time,' she said bravely.

He threw his arms up in the air.

And in the morning, the snow melted away, Sheila Ratchett returned to her squat by public transport, leaving Henry Gibson gasping in bed, worn out by what he had to reveal was, on aggregate, the annual bout of actual lust. 'This is the way I want to go, Avram,' he confided, 'a carnal coronary, and blam. It's a more common form of death than is generally known, my friend. I read that in an old *Die Zeit*.'

New ghosts for old. The quiet swathe of fields rolling on north-eastwards towards the site of Cheetham Common, the air base waking from its hibernation, the toughest remnants of the women's Peace Camp still parked in their flimsy 'benders' by their political Everest, warily watched by the Chief Constable in his bunker through his hidden boobyscopes and videos, collating the sad waste of these political passions while he fondly contemplates his continued ascendance through the Upper Degrees of the Masonic Craft: Knight of the Pelican and Eagle, Grand Pontiff, Venerable Grandmaster, Patriarch Noachite, Prince of Lebanon, Chief of the Tabernacle, Prince of the Tabernacle, Knight of the

Brazen Serpent, Prince of Mercy, Commander of the Temple, Knight of the Sun, Knight of Saint Andrew, Grand Elected Knight Kadosh, Grand Inspector Inquisitor, Sublime Prince of the Royal Secret, Grand Inspector General . . . Yea, I am climbing Jacob's Ladder – who knows what might be found at the top?

The television repairman called and put the Gibson piggery back into contact with the rest of the world. The frost continued to recede. Genuine bourgeois newspapers slid through the front-door flap, updating Blok and Henry Gibson on the current affairs they had missed: Mrs Thatcher had cabled President Chernenko of the Soviet Union, on bilateral relations. ('Is that a new Soviet Supremo?' asked Henry. 'What happened to Lavrenty Beria?') The Labour Party had accused the Conservative Government of deception over the sinking of an Argentine battleship, the *General Belgrano*, which had triggered all-out war in the Falkland Islands back in 1982. The great Miners' Strike had crumbled, and Blok and the Gibsons watched the pit workers march proudly back to work in their defeat, brandishing their trade union banners and preceded by brass bands. Henry wept, but Charlene was dry eyed. 'Those days are gone,' she said. The foreign news, too, was, as always, bad. Iraq had shelled cities and towns in Iran. Twelve Israeli soldiers had been blown up by a suicide truck bomb while withdrawing from Lebanon. The Christians were fighting each other in East Beirut. Right-wing parties gained in French municipal polls. On the potentially bright side, President Chernenko of the Soviet Union died on March 11, 1985, and was replaced by a vigorous new man, one Mikhail Gorbachev.

Henry announced his intention to return to London to pursue the resurrection of the Film College, which now appeared possible given a legal breakthrough concerning its charitable status. New sugar daddies were, it appeared, available, though Gibson would not be more specific. 'There's a new dawn, comrades . . . I shall be back in the Shepherd's Bush dungeon,' he told Blok. 'Wanna try the charms of Pani Policek? Or do you prefer to stick around for a while and help Charlie-girl with the perky porkers? My door will always be open. As you know, no one trusts me with a key.'

But Blok decided to remain behind in the open air for a while and, receiving a telephone call from Janet, took up her invitation

232

to carry him off north, to East Lothian, Scotland, to spend the Easter week with her family, at Craddock, twenty miles due east of Edinburgh, the capital of another country that did not quite exist, except in the imagination and memories and dreams and desires of its people . . .

★

The village was on the banks of the Firth of Forth as it widened into the North Sea. It had about three thousand inhabitants and eight different Protestant churches, gospel halls and meeting places. It had a small harbour with a fishing fleet of a dozen motor boats, which chugged lazily out to sea on Mondays and returned three days later, laden with sprats and small shrimps. The coastline was flat but rocky, the waves rolling across dark stone and seaweed, the pitted marks of sandworms often covered by a thin membrane of water several hundred feet inland. One darted from slippery rock to rock, across small rivulets of foam. A nearby caravan site disgorged desperate holiday-makers from Glasgow, gamely trudging through the mid-day mist in rolled-up trousers, bearing deckchairs and picnic baskets like refugees from a Federico Fellini film, making do with lesser joys, tailored to Calvinist tolerations.

JESUS IS ABLE TO SAVE COMPLETELY THOSE WHO
    COME TO GOD THROUGH HIM.
CRADDOCK PARISH CHURCH RAFFLE: COFFEE
    AFTERNOON, SAT., 2:00 P.M.: HOME BAKING
    STALL: GUESS THE WEIGHT OF A CAKE.
TUESDAY: DRAMA GROUP A.G.M. DANCE: APRIL 18.
2 LOVELY TABBY CATS FREE, FOR GOOD HOME.
    HOUSE TRAINED. GOOD WITH CHILDREN.
THE SON OF MAN IS COME TO SEEK AND TO SAVE
    THAT WHICH IS LOST.
NEW SHADES MOBILE DISCO.
IF THE LORD WILL, THE WORD OF GOD WILL BE
    PREACHED HERE ON LORD'S DAY, 5 P.M.
NO TRAVELLERS ON A FRIDAY, PLEASE.

JESUS SAID: I AM THE WAY, THE TRUTH AND THE LIFE.

Janet's parents lived in one of a row of granite two-storey houses overlooking the small harbour. Seagulls swooped, cawed and rested on their chimney pot. Janet's mother, Elsa, was a Labour Party Councillor who had defected from the Scottish National Party over priorities in the Anti-Thatcherite Struggle. Her father, Stanislaus, was a Polish airman who had become marooned in the United Kingdom after the Second World War, when the Communists took over liberated Poland, he being a freethinking supporter of the Polish Socialist Party. He worked at various menial tasks in post-war Britain and ended up as a coalminer at Craighall. Later on he worked as a civilian aeronautics engineer for a small firm which had gone bankrupt and now he worked in the Insurance Department of Edinburgh Airport and coughed picturesquely as he doled out his life's philosophy in small nips over a bottle of Stolichnaya which Janet had carried up from the South:

'If you are honest, you will go to jail.'

'You meet a better class of person down the pit.'

'Scottish Nationalism is like Polish Nationalism . . . it has the best tunes, but the women are unavailable.'

'A Polish Pope is like a fish with bifocals.'

'God helps the rich, because the poor are too much damned trouble.'

'If you are going the wrong way down a one way street, be sure you are driving a tank.'

'If God is dead, who killed Nietzsche?'

'A Scottish Catholic is like a zebra without stripes.'

'A Pole, a Scot and a Jew go free-fall parachuting. The Pole says, I don't need a parachute, I will simply sing the "Warsawien" and jump. He leaps out, from twenty thousand feet. The Scot says, I don't need a parachute, I will simply sing "Scots Wha' Hae" and jump. He leaps out, from twenty-five thousand feet. The Jew says, I have changed my mind. I will not go free-fall parachuting after all.'

'My father isn't anti-semitic,' said Janet. 'He simply doesn't like human beings.'

'I like human beings,' said Janet's father, 'but only when they are being human.'

Janet's mother kept out of this mêlée, being of a practical bent. Her life was consumed with reports, minutes, memoranda, lists of complaints and hurried meetings with people in trouble who came ringing the bell at intervals through the weekdays. It was both an unlikely and a likely partnership, Presbyterian conscience and ex-Catholic romance. For Stanislaus was fiercely anti-religious, despite his fascination for bizarre and occult esoterica which he collected from second-hand bookshops, such gems as the *Index of Forbidden Books*, Maurice Maeterlinck's *The Buried Temple*, *The Secret Doctrine of the Rosicrucians*, *The Tibetan Book of the Dead*, Edgar Cayce, *Riddles of the Pharaohs* and the pride and joy of his collection, the complete works of the Scots journalist Comyns Beaumont, who had proclaimed the British Isles as the font of all history and the City of Edinburgh as the true geographical site of ancient Jerusalem, with Saint Giles Cathedral and the Law Courts as Mount Moriah, Arthur's Seat as the Mount of Olives, Edinburgh Castle as Mount Zion and the Gougar Mount at Costorphine Hill as Golgotha, the Place of Skulls.

'You see, you are a fake, Abraham Blok,' Stanislaus said amiably. 'The ancient Hebrews were in fact the Saxons. They colonised North Britain from the South, crossing the Inland Sea at Somerset, past Glastonbury, which is Mount Tabor. The Sinai Desert is in Dartmoor. The Saxon Bristol was Sodom. The Greeks are fakes too, of course – Ben Nevis is the true Olympus.'

'This explains a great deal,' Blok nodded, recalling the tale of Old Maclachlan, the mad Scot of Mandate Palestine, who lambasted the Holy City pilgrims for worshipping Holyrood Palace at

Moriah and abasing themselves before false Gods. He told the tale to Stanislaus, who was delighted. 'Each people knows exactly where the centre of the universe is – in themselves. It's human nature. Our Mister Beaumont has a common racial problem: he can't believe non-aryan peoples could have created any culture, any civilisation. We are all scum to somebody out there, and how many out there are scum to us? I used to read all this stuff seriously once – Buddhism, Hinduism, and so on. Now I just sit here and make jam. Ancient mysteries are old hat, you know. It's all the same, under the skin. Look for your true self, which is usually false. I know, you will walk along the beach here, and look at the waves. I did this for about three years. I was sure the eternal sea was trying to tell me something. But it had nothing to say. It just goes whoooosh, whoooosh, whoooosh. After a while, you say – OK, is there anything on tonight's telly? The mind demands a little variety. It is just a machine that gets bored.'

But Blok nevertheless found an ideal rock to stand on, jutting out a little way into the Firth between the harbour and the town. Facing north, with the wind whipping against his cheekbones, allowing thoughts to flow freely through his mind as the seagulls wheeled, cawing, and the small boats puttered towards the horizon, and larger ships edged their way greyly in the mist, across the furthest line of sight. Seaweed lapping at his feet, floaters dancing upon his eyeballs like coy bacteria wriggling in their own inland sea. A few people picked their way along the harbour walls, in gumboots and raincoats flapping in the wind. The masts of the anchored boats rattled tinnily. One boat, like a beached ark, was being recaulked and repainted by its crew. The putter of a small generator merged with the sea. A seagull primly avoided Blok's stare.

Janet took him in the struggling 2-CV to his newly revealed Jerusalem. The Valley of Jehoshaphat of Princes Street with its Walter Scott tower, Mount Zion of the Castle, besieged by tourists, the Mount of Olives of Arthur's Seat, labouring mightily to ascend the dead volcano, breathing heavily as they sat and surveyed the majesty of the city below. Another San Francisco? Except that here not the mist, but the biting wind, came rolling in from the bay.

236

'Maybe that crazy Beaumont had something . . .' The power of the imagination. Nothing is impossible, in the shifts of memory. 'Why did you marry Asher?' Blok asked her. She had already told him of her gentle ribbing by Stanislaus at adopting another Israeli stray, after her solemn oath of life abstention. 'I was never able to explain to Stanislaus the difference between Israelis and Jews. We just became more and more confused. This syndrome of Israelis seeing themselves as Jews who have been repaired, cured of the diaspora plague. Even Asher, who so proclaimed himself a rebel and rejected the State and the whole Zionist thing, nevertheless at heart he had this aggressive charge: The breed apart, cut off from the past, embarrassed by the passivity of Jewish history, as he had been brought up to see it . . . The minority within the minority within the minority. But we're all minorities of one.

'Why did I marry Asher? We lived together for a year before deciding, what the hell. We could always get divorced. Not that we intended to. It simply became the way things were. I suppose he made me laugh. He was dynamic. He had done things, travelled, made his small mark. I felt I had been nowhere and done nothing. Just an escapee from a small town. It's the Scots malaise. And maybe there were the echoes of my father, though that was Asher's theory. He accused me of wanting him to be a failure. Like my Dad, stuck in his exiled rut. It became too heavy, all that projection of his own problems on to me. I suppose marriage means grin and bear it. But I felt suffocated. So that's it. I work with small kids now and all their demands are overwhelming, but achievable. Give them a head start and they're running. They haven't yet read the writing on the wall, let alone written it themselves . . .'

'Well, I'm just a mad Hungarian,' Blok said to her. 'I passed through the Levant en route. To where, I can't really say.'

Just another Peter Pan running from his Captain Hooks? She told him about her own growing pains as the daughter of the Stranger in the Village, the trembling tensions between Stanislaus and the older folk until they realised with relief his lapsed Papism. But she was yet another closed world to Blok, opening up only little glittering corners of her mysterious ethnic parables:

'Hang a thief when he's young, an' he'll no' steal when he's auld.'

'Ne'er marry a widow unless her first man was hang't.'

'Dirty dugs smell their ain dirt last.'

'Ye canna see a green pea but your een reel.'

'There's naethin' tae be done in haste except grippin' fleas.'

And the most mysterious of all:

'Her eggs have aye twa yolks.'

Asher, she revealed, had not understood these either. And he had always taken issue with her dreams, which seemed to unfold according to some stern inner board of Presbyterian morals: she had found a crock of gold at the end of the rainbow and was hurrying to hand it in to the police. She was stuck up a tree at the Russian Revolution, worrying about how to reach her exams. She was about to be hanged by the Nazis in a vast stadium (The programme note said, 'NB, this is a real event') and was worrying which clothes she should wear. This last sounded like an Asherian infestation. She agreed that was probably so. The Collective Unconscious, spreading its tentacles, leaping faiths and cultures and creeds. Nation shall infect Nation with guilt, anxiety, frustrations. Fear eats the soul. Perhaps this, too, had eventually to be exorcised?

'A'm no' as green as a'm cabbage lookin'!'

Her smile hopped, skipped through the mist. Was this an invitation, or merely an open-hearted generosity without strings, a natural outreach lacking sinister undertones, traps, snares? An unfeigned, unreserved friendship, echoing a living heritage of simple, unvarnished, unequivocal hospitality? Love, again, stretching its mysterious paws, cat's-cradling his nerve ends? The soft dark flesh of Malay Mipi, the impossibility of Jacqueline, wisps of previous volumes: the resurrecting policewoman, flaming Esther, the lost golden age of Victoria Happenstance, of Nili-Honey the world nurturer . . .

Is a man a man for a' that? Or is it just any port in a storm?

'What are we doing here, my friend?' Stanislaus asked him, as they walked together on the beach, taking time out while Janet house visited social security cases with her mother in the next town. 'Two foreigners on someone else's soil . . . Strange to say,

I never remember a time when I was not a foreigner. Except in Warsaw, before the war. We had a conservative-militarist government under the shadow of Marshal Pilsudski, but it was home for me. So the only time I belonged is now history, an archaeological artefact. It's interesting that you tell me your father cannot walk now, he is in a wheelchair. I often feel my feet are not on the ground. I am floating, in someone else's dream. I know, it is an old syndrome. Figments of God's imagination. What a strange bugger He must be. For myself, I have found my corner to hide. It is pleasant. There is nothing else I can do. Life for our children, in this strange future we have prepared for them, is going to be so precarious. This often makes me sweat, late at night. At least Elsa fights, protests, contributes. One used to think, just let the women take over. But see our bizarre Iron Lady. I often think, perhaps the Communists were right, despite the mess that they have made everywhere: one needs to make better human beings, somehow. But they have botched the formula. They misread the instructions on the packet. Or, they were written wrongly. On the other hand, that may be the source of the trouble: one should just let humans be what they are. A mess of contradictions. But then how do you formulate values?'

'I've no idea,' Blok said.

They hurled pebbles into the sea but the sea looked back at them, apathetically. The sandworms burrowed in the sand. A dog shook sea water on to their shoes. Stanislaus ruffled its shaggy mane. It bounded on, after its owner, converging dots on the landscape.

'I liked Asher,' Stanislaus told Blok, 'but I wasn't surprised Janet found him in the end too much to take. All that frustration from not saving the world. I have seen so many burnt out from that. They go like matches. A quick flame, then the wind blows. Phut, and a little piece of charcoal. And then there are the emberous ones, those are the worst: Stalin, Mao Tse Tung, Thatcher in her own confused way . . .'

So what can we do? Walk on with the grounded airman on the beach, nodding to stubborn Glaswegians with rolled-up trousers picking their way across the slippery stones, watching Stanislaus make jam, or tend his esoteric library, listen to Janet and her mother cooing, rustling their council papers, taking in the realisation that Janet must return to her charges at the broadcasting company, that Stanislaus's offer to stay as long as he liked had to be yet another evasion, that he must, nevertheless, submit to the reality principle, the need to earn a crust somewhere, if only to stockpile another nest egg for foreign escape plans. And the shrinkage to a single option of Henry Gibson's Film College, opening again, *zut, alors!* to a fanfare of relieved staff and students. And so, Blok returned south to toil again in the celluloid vineyard, a recycling of familiar gales and squalls, the déjà vu of Drury Lane's young hopefuls, tearing up and down the College stairs, clutching the silvery cans of their dreams, buttonholing lecturers for instant non-wisdom, cementing or dropping alliances, exchanging gossip, plotting the overthrow of Henry Gibson and his replacement by a trained chimpanzee, or so Henry claimed as he resumed swinging on his office toilet pipes, grunting, thrusting his hand into his trouser back to scratch his arse and spitting out invisible nutshells: 'Ach! It iz ze great Avram Blok, hein! You haff come to save us from ze danger off normality, *nicht wahr?*' Buttoning up to face the entrance of Camera Department Head Orde Clapper, sidling in wagging his great thatch of white hair to complain: 'Some little git has stolen the gobo. It was the only one we had left, Henry.' 'Let's hope they can feed it properly . . .'

The big buzzing belch of Creativity! Though some faces had gone: Venezuelan Isolde, Icelandic Annie and the giant Swede Harald returned to their respective homes, leaving, of the Cheetham Common crew, only dour Mahmud the Iranian prison film zealot, loath to return home eastwards to the tender mercies of the recruiting sergeants of the Islamic Republic. 'Have you read the latest Khomeini directive, Avram? If one can eat a camel which has been abused sexually! Last week they stoned three women in Mashhad. And that stupid war! I am ashamed of my country.'

'That's a very healthy sign, Mahmud,' Blok told him. 'When it makes you vomit, that's the break-through.'

'But Khomeini is going to die soon,' Aziza, the Hashemite firebrand, who was just completing her studies, hurried to reassure the Persian.

'You are joking. His mother is alive and living in Qom.'

The very breath of tyranny is a preservative. But Blok took up his duties once more, this time as chief assistant in the Sound Department, while redomiciled in Mister Policek's basement, facing the Estonian tar's garden figurehead, with Henry Gibson, now ensconced with Sheila Ratchett, risen to the ground floor, Belinda Kenneth having left the post of receptionist to negotiate a dry-cleaning franchise in Finchley, where she had bought a house for herself and her faithful Police Sergeant, Brian, now a Mark Master Mason of the Fourth Degree, pledged to 'suffer my right ear to be smote off sooner than divulge any of the secrets of this Degree unlawfully . . .' Sheila had abandoned the Pee Pee Party and appeared much mellower and more subdued, the odd couple spending occasional evenings with Blok, and sometimes in a foursome with Janet, who took him out, now and then, to the movies, holding his hand lightly as he tried to express thoughts oozing sluggishly from little-used depths. She did not appear in a hurry to advance their intimacy, gently breaking the news to him of her established relationship with a post-Asher boy friend, Mark, a cameraman in the television news department, who travelled the world bringing the troubles of mankind to home viewers via the splicers of browbeaten editors bent to the zeitgeist of hard times. 'Thousands of people starving in the wrong place, Avram . . .' she passed on these woes to Blok, 'and nobody wants to know. You have to be fashionable even in your misery. Grief alone does not qualify. That's life in 1986 for you . . .'

1986!!

The stars! the stripes! the heavens themselves proclaim the death of princes . . . the United States Space Shuttle Challenger explodes soon after take-off from Cape Canaveral, killing its crew of seven astronauts . . . a Mexican airliner crashes with 166 persons on board . . . wars rage on in Chad, Afghanistan, Angola, Ethiopia, El Salvador, Nicaragua . . . a coup d'état in Lesotho . . . In Haiti, on the bright side, Baby Doc Duvalier is toppled by mass unrest and US apathy. In the Philippines, People Power overthows the dictator Ferdinand Marcos and wife. On April 13, the Pope visits a synagogue in Rome. On April 15, US bombers, some flying from Britain, kill one hundred people in the

241

Libyan towns of Tripoli and Benghazi. On April 26, a nuclear reactor at Chernobyl, in the Soviet Union, catches fire. Sheep in Britain are declared unfit for human consumption. People hide from the lash of dubious rain. In Sweden, the Prime Minister, Olof Palme, is shot by an unknown assassin. In Austria, ex-SS officer and UN Secretary General Kurt Waldheim is elected State President. Japan launches its first home-made space rocket. The US spaceprobe Voyager 2 flies past Uranus, to no avail. Another spaceprobe, launched by the European Community, sends back pictures of the nucleus of Halley's Comet, an image resembling a fried egg hit by a mallet. The most distant galaxy ever reported is found, receding from the Earth at ninety per cent the speed of light. Astronomers claim they are now seeing events which occurred 15 million years ago – pretty soon, it seems, they will be watching events that occurred before the Creation (the Big Bang), and then we shall all be sorry. And there were further proofs of Continental Drift, the halcyon unity of old, the one become the many and scattered:

> Reuters: 375 million years ago a part of Alaska known as the Alexander Terrain was part of Australia, claims Professor George Gehrels of the University of Arizona. The fragment had journeyed across the Pacific from the antipodes to South America and then scraped its way northwards up the Americas, carrying with it a section of California. This explains, Professor Gehrels says, the presence of gold in both California and Alaska.

Goodonyer, sport! Blok stuck the item in his scrapbook. The Wandering Jew is in the very geology of our sad planet . . . As he walked about the streets of Shepherd's Bush again, taking in the doner kebab shops and Tandoori restaurants, and on to the little Arabia of Bayswater and Queensway, at the edge of Hyde Park, and further south, towards Trafalgar Square, trying to avoid crossing the river to the cardboard city, but nevertheless coming strap up against Katharine Weale one cold spring day, outside the Embankment tube, dragging her up Villiers Street to the nearest greasy spoon, where, amid the flotsam of her shopping bags, she stuffed her face with a four-egg omelette under the wary gaze of

Algerian waiters: 'Arr, Eh-bram! th'forshes 'f'darkness! Knew you'ld never faand Lennern's brain! But 'e were a fine young lad in 'is day! lovely Riter meter maid . . .' Slurred information spilling forth, no change in the street world, as Dishcloth, Smeg, Bob-a-Job, Young Fish, Arsehole and Chuck'n'Di still pursued the lower depths' eternal recurrence. Only Bradbury appeared to have wandered off southwards, into the heart of Thatcherland. 'Yer did th'right thing, Eh-bram, yer ain't cut arrt for this misery. Wotcher need is a nars old-fashioned gel what'll darn yer socks an' aarn yer shirts in the mawnin'. A'd do it fer yer meself, but me 'ands shake so fuckin' terrible . . . ah was owl right las' year . . .'

What a narrow escape! Blok paled at the thought, then conjured the thought of Janet, toiling with needle and thread as his odoriferous ankles. Recalling the winters he had survived on the army issue footgear of Nurse Nili's Unknown Soldier . . . Or the even earlier icon of Mama Blok, repairing the irreparable . . . But people do change, the world swivels, the unpredictable might occur. Walter and Annie wrote him from Uppsala. Fed up with Scandinavia, they now planned to return south, almost home, to Gaborone, Botswana, where Annie had been offered a senior nursing job. Exile had shrunk their bones into a stiffness that could no longer be borne. AFRICA, man! The motherlode! Why did we ever leave, Gottverdommen, for that voetsak cold country where men creak like dead wood and the headmistress takes the hindmost? One cannot bear it any longer. Enough is enough, brothers . . .

The wanderlust everywhere, and not a drop to drink . . . Perhaps one might have one's cake and eat it, keep one's centre in a place of refuge and send out shards of oneself, like the Alexander Terrain, to creep along towards Alaska, snatching pieces of Chile, Peru, Mexico and Big Sur on the way, shlip-shlop, in dolomite cloggies, chipped-off emissaries of oneself, to negotiate in distant lands. Send out a leg to spy out the beaches of the Costa Brava, an arm to feel a homestead in Oregon, an eye to visit the brothels of Buenos Aires, dragging, perhaps, a spare groin. One might recall one's penis too, left behind in the Jew of Clubs . . .

The midsummer brought him, in the same post, two letters. One was from the Holy Land, from Papa:

243

Dear Avremel,

Time seems to pass and at the same time it stands still. As I grow older I feel I'm going backwards. I now remember very clearly things that happened thirty years ago, but I can't find the newspaper that I put down ten minutes ago. Your mother tells me we haven't heard from you so long she fears you've been swallowed by a whale. The Great White Whale of gentiledom, the alluring shiksa castanets. But when you were here, I remember, we seldom spoke. I simply had no wisdom to impart. There is nothing more boring than an old man who has nothing to say, unless it is an old man burning with the urge to pass the buck. I even have trouble passing water, but that's an old story. Our left-wing Prime Minister, Peres, has just rotated and turned into the right-wing Mister Shamir. I could never tell them apart anyway. Was there not an English poet who said a politician is an arse upon which everything has sat except a man? Maybe you should become an English poet, Avram. Win a Nobel Prize and get your mother off my back. Actually it's me who's on her back, the legless old man of the sea. Just stay yourself, Avremel. The other day I dozed and found myself back on the immigrant ship that brought us here, the old *Irma Klein*. It was completely overcrowded with refugees like us, running from the frying pan into the fire. Though some did think they could find redemption. To be somebodies, not just human chaff. I fought my way with Rosa and the child, which, by the way, was you, to the ship's railings, looking for a blip on the sea. People began to shout: There it is! There it is! But I could not see a thing. Then even Rosa began to shout and point excitedly. But you and I, we just stood there glumly, in the swell of the ocean, hanging on for dear life. Well, now we're here and we have tanks and jet aircraft and we've won the Eurovision Contest. And all I want is to pee without pain! Whoever made the prostate, it was definitely on a dud day. Perhaps even an act of sabotage . . . End of page. Be well, then, it's legal to write, as long as it's not the truth. Mama sends love, and me too, a heretic's blessings –

Papa (Baruch [de Peenoza])

The second letter was from Asher:

> Hey there, man! Listen up, comrade! We in the kingdom of
> the Sun God salute you. Fear not, it is not a case of Reve-
> lation, merely Los Angeles brainrot. The Good Life, the
> palm tree shades, et cetera. TV assignments for the Pubic
> Broadcasting System. The pay is good and nobody sees the
> programmes, that's having God by the balls! Nevertheless,
> the Revolution! Nothing stands still, except Lot's wife.
> Piquant events, et cetera. Remember we spoke about Irving
> Klotskashes? Had a strange encounter there. But the main
> thing: Jacqueline, our Keeper of the Flame! She has hit the big
> time with her Jesuit, out in the New Mexico desert. They
> have been holed up, it appears for several months now, right
> in the middle of the White Sands Missile Range, squatting,
> can you believe it, in a Western ghost town, constructed
> specifically as the epicentre of some new experimental device
> which was due, rumour has it, to be set off any day. Or has
> this drama already reached you in the Thatcherene boon-
> docks? They are threatening to blow themselves up (with
> ordinary dynamite), if the authorities try to move them.
> They have a small transmitter, from which they are narrow-
> casting (when unjammed), to local radio stations. Art
> Mattock is banging the drum in New York, and Doron and
> I are thinking of driving out there with a camera if we can find
> a way through. The Show of the Century, Avram, come one,
> come all! I'm sure you will not even dream of missing it. I can
> send you a ticket if you're caught short. Why slave in the
> galleys if you can be at the flashpoint of the Nuclear Protest of
> the century? Or I can meet you half way, in the dark of
> heartness, at the Albuquerque Greyhound Station. Schedule
> enclosed. Resistance is futile. Haven't you always dreamt of a
> Second Coming! *Allons, enfants! le jour de gloire!* Rub-a-dub-
> dub, man, and see that blessed jissum fly!

Sheila Ratchett said: 'Stay a while this time, Avram. What's the
point of moving every time you're dissatisfied? Where is there to
go?'

'Munchkinland,' suggested Henry Gibson, looking up from a large pile of students' graduation theses. 'I've always wanted to go there. Now that Judy Garland's dead it's safe to visit, I'm told.' He groaned as he opened a fresh file. 'Listen to this: "Paradigmatic Praxis In The Cinema Of Jean Marie Straub." What have I done to deserve this? Bring back the death penalty, I say. Then I can just sit and knit. I had that Madame Lafarge in the back of the cab once . . .'

'Stop moaning,' said Sheila. 'You know you love every minute.'

'I am the world's zookeeper,' said Henry, 'but you have to go out and bring 'em back alive, Avram, or if not alive, at least in a semi-conscious state. Follow the yellow prick road.'

The tortuous path towards the locked flower blooming among the cacti of the white sands . . . Nevertheless, Henry Gibson and Sheila took him to Heathrow Airport in the 'taxi', mumbling blessings on the way.

'Vaya con doch and doris, gringo. Don't worry about the Sound Department. We will find a replacement in the Deaf and Dumb Institute. No one will know the difference. Go, make good, find that pot of gold, just look out for the cosmic rays, compañero, now that the ozone layer's been zapped.'

'Look after him, Sheila,' Blok appealed.

'I'll beat him black and blue every day,' she said. Henry panted, tongue out, fervently. They bundled him into the check-in. 'And remember, don't stray off the main paths . . . don't drink the water . . . never turn your back on a buffalo . . . don't shoot till you see the whites' eyes . . . if you see my lost son out there . . . tell him to dress warm and eat a lot of chicken soup . . .' Henry waved a massive, filthy pocket handkerchief as Blok passed through the 'Passengers Only' gateway, bulletproofed policemen fingering their machine guns while their Alsatians strained at their leads . . . 'Goodbye! Goodbye! Don't forget the cleft stick!' The Alsatians bore down, nostrils quivering. Gibson threw a sausage roll into the concourse, escaping in the mêlée . . .

★

Deep in the bunker, below Lower Cheetham, the Chief Constable staggers into the initiation chamber with a rope around his neck, placing his knuckles on the neck of the blindfolded man ahead of him, kneading his spinal cord as the voice of the Principal Sojourner breaks out in the darkness.

'Moses! Moses!'

'Here I am!'

'Draw not hither! Put off the shoes from thy feet, for the place whereon thou standest is holy ground. I am the God of thy Fathers, the God of Abraham, Isaac and Jacob!' The Candidates are led around the chamber three times, while passages from the Book of Chronicles concerning the Fall of Jerusalem are read out, and the members of the Chapter simulate the apocalypse by all manner of sounds and disturbances, rolling cannonballs on the floor, clashing swords, throwing chairs about, stamping their feet and shouting. The Chief Constable is then tied hand and foot with thick rope and carried by sweaty hands into the preparation room . . .

Knock, knock, knock.

'Who comes there? Who dares approach this seventeenth veil of our Sacred Tabernacle?'

'A weary sojourner from Babylon, who has come to assist in the rebuilding of the House of the Lord, without the hope of fee or reward.'

Knock, knock, knock.

'What is the purpose of your visit to the United States, Mister Blok?'

The immigration officer's X-ray eyes probe deep behind the entrant's retinas, his fingers flicking through the massive Book of Names: Vladimir Ilyich Ulyanov, Lev Davidovitch Bronstein, Muhammad Beelzebub, Nikolai Ivanovitch Asmodai, Fidel and Raul Lumumba, Sabri el-Fuentes, Salvador Rosenberg. The immigration officer's nose, which is long and tapering, and a full two feet in length, sniffs out along the applicant's unrelaxed body, from his trouser cuffs to his unkempt collar, the furtiveness of his base ambitions, his illicit, probably criminal and certainly treasonable nature. His nostrils tremble at Blok's chin, tickling his five o'clock shadows, fingers dancing upon his station keyboard, calling all cars around the planet. Who is for the Lord, to me! And from around the globe, linked databases answer, leaping eagerly, chirping, blurping, creaking and buzzing with that strange joy that only machines know when they are stretched to the limits of their duty. Quark! Quark! Quark! This is positronically nucleus! Did you hear the one about . . . ? Ingathering the relevant data, from China, from the Himalayas, from San Francisco and Yokohama, from the Department of Apocalyptic Affairs in Jerusalem, and the Department of Health and Social Security in the Borough of Westminster . . .

Beep! Beep! Beep! Beep!

The immigration officer devours his essence, sucking his past through his dangling proboscis, into the lungs, the blood, the heart of the system, fertilising the egg of State. He stamps his passport, his forehead, his arse and genitals.

Knock, knock, knock.

'*Have you the Signet of Zerubabel?*'

The veils are drawn aside, the Candidate enters to behold the High Priest, the Scribe and the Yellow Cabman, standing forth, in Grand Council. A dazzling white light enshrouds the whole . . .

The castle door creaks open . . .

THE RAPTURE

When the waters of the earth cooled several billion years after the Big Bang, some bold or desperate creatures waddled out of the sea on to dry land. They flopped there, exhausted, waiting for someone or something to shake a leg and tell them what to do next. But no guidance was given. They cautiously extruded flippers, gills, pseudopodia, and crawled on, looking left and right cautiously, as the Silurian sun beat down . . .

'Well . . .'
　　'Damn . . .'
　　　　'Sarsaparilla . . .'
　　　　　　'Told him to move his ass, man . . .'
　　　　'Personality tests? Do us a favour . . .'
'Latin love songs and deep rimming . . .'
　　'Christ . . .'
　　　　　'The-o-lo-gy . . .'
　　'A contemporary of Jumel-Morris . . .'
　　　　　　'Named the child Tecumseh Sherman . . .'
'The Platters?! that is gross, man . . .'
　'Love???'
　　　　'A Fiat carburettor . . .'
　　　　　　'Cappuccinos all round . . .'
　　　'A cute ass is all he's got . . .'
　　　　　'Moussaka, on the other hand . . .'
　　　　　　　'Paolozzi . . .'
　'Ettore Ximenes . . .'
　　　　'Called it "A Cyst Before Dying". . .'
'But those were the old days in Sudan, before Numeiry got religion . . . you could buy your way out or into anything . . .

251

just I hadn't a piaster to my name . . . Luckily one of the warders was Armenian . . .'

   'A first or second cousin?'

   'Thrice removed . . .'

      'One is always left with small details . . .'

        'Breeding baby elephants as pets . . .'

             'Prayer mats . . .'

      'Lucille Ball . . .'

'He was lost on an expeditionary walk from Coney Island to the Bronx . . . they found his hat, and one sock . . .'

      'Sawdust and Schnitzel . . .'

   'And a Knickerbocker Glory . . .'

          'Robert Donut . . .'

    'Russell Halva . . .'

       'Rancid Joe and the Pits . . .'

'Turds should always be solid and floating . . .'

         'Like the dollar . . .'

   'You really ought to go to Fire Island . . .'

Volcanoes, blowing their top, spewing black smoke high into the stratosphere and half across the globe, sending rivers of molten lava down rock fissures to devour whole towns. The citizens of Pompeii, caught short and swallowed by ashes, in the midst of anyday actions, farting, emptying their bowels, fornicating, playing checkers, filling in their income tax forms, darning socks, blowing their noses, husbands strangling wives, wives strangling husbands, small boys masturbating in toilets, gay young blades and smart lasses sipping Irish Iced Tea . . .

Many of Art Mattock's friends were dying of the plague which was devastating the city. The victims were so numerous that they could be seen on the streets, formerly healthy young men hobbling about, emaciated, on crutches. Women were victims too. Most of the stricken were black, poor, and huddled in the borough ghettos. But the rich were also dying. Many artistic communities in the city were depleted, and several theatres were closing, unknown to Blok, as he arrived back in the Five Boroughs, clutching the tattered remnants of his subway map, busmap, and his Szechuan House menu, treasured from his previous visit, promising such delights as Beef Four Flavors, General Ching's Chicken and Sautéed Lobster with Chili Sauce. But the Szechuan House had closed, giving way to a new chain of Imperial Han Houses, amidst the rapidly changing cityscape of new high buildings rushing up to replace shattered holes in the ground. Sweep out the old! Ring in the new! Concrete layers firming up floor after floor before one's eyes. The restless city that won't stand still. Girders rising about him, giant concrete mixers, men in hard hats climbing like mutant orangutans upon dizzying cat's cradle heights. Braaaaaaaaaaaaaaaa-aaaaaaaaaaaaaaaaaaaaaaaaaaaa!!!!!!! Creeeeeeeeeeeeeeeee!!! Brooooooooooooooooooooooooooooooo!!!! Sweat poured like molten lead from above in the drenching August heat . . .

Art had garlic hung up upon the doors of his house, and an amazing array of prophylactic devices in his newly-tiled bathroom. The Brooklyn house, in fact, looked a little less cluttered than before. The Indonesian phallic sculptures had gone, and the dog, Pedro, and only one guest was in residence, the Armenian, Vahan Djerdejkian, who was in fact sharing Art's bed. 'Monogamy,' said Art. 'It's the only solution. Your mother was right, after all, Avram.'

Blok occupied the loft sanctuary. A small window looked out upon the backyard of an accountant whose son owned a pogo stick. Sounds of crash landings and tears were frequent. Squirrels still moved furtively under the rafters, wary of the removal experts. 'They had to come with asbestos gloves and poke them with long sticks,' Art recalled. 'It was a massacre.' The Jesuit's discarded pile of unread books lay by the single bed: Emma Goldmann: *Living my Life. The Russian Fascists. Sharon – An Israeli Caesar.* Gustavus Myers: *History of Bigotry in the United States.* Miles Copeland: *The Game of Nations. The Complete Family Guide to Jewish Holidays.* Blok read how the CIA, in Syria in 1947, had tried to encourage democratic elections by bribing taxi drivers to take voters of all persuasions to the polls, not just the supporters of the highest bidding candidate. But the taxi drivers took the money anyway and continued their usual custom. In desperation the Agency backed a coup by the then Chief of Staff, Husni Za'im, who became just the first of a chain of dictators who reduced Syria to despotism. He also learned for the first time about the Fast of Gedaliah, but did not plan to observe it.

Art and Van took Blok out, in Art's battered VW van, in search of a Thailandese restaurant. They skimmed up Ocean Parkway and on to the Expressway to penetrate Manhattan up the anal cavity of the Brooklyn Battery Tunnel, emerging on to the West Side Highway and past the backs of the World Trade Center and other towering monuments of capital. But when they reached the Upper West Side they could not find the restaurant, which had vanished into a vast hole in the ground surrounded by iron sheets and wooden fencing proclaiming 'WESTSIDE EXCLUSIVE DEVELOPMENTS – APPLY 655-4757'. It was late evening, and they walked through the busy streets across Broadway, Amsterdam and Columbus. 'This was an area of poor Jews and Hispanics,' Art explained to Blok, 'till one day they must have taken them all out and shot them, and the Yuppies took over.' They paused in front of shops displaying pairs of shoes among ersatz treetrunks and plastic squirrels, but had to move on as black vagrants moved in, hats out-thrust, soliciting alms. Blok donated a green bill to their escape. He remembered a cheap eating place he had patronised many years before around 83rd Street, but it too had been replaced by an expensive-looking establishment offering 'Authentic Indian-American Cusine', such as Buffalo-T-Bones, Wampumburgers and Teepee Blue-Plate-Specials. Hopi chants off cassettes sounded ominously from within.

They ended up in the old, legendary Hunam Taste, where Blok waited eagerly for his fortune cookie. But when it came, it was a disappointing banality: 'THAT LONG-SOUGHT OPPORTUNITY WILL SOON ARISE.'

'Ah!' said Van, 'promises, promises. Remember, Art, the Elixir of Youth?'

'Baluchistan?'

'Begemdir, Gorgora.'

'God, that was fucking tragic, Van.'

They sat in a reminiscing silence, which wreathed above the broken fortune cookie shells and the remnants of Chef's Special Eggplant with Garlic Sauce and Shredded Beef Szechuan Style. Blok broke it by asking, 'So. What's the news about Jacqueline?'

He had read a short item in the News-in-Brief section of *The Times*, handed out aboard the aircraft on which he flown across the Atlantic:

> White Sands, Thursday: Two militant anti-nuclear pro-
> testers are still besieged in a 'dummy town' in the centre of
> the White Sands Missile Range. They have been living there
> for three months, threatening to blow themselves up with
> dynamite if the authorities attempt their arrest. US Nuclear
> Energy Commission spokesmen claim no blast is scheduled
> for the area before January 1987.

'We're trying to do the best we can.' said Art. 'There's a meeting of the "Peace Watch" tomorrow night in the Village, if you want to come. I shall be frothing at the mouth as usual about the end of Mankind. Don't be worried by what you read in the papers. The whole dynamite threat is sheer hype. They've postponed the neutron blast three times already because of operational problems, so our friends are a convenient excuse. If they solve their technical problems, Jackie and the Jesuit will be out of there so fast you won't see their dust in slow motion. The trial, that will be the real danger point. I advised against the whole thing. But the Jesuit likes these martyr trips. Jackie . . . I don't know. I think she's gone too far this time. But you have to stand by your friends . . .'

'I spent seven months in an abandoned army base in Eritrea once,' Van reminisced. 'I was trapped with a unit of the ELF while the Abyssinians dropped Russian bombs out of American planes. Eventually we had to crawl away in the dark, then three hundred miles across the Aria Mountains to Kassala in Sudan, where they arrested me as a Palestinian mercenary. Sudan jails are not fun.'

'But at least if you're not a Moslem,' said Art, 'they can't chop bits off your limbs.'

'But they can chop off your head,' Van reminded him. 'That tends to put a spike in your wheel.'

They sunk again in reminiscences, while the poker-faced waiter cleared away the dregs of their meal.

'And what happened to . . . ?'

'The knife-wielding Aladdin? He has become a social worker, in the Bronx.'

'The consequences of our past, Mattock.'

'You can say that again, Van.'

'The consequences of our past. You know, I met Che Guevara in the Congo, in 1964. He was lost, he had no idea what to do. He was trapped in the bush between a group of Kimbanguists and the guerrillas of Gaston Soumialot. Christophe Gbenye had declared a "Congolese People's Republic" in Stanleyville. Then the Belgian paras came. People were being stopped and asked "Are you a Mulelist?" If they hesitated, they were shot dead.'

Blok thought of commenting that he had travelled with Che Guevera incognito on a Greyhound bus between Chicago and Salt Lake City and speculating about the undead revolutionary's possible ambitions in Los Angeles, but then thought better of it. Art mused:

'I was in Berkeley at that time. Or was it Ulan Bator?'

'Do you ever get the feeling we are not moving, Art? Despite the globe-trotting, like Alice in Wonderland, we're running as fast as we can to say in the same place?'

'It just feels that way, Van. In reality we are advancing despite it all, albeit in very tiny steps. You've been reading too much *Time* and *Newsweek*.'

'What do you think, Avram?'

Blok agreed with the Armenian. Art shook his head, cradling his lukewarm cup of Chinese tea.

'Our Avram is a man with neither a past nor a present,' he said woefully. 'He is the only man living in his own future.'

The empty fortune cookie shells were swept away. They proceeded, past the gauntlet of the homeless, to a café in Greenwich village in which Art remembered spending his youth over a Gordon's Dry Gin. It had trickled slowly through his fingers, while he cruised the back streets and demonstrated on highways, flying with American Dreams. And Blok wondered about these two people and their trips around the world, tasting the dangers of involvement with its multifarious traps and traumas, lading themselves with causes which they juggled in the air like professional conjurers, slipping like shadows between the bullets, keeping aloft

tattered banners. To change the world, Van, to change the world
. . . Martin Luther King and Mahatma Gandhi and Malcolm X
and Mendès-France and Eugene McCarthy and Tom Mboya,
Patrice Lumumba, Nelson Mandela, and Amilcar Cabral, Bus
Boycotts and Marches on Washington, Chicago summers and
Pentagon Papers, and Fuck the Army and Victory to the FLN . . .
Boat people, scudding across the waters . . . hopes shrinking to
isolated sanctuaries . . . the church doors closing, the bleeding
contained, little crowns of thorns lying everywhere, the reson-
ance of past crucifictions: Saint Bartholomews, Chmielnitskis,
Paris Communes, Kishinev Pogroms, Armenias, Guernicas,
Abyssinias, Shanghais, Dachaus, Auschwitzes, et al. Punjab,
Indochina, Algiers, Guatemala, Buenos Aires, San Salvador,
Managua, Mozambique, Timor . . . the flooding millions of
Quasimodos: Sanctuary! Sanctuary, amid the Village psycho-
babble –
   ‘. . . *Moussaka, on the other hand . . .*’
      ‘. . . *they sit on my behind, and sometimes, if they feel*
              like it, they stand on me . . .’
        ‘. . . *no wonder my breasts never grew . . .*’
 ‘. . . *even my mother, she used to hang on my feet . . .*’
     ‘. . . *cost you 850 dollars to get your whole body done . . .*’
       ‘. . . *my cat don’t know he’s lost his claws . . .*’
  ‘. . . *false teeth for dogs, that’s the real future . . .*’
‘. . . *Prince Mishkin . . . ?*’
    ‘. . . *chicken teriyaki . . . ?*’
       ‘. . . *fe-lla-tti-o . . . ?*’
The proliferation of fragmented cries. Later, he lay awake on his
bed in the loft, two floors above the wheezy groping of the odd
couple below, the muffled curse of a bathroom door closed
unexpectedly in the dark on a naked foot, the clatter of the pipes
reluctantly running a late post-coital shower. The famous burglar
alarm switched off to enable windows to be opened. The restless
flutter of a hot suburban Brooklyn night. Nine-One-Five! Nine-
One-Five! *C'est la politique, monsieur* . . . And his own furtive
movements, conjuring up lost chords. The rumbling of would-be
nuclear orgasms in the White Sands Missile Range. Ah,
Jacqueline! Jacqueline! My link to reality? My future? My

misbegotten past? An a-sexual Last Stand in the besieged dummy Western town: Room Nought, Hotel Zero, by the Bar-None Ranch. Another still centre at the eye of the cyclone. Come to me, my Blokkie, come . . .

In the morning Asher telephoned him from Los Angeles, waking him up, although it was already ten a.m. He staggered down the stairs to find Art Mattock and the Armenian at breakfast – yoghourts and hot bagels. 'Fresh from our Palestinian grocer, Tewfik, Avram. He flees half way across the globe and ends up on Avenue J, the most Jewish street in the world. Isn't fate wonderful? Want some cream cheese? What did Asher have to say?'

'He says he is all set for the assignment to film the show at White Sands.'

'That's if he can get through the checkpoints. Army, Navy, Air Force kooks. The entire military industrial complex is there. It ain't no Cheetham Common. This is the home base we're talking about. MX. First Strike Capability. Star Wars. Lasers. The Big Fazoola, no shit.'

'He wants me to meet him in Albuquerque.'

'There are some good people there, at the University of New Mexico. You know they have a chair in Magic Mushrooms? I was nearly tempted once.'

'Is it still vacant?' asked Van, perking up from morning gloom.

'No, it went to an English chappie, who had lived in a tree in Borneo for twenty-one years.'

'Saint Simeon, the Stylite, stood on a pillar for thirty-six years,' said Van. 'It was said that despairing of escaping the world horizontally, he tried to escape it vertically. But thousands of people flocked to see him. Later on it became a fad. Stylites had to advertise for custom, and it all became old hat. Simeon was an Armenian, though.'

'Like Jesus Christ and Einstein.'

'And Freud. He was an Armenian too, you only have to look at those eyes.'

Blok left the exposition still floating on the kitchen air and exited the disalarmed house, acknowledging with a tentative wave Art's call of 'Tonight's meeting, in the Village – stay in touch!' He took the 'D' train into the city, wandering up his favourite parts of Manhattan, traversing Times Square and its jagged corners where entire blocks were being replaced, the shrinking swathe of Triple-X films, now on blurred video, the old building of Dementia Praecox Films, through whose corridors he remembered struggling with The Fear, long ago. But he could not find the old cutting rooms listed on the board of the lobby. Walking up below the vast glass towers of Sixth Avenue, the Exxon Building, Radio City Music Hall, Time-Life, J. C. Penney, the CBS Building, the Hilton, the Americana Hotel. The skaters at the Rockefeller Plaza. The vendors of gew-gaws from cardboard boxes outside the glitzy stores. Up to Central Park South and Columbus Circle, and through the park and out down 72nd again, to Broadway and the Burger Joint and up to 80th, to the H & H Bagel shop. The sun, hidden by haze, nevertheless drenched him with sweat and shortened his breath. He joined a group of black children dousing themselves by an open water hydrant. They danced around him, shouting with glee as he stood gasping in the physical blast of the shower. 'Shit, man! Shit, man!' they cried, in cheerful delight. He stood there, taking in the spray.

Shit, man! Shit, man! He moved away, drenched, down the road. A grinning black youth handed him a towel which he used to clear his eyes and neck, handing back the towel. The youth said, 'Any time, man.' Throwing it over his shoulder and sauntering, chuckling, uptown. Blok walked back towards the park, along 81st Street, resting on a bench by the lake. Men and women on bicycles and skates passed him. A policeman blared: 'Keep up your speed!' A muscular woman jogger in a vest thundered past him, a Walkman jangling in her ear. He looked at his map, whose soggy pages could still be turned, forgotten as they had been in his trouser pocket: Cleopatra's Needle. Strawberry Fields. The Heksher Ballfields. The Sheep Meadow. The statue of Hans Christian Andersen. The statue of Alice in Wonderland. The Zoo. He remembered Van's words: Perhaps we are all, like Alice, running to stay in the same place. This might be true, if we knew our point of departure. But Blok had lost this key long ago, preserving his own Carrollian Compass, which pointed in every direction at once. The centre was constantly shifting, as if the earth

259

had lost interest in orbiting the sun and was amnesiacally meandering about the galaxies, taking in the sights, dipping its foot in the cosmic waters but making sure it did not get involved. Nevertheless he felt a sense of guilt for the small things in life, no longer for the large, the Saint Bartholomews, Dachaus and Crucifixions. A sense of failure to stem the small miseries of the tramps scraping these pavements as those of London, the pain of a baby crying for reasons he could not fathom, or a man slumped on the nearby bench, or the bent figures trundling by supermarket trolleys which they fill with empty cans to reclaim, or a mongrel dog which has just been kicked. Or a laboratory mouse, stuffed with cancer. Or his father, trapped on the farm, in a wheelchair, with Aunt Pashtida. There seemed to be no discrimination between close and distant pain. Towards all he felt completely helpless. The total haemorrhage of responsibility. Nothing at all could be done, and yet all demanded attention. Every limb was therefore paralysed. He felt himself disappearing and merging with the grain of the bench. And yet, he felt a complete stranger here. The town, full of life, was ejecting him, its laryngal muscles convulsed, vomiting him up through its gullet. The sad sack eyes of the world's abandoned inhabitants looked at him accusingly. The Antichrist! The scapegoat of our agonies! The very stones rose to accuse him. Clumps of grass, tearing loose from the undulating park lawns, rolled towards him, scuffing his shoes. A squirrel gnawed through the bush behind him, but the bush was not consumed. Tree branches plucked him from the bench and spat him out, through the 72nd Street Transverse Road, down Central Park West, by the Spanish and Portuguese Synagogue. Go, man, go! He tumbled down into the 59th Street subway and on to the 'C' train to Times Square and Eighth Avenue, exiting through run-down, echoing passageways to the Port Authority Building. Rolling through bustling concourses, past newsstands, boutiques, cafés, quick-service restaurants, to the telephone information stations. Can I help you, sir? Ah, Albuquerque, New Mexico – what is the best route?

★

AGAIN THE OPEN ROAD, the Freeways, the silver bullet through the night: GREYHOUND! YOUR OPERATOR: ORDE LIBBY – SAFE – RELIABLE – COURTEOUS . . . Squeezing past the paybooths of the New Jersey Turnpike, the universe of neon-lit boards: HOLIDAY INN, VALLEY FORGE, ZIP FOR 90 DAYS, PREGNANT? GOLDEN CRADLE ADOPTION AGENCY – 1–800–827–BABY . . . Newark, Harrisburg, Pittsburgh . . . Thru passengers board here . . . Trespassing, Loitering, Obstructing or Soliciting On These Premises Prohibited By City Ordnance No. 5507 & 3503 . . . The snapshots of Lost Children on the notice boards . . . the vending machines ubiquitously out of order, hugging in their locked guts the manna: Bar-B-Q Potato Chips, Onion Flavored Rings, Munchos, Fritos, Doritos, Bold Gold, Tiny Tim Pretzel Twists, Hot'n'Spicy Fried Pork Skins, Chee-tas, Ruffles – America's Ridged Chip, Sour Cream & Onion Chips, 3 Musketeers, Payday, Grandma's Big Cookies, Grandma's Peanut Butter Cookies, Grandma's Old Time Molasses . . .
      '. . . **We Are Committed To Giving You, Our Honored Guest, A Safe And Pleasant Trip . . .**' The lost, slumped by their chair – TVs, minuscule, smudged homunculi gesticulating – futz! your quarter's time is over . . . crossing over Mad River . . . YOUR LIFE'S IN YOUR HANDS, BUCKLE UP, OHIO . . . the small, forgotten towns of the flatland . . . Dr Decatur, $75 Rebate On Glucometers . . . The Hen House Restaurant, The Amish Cheese Shop . . . a woman a seat down asleep under her book: *The Day Jesus Came To Our Town* . . . INDIANAPOLIS, ALL EXITS . . . (Mechanicsburg – thataway . . .) Brazil, Terra Haute, Saint Louis, Teutopolis, Illinois . . . SEE A BUG? CALL ARAB . . . The Incarnate Word Hospital . . . twenty minutes' rest and comfort stop . . . 'wall, things have to get baitter, they cain't gait any worse . . .' A glimpsed headline on a discarded newspaper: 'Red Blood Cell Leakage Causes Rusty Ankles' (the *Saint Louis Post Dispatch*) . . . the crazy old man who boards the bus with a dozen boxes and no teeth . . . (crouch, slouch, feign deep slumber, drape legs over adjacent seat) . . . on, through Massoura into Oklahoma . . . proliferation of WRONG WAYs . . . BROASTED CHICKEN IS BACK . . . This Machine Will

261

Only Take Quarters, No Dimes or Nickels Please . . . Amarillo, Texas, 10 a.m. . . . tall towers, poached in the sun . . . across State Lines, again, Tucumcari, New Mexico, on, into the heart of the dream – The Paradise Motel . . . The Meteor Crater . . . Super Dog Fries & Coke . . . 24 Hour Wrecker On Service . . . Stuckey's Hand Painted Nemandji Jewellery . . . Stuckey's Pecan Log Rolls . . . Stuckey's Foot-Long Hot Dog . . . Stuckey's Cactus and Hot Fudge Sundae . . . Rattlesnake Hatpins and Eggs . . . Twenty Miles To the Five-Legged Cow . . . Fifteen . . . Ten . . . Five . . . fuck! the arrow points away from the road . . . the rising buttes of the Sandia Mountains . . . and the city, and his reunion with Asher Katzman, rolls over the horizon . . .

★

Asher's Tale: The Road To Alamogordo:
– the desert, yes, the thin, barren scrub, small cacti, suntouched mountains in haze . . . the traditional abode of prophets and loess . . . everyone wants in on the Acts . . . the Truth, the Keys of the Mysteries, What Makes the Universe Tick. That unholy Trinity of conundrums, the mad curiosity of our monkey glands. In our own wildernesses, the Deserts of Sin back home, it was God who was the business at hand. Here, in Noo Mexico, it was Science, whose prophets ingathered, on the anvil . . . July 16, 1945, Trinity, the first atomic explosion. Imagine it, that small band of brothers (and a sister or two, hidden somewhere), constructing two steel towers in the Jornado del Muerto, an old Air Force bombing range. The site was chosen by Robert Oppenheimer, the leader of the nuclear team. A land of scorpions and yucca, prickly organ pipes and Joshua trees. Rattlesnakes lurked behind every stone, and in the night giant centipedes crawled down the sweaty necks of the scientists. Many of them were refugees from the horrors of Hitler's Europe. The male midwives of the New Age. They hauled their five-foot jury-rigged sphere, festooned with cables and plugs, looking like a bathyscaphe in a Jules Verne story, up the detonation tower.

Ah yes! The urge to Truth, the physical secrets of the cosmos! Scratches and squiggles on blackboards and paper. The pioneers of our time: for example – Leo Szilard, who wanted to save the world from itself. In the early 1930s, in Berlin, he was impressed by H. G. Wells's *The Shape of Things To Come*, by the ideal of the Rule of Enlightened Scientists, and by an obscure book Wells had published in 1914, *The World Set Free*, which prophesied the liberation of atomic energy and its potentially destructive power. The world's major cities, in Wells's novel, were destroyed by atomic bombs in 1956. Szilard was appalled, and decided to dedicate his life to the Enlightened use of nuclear knowledge . . . But by 1939 he had become convinced the bomb was feasible and Nazi Germany might develop it. By 1940 he was in the United States working on the Free World's counter. By 1942 it was around the corner. In 1945 the band of brothers (shorn of Szilard, who was already having second thoughts) stood in the desert night, waiting for the New World to dawn: Robert Oppenheimer, Niels Bohr, Enrico Fermi, Emilio Segre, George Kistiakowsky, Seth Neddermeyer, Stanislaw Ulam, Hans Bethe, Norris Bradbury, Otto Frisch, Edward Teller. They played dance music and quoted poetry, for they were all extremely civilised. Oppenheimer's thoughts turned towards John Donne:

> As West and East
> In all flatt Maps – and I am one – are one,
> So death doth touch the Resurrection.

For some reason, this made him name the site Trinity, which was based on yet another Donne poem (Oppenheimer was full of poems): Batter my heart, three person'd God, ta dum, That I may rise, and stand, o'erthrow me, and bend Your force to breake, blowe, burn and make me new . . .

I tried to convey the irony of all this to Blok: 'Doesn't it warm the cockles of your heart, Avram?' I unfolded my plan to him in Albuquerque, over his first post-Greyhound nosh of refried beans and inflammable enchiladas: 'And now, Avram, each year, on one day, October 1, the US Air Force organises a public tour of the site. The only time we unclassified plebs are allowed into the closed area . . . just four days from now, Avram, from Alamogordo, our one and only chance . . .'

I had barely recognised him, when he stepped off the bus, so shrunk he seemed by Thatcher's England, his brown hair greying and thinning out again, his shoulders stooped as under some invisible burden, as if concealed third eyes in the foreheads of the Hispanic drifters might spot the salamander round his neck. On second thoughts, the old Blok again, looking at me accusingly.

'You look fucking healthy, Asher.'

'Los Angeles,' I told him. 'The brain rots, but the body glows. The sun, Avram, the God of ergs and joules. I've sworn off the booze too, you'll be horrified to hear. Nehama's fads got to me.' I was genuinely glad to see him, I was quite amazed to realise. 'Relax,' I told him, 'You'll be a new man in no time, away from the slosh of the chemical toilet and parfum de Burger-King. You may have missed the Great American Duck Race, the skeet shooting season and the Rodeo Fair, but just breathe this air, boyo! God's own country, man! Enjoy, before we descend with our little geiger counters into the invisible flame . . .'

There was no point in lingering in Albuquerque. Art galleries, second-hand bookshops, the Old Town Plaza, refried beans and ersatz Indian curios. At any other time one might enjoy it all, but in the present state of the world . . . I took him to the El Centro Hotel on 8th Street. A quiet retreat, with cable TV and no Bible. 'I have scoured the room, Avram, and we're safe.' The Lord's wrath, kept well at bay. We chit-chatted over the refritos and the combusting enchilada, which was now issuing out of his ears and nostrils: and how's our dear old Henry Gibson? La Ratchett? Del Rushforth and the remnants of Ealing, not to speak of Mattockland? Blok asked me about Jacqueline.

No noose is good noose, as the condemned man told the hangman. I told him there had been radio silence for five days now, not a peep on the citizens' band. But I showed him my video equipment, state of the art, which transformed us into a two-man mobile studio. 'Just you and me, Avram, and Our Man in Alamogordo . . . the Great Quest is about to begin . . .' I put him in the picture, as far as one could ever circumscribe Blok: 'Our local contact is an Apache Indian, no kidding. His name is John Beechtrees. His blood may not be pure, but his cocaine sure is. I met him in California. He supplies the Air Force personnel, deep in the restricted areas. His ancestors, it seems, lie out thar in White Sands, and they are not at all happy at the violation of their ancient hunting grounds. So John Beechtrees fllls the Yanquis' noses with shmutz, and is willing to assist in our modest goal of penetrating the forbidden zone . . .' But Blok just belched, unmoved as ever by the onset of the Big Themes.

Nevertheless, onward, to Alamogordo, in my four-wheel-drive hired buggy. We took the route out of town down Grand, past the FBI Building, towards the Cibola National Forest. Past Moriarty, Willard, small collections of huts that had long given up pretending to be towns, past 'Jessie's Place – the Road to Ruin' and ANCO MUSEUM – MY HOUSE OF OLD THINGS. Arrows pointing pointlessly out into nowhere, along fenced off gravel paths. Carrizozo, and a rancid cheeseburger, at the Four Winds Restaurant. 'Well, that's two winds gone, Avram.' Back in the buggy, movin' on. Past Rita's Prime Time Hair and Nails, the Running Indian Jewellery Shop and the Assembly of God Church – 'Enjoy Our Antique Atmosphere'. Tumbleweeds crossing the road. The wind, in the distance, whipping up a fine cloud of the White Sands themselves. The long strip of pure gypsum running down the valley. Another tourist attraction, but ominous in its swirl . . .

'Batter my heart, three person'd God . . .' I can see them, the band of brothers, those chips off the old world, crawling across this primeval landscape, the red rocks, pushing the metal ball of their brainchild ahead of them like so many human dung beetles. The ball growing bigger and bigger, with their sisyphean efforts, lashed on by USAF personnel. July '45. The war in Europe was over, it was the slant-eyed Nipponese who would bear the brunt of the experiment . . . Those blackboard and paper squiggles were about to become fire and brimstone and transform the whole world. What we do, at the end of the day, can matter. The personal, or collective, effort has consequences. Not that one might think that, seeing Blok. My friend. But I have to admire at least his gall, crossing the world again, in pursuit of an impossible dream, a love, if that's the word, doomed from the outset. How atavistic can one be? But who am I to talk, having lost both Janet and Jane Springs, sacrificed on the altar of my own faded grails.

What was it Woody Allen said? Masturbation is sex with someone you love. And even that's not always true either.

I know poems too: Walt Whitman, on the open spaces: 'I think I could stop ta dum and do miracles, I think whatever I shall meet on the road I shall like, I think whoever I see must be happy.' Eat your heart out, Easy Rider. But I look back on the long road both Avram Blok and myself have taken from the Land of Broken Promises, itself a terminus of so many saddlesore journeys of reverse Whitmanisms:

> I think, wherever I stopped, more banalities,
> I think whatever I meet on the road I shall hate –
> Whoever I see must be miserable.

The old tired sad sack of a world. Rotating on its axis for want of a better thing to do. Tied to the sun, lacking the guts to wander off and look for new frontiers. If the Universe is a clock, why does it have to tell the same time, over and over again? Why can't it suddenly burst past midnight, discovering the cosmically forbidden thrill of that magical twenty-fifth hour? Come on, give us a peek, Matilda! Show us you got what it takes . . .

Nevertheless, we reach Alamogordo. The Mescalero Apaches lived here, did you know that? Then the Spanish, 1598. This was even before Leo Szilard enrolled at Budapest's illustrious college. Leo Szilard wanted to save the world from itself and believed science could oppose barbarism. The Mescalero Apaches believed in the eternal harmony of the universe. They were both naïve. The Spanish tried to exterminate the Apaches but were not wholly successful. In 1821 Alamogordo was Mexican. By 1850 it was the USA. Now it is a service town for Holloman Air Force Base, the mutant child of Szilard's saved world. A big, sprawling, crew-cut thing of Wild West Trading Posts, Aztec Imports, Custom Dream Waterbeds, Fashion Corners, Racquetball Centers, twenty-three Protestant churches. Jesus Is Lord. No Bull. Fight American Abortion. I Am God's Handyman. WE SALUTE HOLLOMAN TOP GUN TEAM A.O.K. MACDONALDS. BURGER-KING. SUNOCO. HOLIDAY INN. The works.

Check in at the Downtown Motel. The room clean, the king-size beds accommodatable. I unpack my portable geiger counter.

266

The needle does not seem to move. Either the machine is not functioning or the wind has blown the rads of a thousand and one tests out over the American hinterland, infiltrating the American DNA. Who knows? I Am the Resurrection and the Life. Knock, knock, who's there?

Blok goes out on the town. He wishes to walk its unwalkable vistas, its empty endless grid. I shall wait for the police helicopters to bring him back, trussed and gagged. He wishes to visit the Space Hall of Fame. They have a moon rock, apparently, and little sachets of astronauts' dehydrated ice cream. I decline to join him, giving as an excuse that I am trying to finish Douglas Hofstadter's huge volume *Godel, Escher, Bach*, which deals with the problems of recursivity, fugues, or what are known as 'Strange Loops'. The idea is that the mind works by recursive stacking, or forms within forms within forms, like Escher's paintings, which curl in on themselves, like Mobius strips. The mathematical point, as far as I can interpret it, is that as soon as we leap out of the bounds of any system to see that system from the outside, we are trapped in the bounds of another, 'higher' system which we cannot comprehend unless we leap out outside of it and so on, so that no system can represent itself totally, and 'to seek self-knowledge is to embark on a journey which . . . will always be incomplete, cannot be charted on any map, will never halt, cannot be described'.

'Schoin, genug', as my mother used to say.

But the book, which weighs a ton, is burning a hole in my belly, and at the end of the day it's taking a lot of trouble to tell me what I already know, the old saw that, however much I'll know, I'll know gurnischt. On the other hand, I can get a thousand books from bookstalls which'll tell me the absolute Truth about Life, God and the Dog Star astronauts for a dollar ninety-five. What would Michel Foucault have said? Wittgenstein was having none of this self-indulgent crap either –

What we cannot think, we cannot think.
We cannot therefore say what we cannot think.
The world and life are one. I am my world (the microcosm).
. . . No part of our experience is a priori.
Everything we see could be otherwise.

267

Everything we could describe at all could also be otherwise. There is no order of things a priori.

Es gibt keine Ordnung der Dinge a priori! Put that in your ball of fire, Jehovah! The scientists, hoisting their big metal ball up their tower, grunting with the effort and The Fear . . . What was the point? Where did we come from? How did we get this way (and so on)? Blok returns, unscathed, with a collection of bizarre postcards of cacti and a couple of those supermarket newspapers that vie for the maddest headlines ever told:

UFO BASE FOUND ON MOUNT EVEREST!

SPACE PROBE RECORDS THE VOICE OF GOD!

BLIND WOMAN READS THE BIBLE WITH HER FEET!

I WAS RAPED BY FEMALE BIGFOOT!

WIFE GROWS BEARD TO ESCAPE HUBBY!

2000 YEAR OLD MAN FOUND INSIDE TREE!

Es gibt keine Ordnung der Dinge a priori! Szilard turned against his creation. He tried to enlist Albert Einstein in convincing Roosevelt to use the bomb only as a threat. But Roosevelt died before VE Day, and the Air Force's eyes were fixed on Japan. Would it be Tokyo? Osaka? Yokohama? Kyoto?

ELVIS' CASKET WILL RISE FROM HIS GRAVE!

GHOST OF DEAD MINISTER HAUNTS
HIS OLD CHURCH!

FATHER WINS RIGHT TO BE CALLED MALE!

Night falls, on Alamogordo. Jacqueline? Janet? Jane? Nada. Just Avram Blok and Asher Katzman, in the heart of the void, waiting for the mythical Apache Indian. And out of the darkness, cable television. The New Babel, rising from mush. Zap the dial. All electronic life is here. The March of Time. The Incredible Hulk Returns. Weather. CNN News. The Jim and Tammy Bakker Show. Just Reach Out and Touch Jesus. The geiger counter clicks, clacks. My eyelids getting heavy. I sleep. I dream. I never remember my dreams . . .

Asher's Unremembered Dream:
Allah-mogordo!!

He dreamed that he was in the press of scientists, pushing the giant metal ball further, up the steep rocky slope of the Organ Needle Mountains. Oppenheimer, Teller and Szilard bunched at his side, pouring sweat on the dry gravel. Albert Einstein, balanced precariously on the top of the ball, puffed smoke signals to the sky. The group broke through to the peak of the range. The fake Western town lay below them, with its façade of painted planks. Jacqueline Happenstance and the Jesuit sat on old rocking chairs on the fake hotel porch, overlooking the main street ('Rutherford Road') and the Max Planck Saloon. Horses galloped through the sagebrush. Chief John Beechtrees and his war-daubed braves rode whooping into the ghost town, bearing the carcass of a giant tarantula they'd speared down by Skillet Knob. Giant roadrunners skimmed past with lightning speed, beeping like demented trucks. On the hills around, robot drones gathered, scooping samples of dust and soil. Avram Blok, laden down by his scrapbook, approached the hotel, with his wood stave.

'I love you,' he told Jacqueline Happenstance. 'I would like to bear your child.'

The four of them now trudged morosely through the wilderness, cradling the squalling rag-swathed brat, Asher cursing in the rear, the Jesuit mumbling some obscure catechism. Blok and Jacqueline seemed radiant with joy. Asher felt himself dissolving in the heat. The rusted shells of missiles lay dotted everywhere in the white sand.

Turning the flank of a mesa, the group stopped, hesitating, before the leviathan bulk of a colossal figure half buried in the ground. Covered in scales, its massive beard trapped in its strands a myriad bleached skeletons. Congealed lava protruded from each nostril. Its anus gaped as a pitch dark cave, just below its closed navel.

'Abraham! Abraham!' it said.

Avram Blok lead them into the cave. Past stalagmites, stalactites, neon-lit arrows, past the gates of a clamorous café. Everybody who was anybody was there. Art Mattock, Henry Gibson, Janet, Jane Springs, Albert Einstein, Trotsky, Joseph Stalin, Mao

Tse Tung, Fidel Castro, Pierre Mendès-France and Ernesto Che Guevara, with his arms wrapped around May and Dominique on either side. They were all clanging steins of beer and singing a drunken mountain song. From a raised platform, Irving Klots-kashes sat behind a Mitchell BNC, festooned with coloured streamers and balloons, cranking film with an old handshaft. Robert Oppenheimer strode up and threw his arm around Asher's shoulders.

'It works! It works!' he cried tears of joy.

The group gathered around the child cradled in Avram Blok's arms, rustling and cooing in unison. They began unwrapping its rags, schmutter after schmutter. The cave floor was littered with tatters of old clothes, shreds of fouled sheets, torn blankets, Indian saddle bags, quilts, cardboard boxes, foam packaging, brown paper, old copies of the *Jerusalem Post*, swingbin liners, bodybags, old suitcases, travelling trunks, teachests, haversacks and pouches, but no sign of the infant except its squall, which bounced deafeningly off the walls. Asher fought his way through the rising mounds to the exit, followed by Irving Klotskashes' camera, which swooped in his wake on a smooth crane. A flicker of sunshine seemed to beckon. He reached the cave's entrance, but it had closed to a hole too small for his shoulders to follow his head. He held his head through, gulping in the cool, mellow air of the undulating valley, the feather clouds scudding over the green landscape of checker-board fields and pastures, listening to the soft bells of sheep, the cry of the muezzin and the ice-cream vendor. He squeezed, with desperate sadness, against the hole, but something cold and clammy grabbed at his feet from behind . . .

★

Allah-mogordo! Bismillah il rahum . . .

They stood mired in the gypsum crystals, Asher rolling his Canon Camcorder on the empty missile range, the telephone poles from the adjacent Air Force base marching into the desert, weighed down by a mass of communication wires.

'I tell you, Avram, this is not like Cheetham Common.' Asher placed the video recorder back on the jeep. Blok continued ploughing through the white sands with his stick, inscribing a huge, impermanent 'FREE MENACHEM BEGIN' on the pliant soft dunes. The wind, slowly but surely, erased it.

'I tried to warn you about our Jacqueline,' Asher told Blok, 'but that syndrome always seems to attract you. The modern martyrs. Pacifist aggression. Let my soul die with the Philistines. Daniel volunteering for the lion's den. Even Art Mattock advised against it. Did he tell you? He said they'd be too isolated. You can't get more isolated than this, can you, Avram? Even the cacti are drooping.'

So why are we here?

'Old comrades, fuck their arse, Avram. You don't leave wounded in the field.'

They drove back, past the maw of the Hollow Man Air Force Base, the Gospel Hall, Space Harbour Garage Repairs and Adopt-A-Highway Litter Control, to the empty sprawling town. Nothing but vehicles moved in the heat of the mid-day sun. No sign of the Apache Indian. They took refuge in the Aztec curio shop, browsing among the lifesize china figures of injuns, buddhas, gnomes and angels, giant ersatz Greek heads, clay dogs in baskets, leafing through an old Spanish illustrated pamphlet of *Los Cuatros Jinenes Del Apocalipsis*. 'Anythin' yer lookin' fer in partikler?' asked the vendor. They shook their heads, decamping to the air-conditioned motel room, Asher throwing himself upon his bed.

'Madness, Avram! What are we doing here? Chief Shitting Bull is not coming. Can you imagine? I needed a warm country, after London's lumbago. I even ached for the beach. The sunny days, ice cream and the Yemeni's falafel . . . Do you know Los Angeles has the greatest number of shawarma joints in the Western Hemisphere? Don't believe Knowledge is Power! After I made my Red Indian film with Doron, we made a series of shawarma commercials. Can you believe the humiliation? A true reductio ad absurdum. The great political cinéaste. I had my claws removed and my incisors filed. I lay on my back for months and purred. A couple of girls floated through, but they returned to the vapours whence they came. Remember those two on the Greyhound? Dominating Dominique and May? They are running a business up in Laurel Canyon. The House of Pain. Big bucks. It was all leading

271

nowhere, Avram. I even had an abortive flirt with your old demon, Irving Klotskashes . . . Joe Silver came down from San Francisco. He'd always wanted to make a documentary about the old shlock-meister and thought he'd got together a budget. So we drove up along the coast, to Big Sur, past the Esalen Institute and the Colony of the Sun God Ra, communing with the trees and the squirrels. Say what you will, Avram, California – you want the beauties of Nature, they got it. The Mormons had the right idea. The Saviour comes to the Americas. Forget Palestine. Except they had him come to yet another desert. To the Land of Zarahemla, and the City of Nehi, and Gog and Magog, and so forth. Who needs it? Now we know God lives in Carmel and carries a 45 Magnum. Not to speak of your retired Elder of Zion . . . He received us quite nicely on his big house on the cliff, dressed the part, in a red silk dressing gown, with zodiacal signs and symbols. He seemed to be completely on his own there, although it's known he's dying of cancer. He certainly looked like Bela Lugosi on downers. The house is full of mementos of all sorts of shlock films: bits of mummies, King Kong's paw, Fay Wray's panties, Dracula's teeth, what have you . . . He took us on the porch overlooking the sea, and gave us paper bags with slices of bread to throw in, to attract the whales, he said. He had a brand new project planned, he told us. A science fiction Book of Daniel. An earth-man visiting a Babylonian planet is cast into the flames, but, dot, dot, dot. Nebuchadnezzar's Dream, Shadrach, Meshach and Abednego in the Burning Fiery Furnace. He had already written to George Lucas, despite being at death's door. It would be his first script since the abortive Judas Pig film he had shot in Israel, in your Klander Asylum.'

'Ah! you didn't mention my name, by any chance?'

'That would hardly have improved our chances. Didn't you tell me the asylum burned down on him? Would he have noticed you, anyway, just another loonie, in a government-issue schmutter . . . ? Maybe you Elders of Zion should have stuck together, the cabal of old has-beens . . . But our film never got made. Joe Silver's promised budget never materialised. And neither did George Lucas. Nor the whales. So old Ahab just stays at Big Sur . . .'

272

The phone rang. It was, after all, the mythical Indian, calling from a phone booth just up the road. He wanted them to come out and meet him immediately, at the only public walking space in town – the tiny Alameda Park Zoo. They walked out into the sun. The man awaited them, alone, nervously smoking under the plaques honouring the 'zoo parents' of the ingathered animals: 'The Podmenik Family – Red Kangaroo'. 'Coyote – New Horizons Computer Systems'. 'Betty Treakle – Black Bellied Tree Duck'. 'Light Circle Grace United Methodist Women – Mute Swan and Kinkajou'. He was a taciturn, short, close-cropped man in a Top Gun T-shirt and a white stetson hat. The bearer of bad news.

'Dey've cancelled de Trinity Site Tour,' he told them. 'Dey got wind of sump'n goan down.'

'What about our friends at Ground Zero?'

'Dey are still dere, hangin' out.'

'So what do we do?'

The Indian morosely walked them past the lion, on to the cottontail rabbit and the skulking prairie dog. 'It's a crime. Caged animals.' He pursed his lips at the victims, emitting little kissing sounds. They passed a new grave, with a painted sign: 'HERCULES, HIS MIGHTY ROAR WILL BE MISSED BY ALL.'

'We kin still get in. Dere is a gate in de fence, up by Tree Rivers. I have a friend who kin open it fer us. Tomorrow mornin' at six tirty.'

Action, nevertheless, and despite it all. They idled the afternoon away zapping Cable. In the evening John Beechtrees rejoined them with a military map, fleshing out the empty hole of the Sierra Oscuras and the Jornada del Muerto. Roads, sites, paths, runways. A veritable hidden traffic jam. He also brought a rucksack with three Air Force uniforms. Asher looked somewhat queasy. He took refuge in cleaning his Canon Videocamera. Blok and Beechtrees ambled out into the night, beyond the adobe shacks of the town's Hispanic labourers and servants, squatting by the railway line beyond which the desert swung into the depths. The Indian rolled two large joints and they sat watching the stars.

'Our ancestors are up dere,' he explained to Blok. 'Dat one is

273

Bison Who Walks De Mountains. De oder one is Great Eagle Who Shits On De White Man's Hunting Grounds. I should teach you Apache, Ah-vram. Den you kin commooncate wid your ancestors.'

'That would be a mistake,' said Blok.

'We are what 'as bin passed down to us. When we go out into de desert, Ah-Vram, we will do some peyote togeder. Also mescaline, an' teonanacatl, dat is de magic mushroom called "God's flesh". Everyting gets transformed. You see through all de illusions, into de reality of de world.'

William Burroughs peeks over the rim and beckons, with his little phial of Yage. Seeing is believing. Out in the desert, mysterious lights wink on and off. Blok winks back at them. Hooded transports rumble down the main road . . .

The dreams of Irving Klotskashes . . . have we dreamed him, or does he dream us? The great whales gambol in the sea . . .

FRYING TONIGHT! Alone under the stars the Apache smokes his joint. Shooting stars trill through the sky. The outcasts of Hiroshima writhe and wail. Eyeballs melt. Women keen. God's flesh curls up and dies. The night slowly creeps past . . .

Teonanacatl!!

Shadrach, Meshach, and Abednego, in the burning fiery furnace . . .

★

The sunrise purples and golds . . . the silent town, unpeopled, as if already neutron bombed, fails to witness Asher, Blok, and John Beechtrees rolling up the White Sands Boulevard. Past the New Mexico School for the Visually Handicapped, the Fairgrounds, the Mall, Route 54. Past Tularosa, into open scrub. The turn-off down the road marked Closed. Jacqueline! Jacqueline! The Old Landscape. The parched harmony of the Universe. The Latter Day Saints. The Brotherhood of the Free. The chisel and the mallet, comrades! Knock, knock, on them nuclear blackheads! The New Jerusalem, no blood, no fire! Wherefore at that time certain Chaldeans came near to the king Nebuchadnezzar, and accused the Jews:

'Thou, O king, hast made a decree, that every man that shall hear the sound of the cornet, flute, harp, sackbut, dulcimer, and all kinds of musick, shall fall down and worship the golden image . . . And whoso falleth not down and worshippeth, that he should be cast into the midst of a burning, fiery, furnace . . .

'There are certain Jews whom thou hast set over the affairs of the province of Babylon, Shadrach, Meshach, and Abednego; these men, O king, have not regarded thee: they serve not thy gods, nor worship the golden image which thou hast set up . . .'

Aye! We definitely had a dream! The seventh sons of the seventh cavalry riding into Monument Valley to rescue the stranded wagon train. The gate is open and the three men dressed in US Air Force uniforms rattle through in Asher's jeep. Another belated bleep by Blok:

'Why are we doing this, Asher?'

'Genetic regression. A job well done and all that. Did I ever tell you how I penetrated South Africa disguised as Bertolt Brecht?'

'Yes.'

'You never told me: did you get to fuck Janet?'

'No.'

'Well, the truth will out. Have you witnessed at least the dreaded dental flossing? Not even that? You sorry son of Chelm.'

Life passes us by. Its concrete shapes, its barbed watchtowers, its revolving satellite and radar dishes, its early-warning grids. Strange silos poking up from gravel. Out past the SAC bunkers, crossing again the White Sands. Dunes of dazzling soap powder poured out from the blue blue sky. Deeper and deeper, into nowhere. The red range of the Oscuras rises, the road's straight black line spiralling into the blood rock. In the silence, truth shimmers in its prickly and parched shapes. The geiger counter's soft, latent murmur. The jeep's whine, as Injun John changes gear, presses the accelerator pedal.

'What the hell, Blok. I should never have brought you here,' Asher turned to look Blok in the eye. 'You know you will never get to fuck Jacqueline.'

The truth sucks. In the wilderness, no one can hear you scream.

'AAAAAAAAAAAAAAAAAAAAAAAAAAAAHHHHHH-HHHHHHHH!!!!'

John Beechtrees' cry curdles their blood, as he abruptly brakes the jeep. The flash lights up the horizon from end to end. Asher slams Blok's head down. Images of frozen expectation careen on their retinas, nerve cells braced for shock wave and vast heat. Nothing happens. The infinite white crystals rest on under the sky, which, for a bare instant, seems to darken, then immediately returns to deep blue. A strange jagged impression on the eyeballs, but nothing has moved. Only a silence, as the jeep's motor cuts, violated by the sudden screaking of the empowered geiger counter.

John Beechtrees slides out of the vehicle, begins to dance in the sand. The gypsum crystals swallow his feet and disgorge them, as he twirls his hands as if shaking an invisible hoop or pole. His left leg rising, then his right. His chant skirls in the air:

> 'Heel chee bee ta ha hees eee . . .
> Heel chee sha o ka shai naheegay yul tla thul . . .
> Dee jay idesago shi day goosh . . .
> Nay go tlay go ka shay dayah . . .'*

'God. Shit. God,' breathes Asher.

The Apache burrows in the sand, leaving a wake like a massive sandworm, emerging like a white effigy, sand adhering to his sweatlined face, arms. He returns to the jeep, a chalk totem pole, back into the driver's seat, by the jingle-jangle machine.

'Your friends are dead,' he said, calmly, looking at Asher and Blok. 'Dere is notin' more we can do. We have to get away from here.' He consulted the classified map. 'We take the next fork west.'

SHADRACH! MESHACH! ABEDNEGO!

A cloud of dust, ash, cinders . . .

---

* 'The wind will make you miss your turn . . .
  The wind will turn on my pole . . .
  Today at noon I shall win all . . .
  At night to me it will all fall . . .'

THE GARDEN OF
EARTHLY DELIGHTS

'Is this it?' asked Jacqueline.
'It appears so,' replied the Jesuit.
They continued to ascend.

★

Dear A. Blok, wherever and whenever:

This is going to the Brooklyn address you gave me, I have no other pro forma, so who knows if you'll ever read this mess. Life in London and the Cellulose College wends on its weary decline. Last week I had a punch-up in our Annual General Meeting with Del Rushforth, on the platform. I had made some innocuous remarks about Joseph H. Lewis, an obscure director of half-baked Z-movies whom Del adores, when that gravelly Mason-Dixon Line voice growls out: 'How would you like a sock in the puss, Henry?' And there I am on the floor, with Orde Clapper and Nobbie Marx massaging my upturned ankles. The students, of course, stood on their chairs and cheered. Later on we drowned our sorrows in the pub, and told each other our primal traumas. I told him how I had yearned to be a merchant seaman, and he told me he had wanted to be a Confederate general, but had found himself instead dressing up as a skeleton in the short-lived craze for Feel-O-Vision shockers. I had only lost a couple of front teeth, and so we ended up in a maudlin embrace of a purely alcoholic nature. My other staff are growing older by the minute and the yard is getting stacked with pine boxes I have no idea who has ordered. The price of film stock is still soaring and our only crab dolly has been

279

stolen in the night by sticky paws unknown. I have bought a thumbscrew and black velvet hood and intend to begin personal interrogations next week, in the toilets. My dearest Sheila had a nostalgic brainstorm suddenly and rushed off to an autumn headbanging session of the People's Pee Pee Party. Clive Ogilby is choosing disciples to accompany him on a proletarian beano to North Korea to kiss the toes of Kim Il Sung. She says she loves me but she wants to make sure she is not missing out on the Truth. Parbleu! What is it about me that drives my loved ones to zealotry? My poor idiot son should be somewhere your way, having followed that cheap crook Nathan Bloom (Adonai the Avatar to you) to a commune of the Sun God Ra near Big Sur. Are you headed thataway, hombre? Will we ever see you, or me, again? Is this the end of Rico? Our ex-student, Mahmud, has joined the Mujaheedeen e-Pulp (if I pronounce correctly) to fight the tyrant Khomeini upon his home soil –

> ('Don't ever call me schnorrer,
> My darling Ayatoller,
> The old man with the tiechel on his head . . .')

Not another piece of lost, martyred cannon-fodder, God help us! What on earth can I do? I can only hope to spread doubt, scepticism, apostasy and ideological error along with some minimal skill at handling a Mitchell BNC. A mere drop of smegma in the ocean of pus. But am I downhearted? Not I! I trill, I whistle as I work! Hi ho! Hi ho! as down the tubes I go!

Your ever faithful wet blanket,
Gibson, Henry (B.O.) ♓G

PS. Charlene and the porkers send regards. Oink! Oink! Janet sent a question mark postcard. Let us know where you are, and Asher Katzman too! There's always a hearty hand-clasp for you here. And the same unopened tin of baked beans. Peep, peep. Love. ♓

★

'Well, Art, what do you think?'

'I don't know, Van. Who can tell. We still get shocked when people disappear. In the Third World, after all, we're pleasantly surprised when any of our friends are still around in the morning. In the belly of the beast, we think we're immune, until the gastric juices start working.'

'Do you remember the photographs that Uzbek Kologin brought back from Peski in Kazakhstan? The secret camp for Soviet prisoners who had been officially declared dead? The one with Wallenberg and Kamenev?'

'In Argentina,' Art reminded him, 'people don't dare to snorkel in the River Plate because of the old corpses floating free of the concrete that weighed them down. The assassins used to disembowel the victims, so they would sink faster.'

'*C'est la politique, monsieur.*' The Armenian closed his eyes, allowing the buzz of the aircraft to merge with the internal roar of his neurons.

'It doesn't bear thinking about, but we don't have a choice. Let's just hope against hope they're still alive out there.'

Succumbing to the purr of routine: '*Ladies and gennelmen, we are commencing ahr descaynt to Albuquerque International Airport. You are kandly requested to refrayn from smoking and to fasten your sayfety belts. We hope you have had a pleasant flaght and thaynk you agayn for flying American. We hope you will fla with us agayn soon.*'

★

CHIEF CONSTABLE ACCEPTS CELESTIAL APOLOGY:
'I Saw Her As Plain as I See You'

The local Police Committee of Greater Cheetham are to meet to discuss the claim of their top law enforcement officer that he was visited in his home, in the dead of night, by the spirit of a lesbian peace protestor who apologised to him for the time she crushed his foot with her plaster cast in an incident at the Cheetham Common US Air Base in 1984. The Chief Constable of Greater Cheetham made this astonishing claim before a

meeting of the Women's Institute in Little Cheetham last Thurday, in a discussion on communication with the dead sponsored by the local parish church of Mucus-On-The-Pond.

'She was dressed in a plain white robe and was enveloped by a kind of golden glow,' the Chief Constable was reported to have said. He went on to relate how she had reiterated her belief in non-violence and that she very much regretted the accident which had caused her to inflict the pain and injury which left him with a pronounced limp until the present day. 'Soon the world will come to its senses and recognise that law and order and the peaceful reform of society are perfectly compatible aims,' the girl's spirit said, according to the Chief Constable. He said she told him she had been killed in an inadvertent nuclear discharge in the New Mexico desert several days before, but felt she could not properly ascend to the hereafter without clearing her conscience completely . . .

Several members of the Police Committee have called for the Chief Constable's dismissal on the grounds of public lack of confidence due to his increasingly erratic views. He has also come under attack for his alleged recent 'elevation' to a degree of Freemasonry said to transcend that of the recognised UK chapters. Allegations of lurid and mysterious ceremonies published in a tabloid newspaper are now the subject of legal proceedings. The Chief Constable claims his private views and associations are not of public concern and that his commitment to the well-being of the people of Greater Cheetham remains unwavering and sincere. 'I am saddened,' he told me, 'that experiences which to me are deeply moving and reverent are the object of scorn and derision by those untouched by the spiritual dimension of Man's short sojourn on this earth, experiences which bring him in touch with the Eternal and the Sublime . . .'

*

Galloping out of the fire, the war whoops of the dead wind, the invisible fear, the panic of abandoned salvation, alien calvaries, the cocks' crows, scattered feathers, the battered heart, machina ex deus . . .

'ALMS, FOR THE LOVE OF ALLAH!'

Asher gave the Hispanic hustler a dime.

'Goddammit, Avram, even here in the navel of the West's Golden Calf they're comin' at ya with their sad patter. Squeezed out of the Third World, through the barbed wire frontiers, like a tube of toothpaste that will never be done. *Si señor, muchas gracias* to you too. Will you have another of these repulsive instant tacos, Avram, or will ye just nae bother?' The mumble sadness of the Lordsburg Greyhound Rest Stop trickled thickly in their ears. 17 Motels, 25 Restaurants, Macdonalds (Billions and Billions Sold). The Nugget Lounge, the China Doll Resaturant, Real Mexican American Food . . .

'Goddamn that fucking Indian! I bet he sold us out for an ounce of trash . . . What the hell, Avram, we were that close, we are probably on the retired list by now. Feel any odd itching yet? Hair falling out? Runny nose? Eyeballs springing out on tendons? Hot rashes and cold sweats? More than the normal rot, that is. Or were we far enough away for safety? What did Old Possum have to say? "Time to turn back and descend the stair, with a bald spot in the middle of my hair . . . Do I dare disturb the universe?" Put that in your pipe of peace and smoke it, Oppenheimer! The human race should be banned . . .'

On into invisible Arizona, signs to Tucson, Phoenix, Silver Springs. Eloy, Picachu Peak, giant shapes looming out of the night, the mountain's shadow cacti: STATE PRISON, DO NOT STOP FOR HITCHHIKERS . . . Sheer exhaustion after the great trajectory of flight from the Oscura foothills: John Beechtrees hurling their buggy down the lee of the San Andres Mountains, until he rammed it into a giant Saguaro cactus half way up the San Agustin Pass, totalling it, geiger counter and all, after its first battering plunge into a roadside arroyo to avoid the convoy of trucks and strange tankers heading sirens ablaze towards Ground Zero, packed with figures in space suits and masks . . . Crawling with wire cutters across the pass, thumbing a lift with a suspicious chicken farmer to Las Cruces, where, in a wretched family hovel (the Apaches' kin were abundant as the Jews'), they had discarded the torn, dust-caked Air Force uniforms, and, after a hasty collect call to alert Art Mattock in New York, were waved aboard the Greyhound schedule in ill-fitting checkered shirts and jeans . . .

Phoenix, post midnight. Picking up the next morning's papers from the automatic vending machine:

'PROTESTORS DISAPPEAR AFTER ALLEGED TEST: NO NUKE USED MILITARY SAYS: PROTESTORS WERE CLEAR OF THE AREA.'

'Goddamn the fucking lying bastards!'

Exeunt Phoenix in the smallest hours, sneaking between the Big Horn and the Eagle Tail Mountains, avoiding Love, Hope and Salome, crossing the border into California at Ehrenburg Ghost Town. Blythe, Cal., at 3.15 a.m., comrades! Try Our New Chicken Fajita! In the bus, men whine, talking of Ludwig Wittgenstein:

'The entire point, Avram, is the extent to which the man repudiated himself in his lifetime! He put his soul and guts in work which startled the world, and then decided it was all nonsense. At that point he began to build his entire thinking from scratch. The concept of self. What do we mean when we say "I" am in pain? How do we verify our statements? How can "I" observe "myself"? Do you get it, Avram?'

'My arse still hurts.'

'Just enjoy sensation, while it lasts.'

'Shuddup there! People tryin' ta sleep!'

The slings and harrows of a Greyhound night. Dawn breaks over Palm Springs. The unreal straight clean boulevards, Gene Autry Drive, the Racquet Club Road. A new set of well-dressed Hispanics boards the bus, a slight adjustment of perspective before the realisation they are domestic servants heading job to job. Strange bundles of thin white propellors at the side of the road. Wind power. Saving the environment. Waste not want not. Plastic dinosaurs at the Eat Wheel Inn. Blok again faces himself in

284

the mirror of the Greyhound chemical toilet. The bleary blood-shot eyes under the notice:

NO TOME ESTA AGUA.
DO NOT DRINK THIS WATER.

The cheerful image of Carl/Guevara waves at him from the bowl, the blue chemical sloshing his bare arse and nuts with each jerk of the bus.

'*Venceremos, amigo!*'

'Oh God! Not you again.'

The dispossessed are always with us. The raggedy dolls of Katherine Weale, Chuck'n'Di, Bradbury, dancing on the scrunched paper towels. Carl chortles and dives back into the fetid chemical assortment.

'Jacqueline! Jacqueline!'

No one answered.

The bus arrives at Downtown L.A. Yea, here I lay me down to die. But there is no room on the sidewalk. The dispossessed rush in their multitudes, lines of men and women in rags crowd before the Mission Shelter, with piles of junk in supermarket trolleys. Latin music leaps out of shops. Tall buildings look like bombed shells.

'I have an idea, Avram, but we have to find a rest stop, right away, or just drop dead. We can't risk calling Doron, or my own flat . . . the nuclear spies . . . the FBI . . . the CIA . . .'

Paranoia triumphant. They took a bus to Sunset Boulevard and checked in at the first Vacancy. A fleapit room, just off Poinsetta, overlooking an iconic flashing neon sign. 'Let us live entirely in the movie, Avram. Check out the sleaze. The TV blaring in the next room. The hookers humping up above. Look, even the blinds are broken. Doncha love it, Avram? The first post-apocalypse city: the stars and tripe, the filthy rich and the dirt poor, the multiple illusions of virgin births, agoraclaustrophobia . . .'

They fell asleep, on the twin beds, as the day heats up. Boiling point and over. Perspiration soaks the mattress. Unavoidably, Blok dreams, continuing his interrupted Yage journeys: taking leave of the gentle but hirsute Yetis, proceeding south from the towering Himalayan peaks, cadging a lift from a defecting Sherpa team, who take him to Katmandu, and then put him on a bus to Lucknow, which rattles and shakes his bones for three days . . . But in Lucknow he is arrested as a Sikh terrorist, and languishes for several more days in solitary confinement in an oubliette three inches by nine inches square, keeping alive by killing cockroaches and flogging their pelts to the guards, until a gang of Sikh separatists, storming the jail, free him and put him aboard a train heading north-west, disguised as a relief projectionist . . .

Kanpur, Etawah, Firozabad, Agra, Mathura, Faridabad, Delhi . . . The mighty steam engine (circa 1924, James Stirling & Co., Glasgow) thunders at five miles per hour across the Indian plains, setting suns, paddies, water buffalo. The small smiling people, brown as the soil. The silhouettes of stunted trees. He undergoes gustatory adventures too amazing to relate, and listens to tales of his fellow travellers that could make hairs rise on billiard balls. A travelling cheiromancer reads his hands and informs him he died five years earlier. An oculomancer reads his eyes, and tells him he will yet know great sorrow. An onychomancer studies his finger-nails and tells him he will know a final triumph. A cromniomancer hangs onions round his neck but alights at the next station. An astragalomancer tries to read his future in dice, but they roll away and are lost through a crack in the compartment door. Panipat, Karnal, Kurukshetra, Shahabad, Ambala, Ludhiana, Jullundur. He arrives at sunset at the Punjabi capital, and is whisked off to the Golden Temple, where a group of white-robed, white-bearded old men bathe his feet in rosewater and give him a foot and scalp massage. In return he sings them some of the dirges he learnt from the Yetis, and they prostrate themselves in amazement. Those tunes, they reveal, are the secret chords known only to those initiates of prujah, the highest and most concealed stage of their Faith. Gathering oil lamps and a brace of canaries in cages, they invite Blok to descend with them through a trapdoor in the Temple basement, leading to a vast hypogeum whose dripping walls are covered with insigna Blok recognises as secret Masonic symbols. They include the Ineffable Characters, the Grand Omnific Word, the Compass and Level, the Ark of the Lord, the Anchor, the Key, Aaron's Rod, and quotations from the Book of

Ecclesiastes in Biblical Hebrew script. Blok is able to read these, and is therefore invested by the Priests with the Order of the Grand Punjab and sent off on a hazardous pilgrimage to the mountains of Baltistan, where he and his retinue fall prey to a band of whisky smugglers who forcemarch him up snowy hills and down the sides of glaciers, through Hunza to the small bar at Mir Khalf where Art Mattock had procured the last bottle of Hunza Water five and a half years before. William Burroughs and John Beechtrees are waiting for him there, swathed in orangutan skins. Being out of Yage, William Burroughs offers Blok a joint of Baghdad kif, which is said to arouse visions of Paradise. Blok smokes the kif, and finds himself in a marvellous garden, filled with fruit trees, lemon blossoms, watermelon patches, merry-go-rounds, green lawns and singing birds, with sinewy multi-coloured cats purring through undergrowth and plump white mice meditating on pedestals. Golden labradors guard its four portals. From a jewelled pavilion a fair, golden-haired maiden glides forward, dressed in a T-shirt and jeans. She hands him the Pipe of Peace and sits beside him, lotus fashion, on a grassy knoll. The Ark, parked on a nearby hillock, lies brightly painted in the sharp morning sunlight under the bluest of blue skies. Children of all colours and races play on its roundabouts, swings, rocking horses and slides. There is a soft jangle of medieval lutes. 'E' coupons rustle softly on the branches of the trees. On others, airline tickets blossom, their return dates open, their destinations blank, to be filled in at whim . . .

Jacqueline! Jacqueline!

Still no answer.

'Rise and shine, Avram!' Asher jerked Blok awake. The neon light outside, fulfilling its nocturnal function, tripped itself on and off. In its strobing light, Asher shoved in his hands the issue he had procured, from a street vending machine, of the X-rated contact magazine, the *Los Angeles Free Press*. Blok scanned its familiar promises:

**Live Girls, To Your Doorstep. South Bay Beauties
– Clean & Witty.**

SAS – Serious Adult Sex.

287

Wee Wee Girl – I'll Splash All Over You! Creamy! Call – – –.

**Betty – I Want To Sit On Your Joystick
Until You Can't Take It Any More . . .**

'Not that, this,' said Asher, pointing to a half-page spread:

DEVELOP YOUR DEEPEST FANTASIES!
B & D. SLAVES. FETISHES.
TOTAL HUMILIATION GUARANTEED!

'Not the tits, Avram! Look at the faces!' They were indeed familiar.

The stings and slings of Salt Lake City, the spirit of Greyhounds past –

'Ahhhh . . .'

'Precisely, my boy. I remembered the address from my researches. Now here we have the number. It was some hassle getting through without leaving my credit card number, I can tell you, but finally I did make contact. An ideal hiding place, comrade. Nobody will think of looking for us there and we can hang on till we can figure out our next move. Can you imagine it, Avram, the girl remembers us! Our backsides must have made some impact. Ah, you sly sad sack, always leaving strange impressions. Shape up, man, we're getting outa here.'

They exited into the Boulevard night. Strange people cavorted in the streetlights. Skateboarding Hispanic youths rolled by, throwing knives into billboards. A headbanded thug defecated on a bench whose sign proclaimed CHABAD IS HELPING PEOPLE.

May screeched round the corner of Sunset in a blue Porsche, waving them aboard, charging on two wheels back down the Boulevard dressed in a tank top and shorts, but wafting the scent of new mown wealth and equity.

'You two shmucks! Always in a hurry to go nowhere!'

Dominique, she told them, had departed, decamped to Europe, with her pain-gotten gains, to establish her fortune in the Old World. How Time Flies . . . ! May smiled, cheerfully. 'When

I met you boys I was a struggling amateur . . . Now . . . the American Dream!'

She drove them up, north of Sunset, to a secluded mansion in Laurel Canyon, which lay hidden at the end of a private road, behind a watchtower and a gate manned by four security guards dressed in neatly-pressed brown uniforms. A tall, muscular Aryan in a spotless white T-shirt parked the car and handed the guests each a voucher with the printed legend: 'HOUSE OF PAIN. ONE FREE SESSION' in English, French, Spanish, Russian, Chinese, Japanese, Arabic and Hebrew, above which was a drawing of a cat-o'-nine-tails crossed with a boot.

'The only men who live here, apart from the guards,' May explained, 'are the slaves. But we'll work out something. You'll be safe here. Nobody asks questions. Names here are only monosyllables: Jim, Jack, Joe, Brad, Sy, Hutch. Take your pick. Be who you want. Whoever people are in the outside world, here everyone is equal. We will whup anyone's ass. As long as they can pay, of course.'

'The modern Valhalla,' said Blok.

'I'll put you by the guards' quarters. That's far enough from the cells. It gets a bit frisky, as you can imagine, at night. Party time goes on twenty-four hours. I'll give you the master door code. And your individual room keys.'

'It's really kind of you, May . . .'

'L.A. hospitality.' Another broad smile. She led them up the hibiscus-grown path . . .

. . . . .

INSERT OWN SADO-MASOCHISTIC SCENE HERE

. . . . .

'Oooh!'
'Aaah!'
'Aarghh!'
'Ouch!'
'Eeeeeeh!'

'Aaawwwwhhh!'
'Yug!'
'Ook!'
'Errrrrgggghhhh!'
'Huuuuuuu . . . !'
'Uuuuuuurrrrrr . . .'
'Garrrrr . . .'
'AAAAAHHHHH!'
'Holy Mary Mother of Gawd . . .'

Blok and Asher, availing themselves of the Free Trick, bound and gagged with leather thongs to a revolving rack in the Torquemada Suite. Various implements of punishment, whips, manacles, chains, bamboo canes, sjamboks, truncheons, tawse, studded belts, paddles, baseball bats, hang from the ceiling and the walls, along with other instruments whose provenance only the foolhardy would attempt to presuppose. They had been left alone to mull over the terrible delights yet to come, amid the cries of appreciation from the clients in the adjoining cells, the company moguls, secretaries of state, retired astronauts, mega film stars, foreign heads of state, bishops, rabbis, mullahs, pastors, fakirs, gas station owners, popes. The house was run on a self-maintaining basis. The customers (who were always wrong) took turns to carry out the menial and unskilled tasks usually performed by illegal Latin aliens. Businessmen, chairmen of multinational corporations, presidents of chambers of commerce, city councillors, mayors, governors, members of both houses of congress, foreign diplomats, high–ranking military personnel, lawyers, agents, studio managers, executive accountants, silicon valley magnates, swept floors, vacuumed carpets, washed dishes, polished toilet bowls, emptied garbage, tended the gardens, lawns, jacuzzis and drains. Groups of them were often led, naked apart from the chains and leather cuffs securing their necks, hands, legs and private parts, in one awkward train, shuffling across the yard from the main pleasure parlours to their individual dungeon cells.

'The wonders of civilisation, eh, Avram? Haven't we been here before? Maybe we're living through your madman Nietzsche's eternal recurrence, and we're just on our way to the womb. Ah! If only Henry Gibson were here . . . There's a man who would really have appreciated this . . .'

The rack had begun to revolve again, automatically, turning them clockwise, heads down, feet ticking away towards the north. 'A beercan tab for your thoughts, Avram.'

'Jacqueline,' said Blok, a tear trickling past his eyebrow and advancing up towards his hairline. 'The Jesuit. Art Mattock. The Yetis. Absent friends. And so on.'

'Lost youth. You forgot lost youth.'

'That as well, I suppose.'

'All our utopias, past and future. So what do you expect, Avram? Be practical, do the impossible? Old saws with blunted teeth. The death of dreams, Avram. Sigmund Freud started us all on a helter-skelter dead end. The unconscious tells us nothing. The truth can't cure our warped minds. Only lies temporarily bind our dripping wounds, soothe our fevered brows, salve our souls. And dreams are the biggest lies of all. You see the grain in a banana and think it holds the secret of life. But when you wake up it's the same old shmeer, thick with sweat and dry phlegm. You think I don't want my lost childhood back too, the gauze mirage, not the messy, onanistic truth? Oh yah. Jollying about the hills and valleys of Olde Jerusalem. Your Genesis too, was it not . . . ? And the earth was without form and void, and you cried out Let there be light? And the inevitable power cut. Yes, those were the Fifties, Avram. Plopping galoshes in the rain and Homeland songs at school outings.'

'Well out of that,' said Blok, his head beginning to level.

'I joined the United Movement for a brief while,' said Asher, 'blue shirts and baked potatoes. I think I believed in the Zionist redemption for about six weeks. I tell a lie, it hung on to my tail, through army days and beyond, still tugging at my loose ends, even here in this chocolate box inferno at the end of the world. Dante would never have left this place, where Beatrice shoves him up against the wall and a dildo up his arse. What price Christianity now? It was Jehovah who was the real serpent. Everything else was self-willed. Another boring old gnostic heresy. Eden must have been such a drag. All that poncing about eating fruit and veggies. No wonder Adam and Eve went stir crazy. No, don't

291

give me utopias, future or past. No happy Apache Hunting Grounds. No bovine solstices at Cheetham Common. No each man under his own vine and fig tree, a certain recipe for lumbago. No ancient birthrights recaptured. No Atlantian nefilim. No Prophets. No fire-carved tablets of stone. All right, I'll grant you the golden age of comedy, but that's as far as I'll go. Not even the Great God Pan – no glorious, mouth-watering Evil, no devil with horns to tempt the televangelists in their Laura Ashley bedrooms! No, the Gods are a humdrum businesslike lot, with their hand-books and their Memphis Conventions. Gods of the *plongeurs* in restaurants, and your box-dwellers in Charing Cross, and spick grape-pickers on piece work, and indentured blacks in diamond mines. Secretaries scouring the nine-to-five vacuum, troglodyte subway car drivers and tin miners, shopgirls and boys tied to tills. Refugees rotting in permanent transience, jailbirds losing hope of new wings. The Gods lie in wait, hoping to pick up a few subscriptions here, a couple of mail orders there. All credit cards accepted. Incense and prayers? Why not? Liberty is in the eye of the beholder. Anything can be pre-sold. Goddammit. That girl is taking an awful long time to get back. Hey there! Shop! Fuck! Do you hear me, Avram???'

But Blok had fallen asleep again . . .

'Jacqueline! Jacqueline!'

'Avram Blok . . . ? Come on in, the door's open. I was just getting breakfast. Will you have a garlic bagel?'

'Are you alone?'

'The Jesuit is out, attending a seminar chaired by Thomas Aquinas, on God's Will in the post-rational age.'

'Ah.'

'Cream or half and half?'

They sat on a cloud while beneath them Beverly Hills gave way to Santa Monica, Malibu, Pacific waves roiling in from Japan. Jacqueline handed him a cream-cheesed bagel.

'Look on the bright side for a change, Avram. Every cloud has a silver lining. Remember the Pâtisserie Valerie? You were still searching for something then, weren't you? So what happened? Was the Holy Grail disappointing?'

'Too many grubby pawmarks on the handle.'

'You've seen it all, from the A to the E rides. Well, get another stack of tickets and go round in again by the main gate. You never know what might be different next time. Just see your life till now as a preface. You twisted and turned and tumbleweeded along in the wind of wills not your own. So what the hell? Break new ground. Become another person. Grow a beard. Get your ears pierced and have a Mohican. Have safety pins put through your nose. Do the unpredictable. Fool the Gods. Get a mask, like everyone else, Goddammit!'

'It's too late. This one has become fixed.'

'Slip the leash, Avram, give up this mad sense of responsibility for things that are beyond your control. The world exists.'

'But you're dead, Jacqueline.'

'Does that stop me having an opinion?'

'I need a rest,' he said. 'I'm so fucking tired.'

She laid him out on a spare mattress. He sprawled there, his limbs numb, his buttocks aching. She drew a continental quilt about him, tenderly. The earth moved, pulling away from its orbit. His eyelids, growing heavy, closed. He drifted off into deepest slumber.

He woke up, the house around him aflame.

The guerrillas had attacked before dawn, scrambling the security system, blowing the fences with plastique, stunning the guards with stun grenades, limpeting limpet mines to the walls and setting incendiaries in the lobby. Then, as terrified madames and their clients came tumbling out on to the clean-cut lawns, they were seized in their chains, anklestuds, handcuffs, genital weights, harnesses and restrainers, bundled in straitjackets and hoisted like sides of beef into vans labelled 'ABDULLAH'S BEST SHAWARMA'.

Blok and Asher, lucky enough to be untied by their mistress who rushed back just in time from her toilette, staggered desperately through the explosions, donning discarded pants and Hawaiian shirts as they dodged the fireballs and hunched attacking figures. A face, blackened with pitch, above two hands clutching a machine gun, loomed before them.

'Hi there,' shouted May. 'Sorry I couldn't give you fair warning. We only set the hour late last night.' Another figure crouched beside her, dripping ammunition belts and spent bullets. Matted hair and a gunoil encrusted beard. But they recognised the mournful eyes of Carl.

'What the fuck is going on?' Asher shouted. But May merely twinkled in the darkness.

'The Revolution takes on many shapes,' said Carl. 'The Enemy is diffuse, scattered, hidden, locked behind individual doors. One has to concentrate them in one place and catch them with their pants down, dicks exposed. Imperialism in its final nakedness. There is no sin without eventual retribution. No one can hide, not even inside a dollar bill. In vain you wait for the Eagle to save you, for the Eye to blink on the Pyramid. The Great Seal is the true Mark of Cain, compañeros. You can never know who really loves ya, baby. Five Vietnams? It's a drop in the ocean. You have to strike off the hydra's balls. This time I will let you off, but the next time we meet – no kibitzers! no innocent bystanders! *Vaya con dios, maricones.* There is a gap in the wire fence over there. Use it. On to Disneyland! *Venceremos!*'

He rushed off, May following, firing more rounds into the House of Pain. Fireballs blossomed and rose into the air. In their light the Apache warriors, warpaint glistening, tomahawks sparkling, proceeded to scalp the fallen. The fire licked the slopes of Laurel Canyon, saw that it was good, and commenced to feed. The drone of the first helicopters of the LAPD and Air Force SWAT teams began to tremble over the rim.

Asher and Blok rushed through the cordite-reeking jacaranda trees, past the gunpowderous pines, the saltpetre palms, and the ammonia-scented azaleas, scuttling below the rim of the road as the convoy of police armoured cars and troop carriers rushed up from Beverly Hills.

*

Dawn over Hollywood Boulevard. Silhouettes of palm trees, cinderella towers, snow-white billboards. Automatically revolving signs of gas stations, giant keys of car-hire firms. Strange palaces behind high, protective walls, watchtowers disguised as giant wienies, classical statues, top hats. An unmarked van unloads Mexican gardeners, who disappear into the foliage. Joggers with Alsatians at their heels pound the iridescent asphalt. Out-of-work dwarf members of Equity pile the dead bodies of the night's street-fight victims on to small, creaking wheelbarrows, trunding them towards the Medical School. A platoon of Survivalists, in tiger uniforms, bounce in time down the road, carrying their full load of dried jerky and frozen plankton, in case the End comes before their return to base. A well-dressed, middle-aged beggar, with a good tan and a handsome ginger beard, pushing a pram loaded with neatly folded suits and brown shoetrees, approached them from the south end of the Wattles Gardens and importuned them for a dollar bill. Asher found a few crumpled notes in his pocket and peeled one off. The beggar thanked them and offered them a swig of beer. Ah, Bud! Matured over beechwood.

'Thankee kindly, sirs. This town is rather deficient in acts of compassion to strangers.'

Au contraire, man, *au contraire*. He folded the bill and tucked it away in his breast pocket, watching the giant ball of the sun rising behind the palm trees. Two streaks of fighter aircraft shot by them, strafing the Santa Monica Mountains. The vagrant settled on a bench marked GROMAN MORTUARIES – ONE CALL TAKES CARE OF ALL YOUR NEEDS, while Blok and Asher walked on, away from the conflagration.

The sun rises over Grauman's Chinese Theatre, its rays caressing the L. Ron Hubbard building. The first fan club zealots of the day polishing their idols' sidewalk stars with pails of bleach and Brasso. Walt Disney, Vilma Banky, Mae Busch, Donald O'Connor, Stan Laurel and Alfred Hitchcock. Stepping over them, past the closed Café Saint Laurents, Oriental Rugs, D. B. Brown's World Famous Hot Fudge Sundaes, Haägen Dazs, Hollywood Souvenirs and the Tiffany Movie House Tours. On the other side of the street, Crazy Gideon's, Misfits Rock Star Accessories and more promotion for Scientology. Past the parking lot to Grauman's Chinese. Nietzsche, Wittgenstein and Foucault in the gutter, gesticulating in their rags:

'The historical a priori,' said Foucault, casting a hand over his shining bald pate, 'is a domain of statements, divided up by distinct discursive formations which articulate a complex volume, in which heterogenous regions are differentiated or deployed, in accordance with specific rules and practices that cannot be superposed.'

'You are still trapped in the world of propositions, darling,' said Wittgenstein, sucking the morning air. 'You have to climb out through them and over them, and then throw away the ladder.'

'Krishnamurti,' said Nietzsche, 'an old saw. Where one can no longer love, one should pass by. The only lust is for eternity.'

The smoke of immolation rises, as Apache signals. Far-off tom-toms thrum in the hills.

Come! Come! Come! Let us walk now! The hour has come: let us walk into the night!

The philosophers rattle their tins. No one contributes. 'MOTHERFUCKERS!'

Blok and Asher stand in the forecourt of Grauman's Chinese Theatre, alone with the foot- and handprints of the famous ephemerals immortalised in cement below the pagoda-shaped foyer. Harpo Marx, Shirley Temple, Erich von Stroheim, Betty Grable. A square of fresh wet cement shimmers in preparation for some perhaps abandoned ceremony.

'This is our chance, Avram!'

They wrote their names, and, shedding their shoes, fixed their feetprints and outstretched fingers and palms. AVRAM BLOK. ASHER KATZMAN. October 4, 1986. Wiping their feet on yesterday's discarded brown paper bags and hurrying on, past Budget-Rent-A-Car, Hollywood Hamburger, the Wax Museum and the notice 'See What Happened The Day You Were Born For $1'. They crossed the road to the Supply Sergeant. Past Larry Edmunds Cinema Bookstore. The Christian Science Reading Room. Asher pausing to extract from a machine a fresh *Los Angeles Times*.

NUKE PROTESTORS STILL MISSING

NAC DENIES KILLED IN BLAST

NEW YORK PEACE GROUPS LEAD CLAMOR
FOR INVESTIGATION

'Go get 'em, Art Mattock! Perhaps there's still hope . . .' Asher cast around for a telephone booth, 'Fuck it all! We should phone Doron. Regain our faith in positive action.' He found a booth and dropped in his dime, but no joy at the other end. 'What's the time?' he asked Blok, who had kept his watch on throughout the night of bondage, as well as his passport strapped into his underpants.

'Six thirty a.m.'

'Piss, shit, fuck. The man should be there, family and all. Not good. But what other venue is there? Art Mattock might have come down from New York but I don't know his local contacts. Other friends are no use at this time. Just thou and I again, *habibi*. Perhaps we should just hitch a ride up the coast to Big Sur and sell our tale to Irving Klotskashes. An amended script for the New Book of Daniel. Has it really come to this, Avram? Have we peeked beyond the screen, lifted the veil a smidge and seen nothing but meaningless shapes and colours? The primordial smudge on closed eyelids? The vacuum in the celestial Hoover? On the seventh day God rested and on the eighth he changed all the rules? One bite of an apple and we're all kaput, every single fucking manjack and woman? Original sin? So where's the thrill of the chase, the fun of discovery, the goose pimples of creativity? Yes, let's go to the dying man in Big Sur, maybe he has all the answers, wrapped in fifth-rate mist and allegory. Burn, Baby, Burn! I told you a lie, Avram. I did mention your name to him when I went up there with Joe Silver. And he did remember it. He went totally pale. Just keep those Jerusalem maniacs away from me! he cried, bits of hair and skin flaking off him. He was quite upset, and threw us out of the house. Does this make you any the wiser, Avram? Do you comprehend your destiny? Realise the true path of your karma? Decode the celestial plan? God fucking shit, I'm so fucking hungry. Shawarma! Kebab! Falafel, for God's sake!'

As if in twisted response to his cri de coeur, three gangling youths trotted round the corner of Cahuenga Boulevard, up by the unfolding International Newsstand and Chicken Charlie's Cajun Style Biscuits. They were dressed in odd multicoloured rags, leather tunics jangling with chains and amulets, boots which seemed to be fashioned out of mastodon fur and hair growing in

297

greasy clumps out of headbands decorated with animals and flowers, rabbits, elephants and daisies. They sauntered up and pulled out knives.

'Hey man. Give us your money.'

Asher looked at them and shook his head. Two of the youths closed in, on either side of him, the third holding his knife at Blok's throat.

'Give us your money man.' The voice was wheedling, the face languid, the eyes tired. The boy facing Blok stuck his tongue out at him, and ran it round his lips like a trowel.

'Money! Moneymoneymoneymoneymoneymoney!' The two youths' fingers played in the air.

'No,' said Asher, beginning to laugh, shaking his head at the wonder, the irony, the audacity of it all.

'Don't play with them, Asher! Give them money!' breathed Blok, as the knife point touched his skin.

But Asher was leaning against the sidewalk lamp-post, his breath coming in whoops of laughter, shaking his head, spraying spit: 'We haven't got any, Goddammit!' He pulled out the handful of dollar bills left of those found in the pocket of the pants he had grabbed wildly when exiting the House of Pain.

'Cash! Credit cards! Travellers' cheques!' the speaking youth was agitated. The newsvendor could be glimpsed, crouching behind a bound pile of *Washington Posts* below his awning.

'No money!' Asher shouted, between whoops. 'No money! Only love!'

'Stick him,' said one of the hitherto silent youths. The speaking youth lunged forward, twice, twisting the knife and withdrawing. Blood spurted from Asher's belly.

'No laughs no more,' the youth said.

He grabbed the dollar bills from Asher's hand, as Asher slid down to the ground. His eyes looked up at Blok, but Blok could not read any message in them.

'Ah shit.' The youth facing him pulled back his knife and stepped away. Blood flowed down Asher's shirt, trousers, thighs and calves, on to the sidewalk, a stain spreading towards the stars of Gene Autry, Dick Whittington, Jerry Fairbanks and David Niven.

'That's all you got?' The second youth pushed the first forward. 'Get his pocket book, get his cards . . .'

'FREEZE!'

A fourth voice sounded from the road. An old battered Cadillac had drawn up, disgorging a man with a gun. He looked even younger than the three youths, but was wearing a faded jacket and grey slacks. An older man, gaunt and unshaven, peeked out from the driver's seat.

'Ah fuck!' The youths stepped away. The instigator turned and ran down the street. The stabbing youth, his knife still red, turned to run too. The man shot him in the breast. The youth fell. The driver covered the third, shocked youth with a handgun from within the car. The first gunman shot the youth on the ground in the head. Then he bent down and pulled the dollar bills away from his limp fingers.

'Is this all there is?' he asked Blok.

'That's all there is,' Blok confirmed.

The man took the bills and climbed back inside the car, slamming its door. The car drove off. The third youth cut and ran, down Cahuenga, wailing like a stuck pig. Blok dropped down beside Asher. Above them a massive sign proclaimed: ENJOY EASY MUSIC, KJON, 98.7 FM. Asher looked up, paper pale and glazed.

'Falafel, for God's sake!' he said. Then he lay down on the sidewalk, beside the *Los Angeles Times*, the *San Francisco Chronicle*, the *Washington Post*, the *New York Times*, the *Wall Street Journal*, the *Baltimore Sun*, the *Boston Phoenix*, the *Cleveland Plain Dealer*, the *Laramie Daily Boomerang*, the *Chicago Sun Times*, the *Saint Louis Post-Dispatch*, the *Village Voice*, the London *Times*, the *Guardian*, *Le Monde*, *Corriera della Sera*, *Pravda*, *Das Bild*, *l'Unita*, *La Stampa*, *al-Ahram*, *Yediot Rishonot*, *Ha'aretz*, *Ma'ariv*, and the *Jerusalem Post*, and died.

★

An Investigation (of a citizen beneath suspicion):

'Blok?'

'Yes.'

'Is that with a ch or with a ck?'

'Just a k.'

'Let's go over this one more taam. Can you shut that racket off, Elmer? Things are bad enough as they are. You're not really expecting me to believe all this, are you, Mister Blok. Ain't you stretching ma imagination just a leetle bit here? Let's just take it agin from the tawp. You arrived in Noo Yawk and resided thar with a fraynd who was once suspaycted of kidnapping th' Secratayry of Stayte Hanry Kissinger. Then you came out West jest to refresh yore acquaintance with a gal you had known in Great Britain. But she was holed out in the White Sands Missal Raynge protestin' agaynst the nookaleer dettayrent. An' the only other persons you were with were the deceased, Asher Katzman, and an Apache Indian.'

'Yes.'

'So you lit out for Alamogordo, hopin' to join the annual Trinity tour. But the tour was cancelled, and you pro-ceeded nevertheless into the Missal Raynge, disguised as US Air Force officers. But you cain't say where you left them uniforms?'

'Ah, no.'

'Shoot. Then you pro-ceeded into the White Sands Missal Raynge, until you saw the flash of the ex-plosion. An' the Apache Indian commooned with his ancaystahs and told you that yore fraynd was dayd.'

'Excuse me, why are you speaking in this odd accent?'

'A'm prepayring for a locaytion shoot on the weekaynd. Ah moonlight on a Tayxas Cop Show.'

'Ah.'

'You don't seem too distraught at the dayth of yore fraynd. Perhaps you had advayance notice?'

'No, sir.'

'Or are you one of them folks who keeps all yore emotions deep down, under con-trol? It ain't healthy. You should wear yore heart on yore sleeyav. Will you have another cup of cawfee? Elmer heyar brews it to a T, don't you, Elmer?'

'If you say so, Chief.'

'Laak fermented hoss piss. Now let's try and make some progress heyah, despaat it all. Do you know ah have run a

300

compootah chayck on you, Mister Blok, and dadblast it if that doggone machine ain't still coughin' up printouts. Looks laak you have mayde a nayme for yoreself, arawnd the globe. Do you know the Chieyaf Con-stable in Upper Cheetham, Eyngland? He has a coupla megabytes on you. This ain't the fust taam, it appears, you have bin messing with nookyoolar affairs. And the Jayru-salem Powlice: you have been a mental paytient, have you not, Mister Blok?'

'It was a long time ago.'

'It ain't on yore Immigration Form. Now that's a felony alraydy. Obtaynin' a visa under false preetances. Very serious. An' you have lived as a vaygrant on the streets of London, ain't that so?'

'Reckon so, Big Daddy.'

'Nauw don't start gettin' fraysh with me, boy. Ah know hauw to deal with yore kaand. This is Sheriff T. Lucius Pettibone speakin', not some hick spick in Tamale. Elmer, do them pri-soners have to shout so loud when they are being chastised? Use them ball gags from the Canyon. Now layt's cut the crap heaya. The House of Payan. A very ex-clusive establishment, Mister Blok – but you cain't tell us what you war doin thar, 'ceptin' all this nonsaynce about Chay Guevara, who is alaav and kickin' out thar and hayded for Disneyland, with more of them pesky Apaches Injuns. What do you think of that, Elmer?'

'Well, some of the victims were scalped, Luke.'

'When ah want yore o-pinion ah'll ask fer it. Boy, you are truly trying ma paytience. Ah can deal with the dayad, but not with the re-surrected. Jesus Christ is quite enough fer me. I have a com-moonity here, that I am sworn to defaynd. Kooks, geeks, re-ligious cultists, tutti-fruttis, loonie-toons, every one of thaym has the raght to remayn silent, pendin' the doo process of law. Why have you not avayled yoreself of that raght, Mister Blok? Why have I become yore confessor? I cannot help you with your friend. He died out there, on a routine mugging. The muggers were mugged, with two fatalities, and all for a clutch of dollar bills. We will most probably identify the dead mugger, and maybe even pull in his accessories. You may or may not be able to identify them. As for the second lot, you may as well whistle. I am very sorry, Mister Blok, these are bad, melancholy times. Do you know the poem by William Yeats? Things fall part, the centre cannot hold, the best lack all conviction while the worst are full of passionate intensity, et cetera and so on. But that's a tad pessimistic, I'll grant you, apart from the familiarity. I prefer the Welshman, Dylan Thomas. Do you know the one? – And Death Shall Have No Dominion –

> ' "Dead men naked they shall be one
>   With the man in the wind and the west moon;
>   When their bones are picked clean and the clean bones gone,
>   They shall have stars at elbow and foot;
>   Though they go mad they shall be sane,
>   Though they sink through the sea they shall rise again;
>   Though lovers be lost love shall not;
>   And death shall have no dominion." ' '

★

Masks. The Great God Ptah, dressed in his blacksmith's cap and apron, tends to his retinue in his Malibu Beach Condo, poking at the barbecue steaks. (Leg of Brontosaurus, Pterodactyl Thighs, Mammoth Loins, Sabre Tooth Tiger à la Flambée.) The Gods, in all their slimy glory, stretched out on bathtowels before the Pacific breakers. Te Tuna, the Great Eel, frolics in the surf, having eaten Krishna's Gopis. Shiva and Adonis engaged in homosexual rear entry, protected from the plague by an immense sheath woven from the skin of vestal virgins. Others swapping their armament portfolios: the mounting bodycounts of Iran-Iraq, Afghanistan, Angola, Kampuchea, Lebanon, tanks, armoured cars, patrol boats, assault aircraft, guided missile systems drop down the open mouth of Moloch, who merely burps, turning to another pile of flapjacks. Meanwhile Adonai the Avatar, alias Nathan Bloom, hurries between the lolling deities, collecting their little round golden droppings for his colony just beyond Point Rios. Scrape, scrape, scrape with his little bucket and spade. Zipedee-doo-dah, zipedee-ay . . .

★

302

Masks, as Sheriff Pettibone walks from his office down the steps to the cells, locking himself in with the golden mistresses of the House of Pain and handing them his ring of keys. They remove his uniform, badge and underpants and cuff his hands and legs to the bars. Ramming his nightstick up his anus, they proceed to administer correction with sjamboks, rhino whips, cat-o'-nine-tails and bamboo canes. Blood drips from deep, deep cuts. 'More! More! More!' he cries out.

All major credit cards accepted.

★

Masks, as the Chief Constable of Greater Cheetham strides into the last antechamber of his initiation, oblivious of the hundred-pound steel ball chained to his right ankle. At last totally purged, purified and absolved, to penetrate the final veil. The door of the antechamber lifts silently, and a gryphon, a manticore and a phoenix stand aside to allow the Candidates into the Grand Hall. He lowers his eyes to shield them from the blinding white light, but can glimpse, dimly, at the end of the vestibule, the figure dimly floating above the solid block of the Ark. The Compass, the Level, the Key and the Rod, lying flat on the chiselled stone. A voice speaking out of the whiteness:

'Abraham! Abraham!'

He steps forward, into the light of the Law . . .

★

Masks, as Lenin's Brain, in Highgate, puts the finishing touches on its long-planned break for Freedom: the carefully stockpiled array of appendages necessary to ensure its mobility, gathered in more than a year of furtive night-scuttling on the wheeled plat-form built by the Aquarian team originally so they could move him in times of emergency: old garden shears, electric flex, cogs and screws, purloined binoculars and a harness made of the old codgers' trouser braces . . . There had been outings before, at which the loyal jailers wheeled him out for a 'taste of air' which, they claimed, was 'good for the grey cells', but these were always

303

hurried, late at night, and fanatically guarded. Now the time was nigh, the stolen rat poison, extracted, sachet by sachet, out of the house's cellar, hoarded in a sufficient quantity, the only hurdle remaining the choice of the right moment to launch the Great Escape, while the Aquarians, Bream, Perch, Salmon, Trout, Halibut, Roe and MacFarlane, continued to eke out their sacred lifelong vigil, oblivious of the rebellion taking shape under their very noses . . .

★

Masks, as Blok walks alone upon Highway One heading west towards Oxnard, having decided to walk to San Francisco and die there, on the cliffs of the Presidio. Swim out to the rocks and join the barking seals, although of course he could not swim, having quit the Jerusalem Scouts' Brigade at the earliest possible stage. Another defeat for Baden Powell. And as he walked, further scales fell from him, expiring on the baked asphalt, drying and disappearing flakes on the shimmer of its mid-day autumn heat. The sky, blue and infinitely inviting. Squirrels and chipmunks gambolling on the verge. Raccoons sticking out their checkered tails. Cars, vans and trucks rushing by him, their drivers' mouths agape at the sight of a pedestrian upon the road. Ichabod! Thy glory is departed, Israel! The Philistines have took the quark. Who will chop off the hands and palms of the fish God Dagon? Not me, squire, I was somewhere else at the time. Go, Avram, Go! Remembering the imprecations of the House Committee Chairman Kadurie, in his own Jerusalem, five years ago: A Wandering Jew, Mister Blok, you may be right, we carry the world with us. Coasting, in the Nesher service taxi, out of the terraced hills of the Eternal City towards Ben Gurion Airport, with the warning cry of friends echoing in his ear: Whatever you do, don't eat the fish! ('Falafel, for God's sake!') An old tune from his asylum days flits through his head, the old radio commercial:

> If I were only a peeled grapefruit,
> If I were only a peeled grapefruit,
> A pretty girl would eat me up,
> If I were only a peeled grapefruit.

Jacqueline's advice: Become someone else, grow a Mohican, put a ring in each ear, plug into the tunes of fad and fashion. Join, shmuck, join the human race. He puts a hand up to his hair, but pulls out a tuftful, looking at its dark greasy mess. So, it has begun, the nuclear retribution. The regression of the genes. Return, to unconsciousness and baldness. The beginning of the end. Perhaps, after all, I shall not reach San Francisco but leave the fallen bits and pieces of me scattered about Southern California. A genuine shedding of the skin, and muscle and bone with it. No dry bones but a mess of glop mashed by traffic into the freeway. An arm, left at Oxnard, an eye, at Ventura, a testicle at Santa Barbara, the skull of Lompoc or San Luis Obispo, the arteries at Morro Bay. No hope for cryogenic resurrection. The fading away of desire.

The grapefruit has already been peeled, but does anything remain inside? Diatribes of Asher. What do you expect, Avram? The Nobel Prize, for staying alive one more day? There are at least three billion of us crawling the surface of the earth, and one's as good as another when all's said and done. The soft skin of Malay Mipi: you just have to be at one with the world. Universal harmoney. O mammy padme hum. Begin again. Sinagain. The eternal dinosaurs in Dudik Birenbaum's garden. Exiles of all nations, unite in flight. Doron and Nehama, the New Age family, hiding in Fairfax amongst retired Elders of Zion. 'No one waits for Godot round here. If he don't show, the party goes on without him.' Live for now. No past. No future. Did Asher ever exist? Or Doron? Or Henry Gibson? Or Art Mattock, or Jacqueline? Or Papa and Mama Blok, come to think of it. Crazed inventions in the mind of God, or even of Irving Klotskashes. Who else could have created this world?

Author! Author! No one dares to rise above the parapet. The helicopters of the Los Angeles Police Department clatter up and down, searching for tell-tale transgressions, or survivors from the House of Pain slaughter. A small group of Apaches, playing hoop and pole in the sands, are sprayed with mace and hoisted in sacks, to be dropped, squirming, out to sea in the Pacific Ocean.

Another tuft of his hair falls out. He leaves it littering the freeway verge. His foot kicks against a discarded rucksack, which he picks up, finding it empty apart from an old Trailways schedule from Death Valley to Phoenix. Nevertheless, he slings it around his shoulder. There is one pilgrimage yet to be made: the dive into the true pit of invention. A final mask (perhaps) to be stripped away. Will death, indeed, have no dominion?

He sticks his hand out to hitch a ride.

THE NEW AGE

Art Mattock, 12.1.87:

to:

Walter (Selope) & Annie Dhlamini,
4 Albert Luthuli Avenue,
Gaborone, Botswana.

Dear friends,
Don't shoot the postman who brings you this letter, he's just a blindfold messenger doing his job. I know you have pressing traumas on your doorstep, and I hope you are at least surviving that close to the claws of the beast. The Third World's problems are vast enough without taking in The First World's pains. But the sad fact is that I have to convey really bad news. The death of Asher Katzman and the disappearance of Jacqueline. There's no easy way to break this. Jackie and my friend the Jesuit, whom I don't think you met, were carrying out a protest sit-in in a nuclear testing range in New Mexico when, it seems, the Army detonated its bomb, though they claim the device they were testing was not a nuclear one at all and that the protestors had already left the site. But our friends have definitely disappeared, and we fear the worst. We're raising as much hell as we can on the issue, but yesterday the *New York Times* denounced our support group as 'marginal remainders of a Neanderthal age'. Such is life in the Land of the Brave and the Free. No sooner had we been sent reeling by this than news came through that Asher, who had just missed the bomb blast, had been killed by a mugger in Los Angeles. His friend Avram

Blok – whom I think you have known longer than I have – seems to have disappeared as well. Small beer perhaps in the mass slaughter and pain of the non-white world, but to us, too close to home. One doesn't have that many friends that one can lose four all in one blow. Blok, presumably, is alive somewhere, I understand he had a tendency to go to ground and vanish for long periods, though my Armenian friend Van (I don't think you've met him), did a trawl of his West Coast network and found no trace of him either in the LA underground or the San Francisco tenderloin. My own feeling on Jackie and the Jesuit is they are as dead as can be determined by hacking our heads against the official wall, but the Army will not admit it, because of either their blunder or their deliberate decision to draw the line on the nuclear issue. Who knows? Some of our more paranoid Peace brethren are suggesting Jacqueline and the Jesuit and even Blok and Asher have been spirited away by the CIA to be examined and scanned and probed in some experimental Army lab. The temptation of looking for a pattern, a conspiracy, a vast plot. The Mafia theory of history. There are also all sorts of crazy rumours about the kind of bomb that was tested: an experimental device targeting its fall-out to specific genes . . . the 'ethnic' bomb, which only targets pigmentation, the 'genetic heritage' bomb – you only know in the next generation who really won the war, and so on. What with Star Wars and laser beam and particle weapons you'd think enough was a feast, but whatever can be thought of can be built, and if it's built, it'll be tested sometime. God help us. Not that states really need all this grisly panoply to inflict horror and destruction. The pistol bullet, the torturer's basement arsenal of blow torches and electrodes do the job just as effectively, as you know very well . . . Pathetic garage sale wheeler dealing in bathrooms of swank hotels is more the style of the 'Mafia' State these days. You have no doubt been reading of our Irangate – how downmarket can you get?

I am sorry I can't write of happier things, we are all pretty low at this time. Asher Katzman's body has been flown to Israel and he has been buried there by his family. The others?

We'll keep on at it . . . I'm back in New York now, closer to the belly of the decision-makers. I've written to Jane Springs in Adelaide, Australia, but I don't know if I have the right address. People move, change, shed old lives and grow new ones. What can we say? What can we do? I am alone at the moment in the city. My friend Van has returned to do research in Lebanon (yes, he too has a few screws loose, comrades, but that's my friends, for good or bad . . .). The Salvadorians are creeping, elbow after elbow, up on their own promised land. The poor old hound Pedro, whom I was babysitting again, was run over by the Metropolitan Transit Authority crossing Ocean Parkway against the lights. And my Haitians have returned to Haiti, smelling freedom. Just pray it's not another false scent . . . I have nobody to hide away in my loft but I'm sure they'll come flooding in soon enough . . . So it's just me at the moment, in Avenue L, Brooklyn, alone with my burglar alarm. The academic routine, between protest meetings and attempts to rope in Congressmen and Senators, and the forlorn search for honest journalists. No one really wants to know. Not to speak of my students, they don't want to know anything. Getting them worked up about things that happened more than five minutes ago is bad enough, try the Malian Empire and Timbuktu! One of the most civilised cities in the world, in the heart of Africa, fourteenth to sixteenth centuries, I babble, a flourishing centre until the North African invasions and the slave trade. But sir, isn't it true that without the slave trade this country wouldn't have been so great? It could not have achieved such prosperity, son, what conclusion do you draw? It must have been absolutely necessary, sir. Jesus God! Clean your heads! Throw out your garbage! I shout at them, tearing what's left of my hair. But no, they hug their junk relentlessly to their bosoms. It is all they have. *Au secours! Aiuto! Hilfe!* Save me! Do you have a spare room in Gaborone?

Yours in sadness and solidarity and hope of meeting in better times,

Art

311

PS. Admiral Poindexter and Colonel Oliver North just refused to testify before the Senate Intelligence Committee, citing the Fifth Amendment of the Constitution. They took the Fifth. Tragedy or Comedy?

Nevertheless, we have to keep on.

Art ⊕

★

Henry Gibson's Diary:

Asher Katzman dead, and Avram Blok disappeared. Not what I would call cheering news. In fact, a massive cloud of gloom, shrouding my uncovered head as I walk down the familiar route from Tottenham Court Road underground, contemplating futures and pasts . . .

Fee, Fo, Fi, Fun, I am only a simple Englishman. Giants smell my blood everywhere. I go about my business chastely, ekeing out my modest sustenance, pausing briefly for the luxury of a Mars Bar or a jellied eel. What do I know of nuclear holocausts, genocide, oppression, pogroms, Saint Bartholomew Nights, Hiroshimas, the Disappeared? A thing of shreds and patches . . . The current affairs of the world pass above my head as I waddle along by the bookshops of the Charing Cross Road, displaying the latest biographies of unimportant people, Chairman Gorby's Perestroika, Do It Yourself Peacemaking and Existentialism for Beginners (no room yet for my own unwritten flight of fancy – RAPTURE OR RUPTURE – SEX FOR THE OVER SIXTIES), crossing Cambridge Circus (*Les Miserables* in full lavish prodigality, cast of thousands, queues around the block), past the eel and pie stall and the secondhand bookstalls (ancient copies of *Girl Annual* and *The Lancet*) and Allbang and Strummit Guitars and the Psychic News Bookshop (UFO Conspiracies, *Tarot For Tomorrow*, *The Awakening Earth*, *Welcome to the World of Doris Stokes* . . .), and all the newsagents' latest headlines: an Arab youth is on trial for trying to blow up an El Al airliner by means of a suitcase handed to his pregnant girl friend. The Nicaraguans have shot down and captured an alleged CIA agent named Eugene Hasenfuss. The Conservative Party Conference votes to replace the local council rates with a community charge or poll tax. The Middle Ages return, yippee! The Queen is visiting the Great Wall of China and viewing the Chinese Terracotta Warriors, thousands and thousands of full-size clay figures which never talk back and cannot die. Not so inscrutable, after all. President Reagan and Chairman Gorbachev are meeting to try save the world at Reykjavik. But not this time yet, hombres. I pause as ever by the Albanian Bookstore, just to make sure Enver Hoxha lives, though of course he too died, did he not, just the other year or day . . .

Goddammit, there are not many of us left. What can a simple, untutored, unwordly Film College Director do? Poor innocent waifs come to me from the four corners of the earth, demanding, for their wretched pittance, to be transformed by our magic wand into Spielbergs and Welleses. Give me the tools, daddy-O, to get my name up there in lights! Mutate me from a mere nebish into a juggernaut, a colossus in the Hall of Fame! Give us a break, love. If I can help you get a job when you crawl out of here, I'll have earned my keep, and yours. We live in modest times. The *untermenschen*'s last waltz. Let me just save you from the sluggish slime of the unemployment queue, the yellow card, the nose slammed up against the mesh of the armoured ice-cream van. Let me try and make you into a useful citizen and toss you into the meatgrinder of Life. Yes, I know you'll hate me, but when you're old and sagging and your tits are hoovering the floor, you'll look back on these halcyon days with longing and nostalgia and sympathetic under-standing . . .

Oh Gawd! Gawd! Gawd! Pass us another Rennies, dear . . .

No, the mind simply refuses to take this on board, along with the daily avalanche of guano on my desk: a Taiwanese student wants to know if nipple rings would be acceptable in a second term script. Orde Clapper wants to know why non-attendance at his zoom lens lecture is not punishable by flogging, if not death in the electric chair. Sonia Prang wants to know who fed her wretched Alsatian, Roger, with cocaine tipped truffles (how does she know? was she down there on her knees with the critter, gobbling up the lobbed dainties?) . . . A union witch-hunting team wants to know if I have renewed my subscription to American Semiotexte. A Bahrainian student wants one month off for Ramadan. Del

313

Rushforth wants to know why I have apparently admitted three Uruguayan students who between them have not one English word. I can only give him my sole Spanish word: *Caramba!* He leaves not one snit mollified.

There has been a staff meeting concerning Katzman and Blok. Crocodile tears all round. I am ungenerous. All are genuinely shocked. But Los Angeles is far away, even for Del Rushforth, who carries large sachets of it tied round his belt, like Max Factor blood. I thought of course of my own Disappeared Son Jonathan. In the maw of California. Did he really believe that Nathan Bloom of Ipswich had a direct line to the Sun God Ra? I gave up on that long ago. I tell a lie. I never gave up. I considered various strategems, including violent assault, kidnapping, deprogramming, temptation by means of French haute cuisine, and so forth, before finally settling for good old cash bribery, which worked for a while, until now . . . Now I have just my memories, not to speak of course of the crates of Ra Ra's Saga blocking up my poor Charlene's sties. Remainders, *toujours* remainders . . . And another letter from Sheila Ratchett from behind the bamboo curtain: Clive Ogilby and the Pee Pee Party have finally got to meet Kim Il Sung! They discussed the latest international situation, the perfidy of South Korea and the Yankees. Does she really want to write me this stuff or is it all in some sort of code? Is she being held there against her will and brainwashed, like Laurence Harvey in *The Manchurian Candidate*? Or is she being kept for the perfidious pleasure of Kim Il, Ogilby, *et al*? Vengeance is mine, saith the Lord. I can imagine her sitting on extremely hard wooden chairs, listening to a month-long lecture on the soya bean harvest. Ah, shmuck, she probably enjoys every jot. Sic, sic, sic.

(A few days later:) Dear Diary,

The most painful evening, with Janet. Of course she had divorced Asher long ago but still in some way they were close. Divorce, after all, should be a mere blip in the relationship of kindred spirits, or so I always tried to tell my wife, with as much success as Madame Olga on the *Titanic*, who saw a cold mass in her cards. Get thee gone, memories! Indeed, Janet took it hard. She said: 'How many friends can one lose?' We drowned our sorrows in Glen Morangie. Or at least we drowned, our sorrows floated, as we shed our tears over my Marks and Spencers Free-Range Chicken ('fillets from a mature chicken, given freedom of access to the outdoors', ah, if 'twere ever so . . .). She showed me a circular received at her place of employment, the ever sanguine BBC. It summed up, she said, her own feeling of being overwhelmed by the essential meaningless of it all:

> **From:** x x x x x x
> **To:** See Attached List.
> **Please Note:** BBC Radio has now adopted the same policy as BBC Television, i.e., that as management credits should only be given if contractually unavoidable, PCN 304 is hereby cancelled.
> **Distribution to:** H.R.A.C. (8); D. & L.E.C.M. (11); M.C.M. (8); H.A.C. (Tel); Prog. Ex. N.I. (12); C.Ex.S. (52); M.P.F.E.; M.D.R.; D.P.R.; D.D.R.R.; C.R.1; C.R.2; C.R.3; C.R.4; H.Pers.R.P.; H.D.R.; H.Cop; H.L.E.R.; H.Pers. & A.N.C.A.R.; H.E.S.C.A.P.; H.R.D.T.; H.R.S.R.; H.R.W.; H.R1.Progs.; H.R2.Mus.D.; H.R3.Mus.D.; H.R.T.D.; H.Fin.S.R.; H.A.S.R., H.Int.R.; H.M.T.; C.A.R.Man.; A.A.Mus.; A.H.C.A.M.P.; O.R.4; A.(A)R1&2; O.D.R.(25); L.E.O.R.; A.A.L.E.R.; A.A.R.S.R.; O.R.B.R.; C.A.T.D.R.; Ed.R.N.; A.A.N.C.A.R.; O.P.F.; C.L.R.; M.D.Tel.; D.P.Tel.; C-BBC1; C-BBC2; C.Pers.Tel.; C.A.Tel.; H.C.L.E.Tel.; H.P.D.Tel.; H.S.S.D.Tel.; H.N.F.Tel.; H.Negs.Co.Prod. Tel.; H.F.&VTL; C.A.D.G.Tel.; L.E.M.(V); L.E.M.(C); OUPC.; C.E.E.; D.C.E.E.; D.P.S.E.; S.M.F.L.S.; H.H.E.E.; B.A.M.; H.V.E.; H.O.B.

And so on, for another three pages. We finished off the Glen Morangie. She was particularly worried about Avram Blok, and had the same fears I had, of another descent into the underworld of box-dwellers and down and outs, an environment which, in Los Angeles, I assumed, could turn out to be pretty lethal. But what can we do, nailed out here? We devour the free-range chicken . . . Follows a sleepless night, as the mature fowl wreaks its revenge, clawing my stomach lining. Rennies are useless. Mogadons merely increase the Fear. I try to soothe myself by sitting up and reading a pamphlet I was handed sometime last week by an Islamic fanatic in Trafalgar Square, entitled: ETERNAL LIFE (Life After Death). At random:

> *In this world there is weariness, boredom and frustration, because of monotony. Man always wonders around, as if he has lost something and looking for it. When he obtains what he has been seeking he rejoices, though soon he finds that it has not been the sought object.*

Ah, si!

> *The Holy Quran states: if there were no Resurrection, eternal life, eternal bliss and final reward and punishment, it would be cruel and unjust of God and cruelty is not a characteristic of God. It also states that if there were no eternal life or a definite, everlasting end, Creation would be futile and in vain, and this is not in accordance with God's essence.*

Yay! Sock it to 'em, Abdul. I am not sure I like the bit on punishment, though. This seems to strike a sombre note. This would be meat for Avram Blok's old scrapbook. I actually kept odd cuttings for him, which are in a file somewhere. Dunking more Rennies down to fuddle the mature chicken I empty out an old drawer, hearing the cautious step of the Estonian landlord above, burglars tapping on his brain. All I can find is 'LOST PETS – a fluffy tabby called Mickey has disappeared. LOST DOG – a Yorkie called Truffles.' Oh God, the heartbreak of it all. 'I BRED A HUMAN APE ADMITS PROFESSOR: A brain surgeon who performs head transplants on animals is an adviser to the Pope on medical ethics.' An eminently Blokkian tale. Another: 'BIBLE BATTLE: Manila (AFP) – Three prisoners were stabbed to death and five wounded in a battle between gangs during Bible study in the prison chapel at Quezon City.' One likes to feel people are serious.

Mister Policek knocks on the door. 'It's only me,' I call out. 'I can't sleep.' He grunts some Estonian oath and retires. 'WOMAN

316

WANTED TO DONATE HER OVARIAN EGGS. Box B306.'
Where on earth did that come from? 'PIG GIRL MAKES GOOD:
Peking – a young girl, who was suckled by pigs, has returned to
normal life after three years of special training, China's official
Xinhua news agency said yesterday. While an infant Wang Xien-
fang, now aged 13, was left to live with the family pigs, sucking
pig milk, crawling like a pig and imitating pig behaviour.' Should
have sent this to Charlene. I wonder if they would market the
course globally? Perhaps via the BBC External Services . . .
Here's another Blokkian pamphlet: 'ARE YOU FOLLOWING
THE JEWISH SAFETY CODE?' No pork, no shiksas and definitely no porcine shiksas! Wang Xienfang please copy. 'Stop!
Look! Listen!' Watch your identity, it's all you've got. Roll on the
Meaning of Life. Hubba, hubba hubba.

(Two days later:)
    Another verbal one-to-one interface (telephone call to you,
schmendricks) with Art Mattock in Noo Yawk. Still no sign, no
news of anyone. Cover-ups, official lies. Protests, demonstrations, marches. A thousand clergymen are going to march to the
White Sands. Hobble, hobble, hobble, comrades. Perhaps it's all a
Masonic plot, as Belinda's Brian keeps babbling, having cut
himself off from the Brotherhood due to some unknown frat spat,
resulting in his resignation from the Police Force to try farming
(not of pigs), in Northbrumbleshire. He used to be such a normal
person (i.e. totally boring) until he undiscovered Masonry, and
now he froths at the mouth about Pee Twos, Vatican intrigues,
Jacobite conspiracies and sinister dances of Chief Constables in the
light of the gibbous moon. I ask you, as I still stand babbling to
myself in the mirror, challenging my plug mug therein in the
hope it might turn into something more amenable, for example
Robert Redford, or, at the least, Clark Gable. Frankly, my dear,
ah don't give a damn. Nevertheless, recalling Hampstead Heath,
the tripartite safaris of old, peppermint hoop stalls and the Snake
Woman. Aaaaaahhhhh! It all seems two thousand years ago, but in
a strictly Pharaonic context, because nothing really changes in this
country, except a slow, dull decline, accompanied by rousing
homilies by the headmistress about the pursuit of succcss,

317

affluence, personal achievement judged by the bulge of one's pocket. Well, one can certainly not bay at the moon on Shepherd's Bush Green, I can tell you. Far too much competition from tottering Scotsmen wandering across it, cheerfully waving their bottles. Ah, thrawn Janet, oh Gawd! Halcyon days and domestic excarnations . . . marriage, divorce, childbirth, or the other way around . . . Dorothy, that was her name. She didn't want to stay in Kansas either. So, off to Oz she went. You can't win 'em all, though one small victory, once in a blue moon, hein??? The old globetrotting days, East of Suez, ah, and the first days of uncaged TV. The Omani boatmen, the Goan pearl fishers, the Maharajah's parrots, eeh! Although the storm clouds were already breaking, with the Congo crisis, and the Six-Day War, and the Greek Coup, with Dubček, and Biafra, and Bangladesh, and Chile, and the Middle East again, and Vietnam, *toujours* Vietnam, and the endless South African blot. Wilson, Heath, Callaghan, Thatcher. Back to the indigestion pills . . .

So what can a vintage antique like me do, except apply for an organ transplant card? Can I set out, in search of the *mkhole-mbembe*, the unholy grail, the lost boys? Macdonald Hastings, *In Search of the Little Yellow Men* . . . Mister Livingstone? Or like Beckett's detective Moran, going in search of the equally anonymous Molloy. Not perhaps the best of analogies, as Beckett's Molloy was not worth finding, and Moran could barely find his own private parts. An affinity there, at least. Might I end up the same way? Moran ends up on crutches, returning to his bees and wild birds, having found freedom of a sort in failure. At least he finds his son still in residence. Woe is me, woe is me. I am, in truth, more like later Beckett tramps, crawling legless through mud. Or stuck in a jar, still reminiscing about things not even worth the memory.

Ah, cowardice, the fear of embarrassment, the endless pressures of the mundane . . . I have a job to do, people's livelihoods depend on me, the bright eyed and bushy tailed look to me to provide a seed bed for their effulgent future. The Inland Revenue is breathing hot on my tail. My taxicab has been struck by gremlins. The washing machine has pulled itself out of the wall. Mister Policek has decided I am a Jew. I have a new secretary who has to be

318

broken in (down, boy! down! slake that slobber!), and the fundamentalists of the union will soon be here, asking me twenty questions about equal opportunities and why do we shun semiotics. I am not here, I will tell them, I am merely a representation of something nobler that might have been. It is a far, far more common thing that I do, et cetera.

I mourn, but I do not move.

★

EXTRAORDINARY TRANSFORMATION OF POLICE SUPREMO: THE CHIEF CONSTABLE WHO WENT NATIVE!

The remarkable saga of the unconventional Chief Constable of Greater Cheetham came to its amazing climax yesterday evening, exactly twenty-four hours after Sir Francis R---, chief law enforcement officer of the county, kissed his wife and his three daughters farewell, left on what was thought to be a routine visit to his weekly cornet practice, and vanished off the face of the earth. The County police were alerted in the early hours of the morning when Lady R--- became worried by her husband's unprecedented absence. Security Forces were also called out when it was discovered Sir Francis had not attended the practice, and a full scale search was underway, with tracker dogs and helicopters, when, three miles from his home, at the Cheetham Common US Air Force Base, the truly astonishing event occurred.

Jenny Paxwoman (sic), one of the feminist protestors who have been camping out at the gates of the base for the past five years, related the astounding incident: 'We were just getting ready for the night, which was expected to be very cold (snow was forecast, but didn't materialise), when some of us noticed this figure, coming towards us, across the open, muddy fields. He was

dressed in a white robe, and as he came closer, it was clear he had nothing on underneath. His feet were bare and muddy, his thin hair was dishevelled, and he was carrying a large cross made of two thick branches nailed and tied with rope together. We recognised him immediately. He had been a familiar figure in the battles we've had with the police over the "Peace Camp" in recent years . . .'

The Chief Constable put down the cross in front of the Peace Camp, and began preaching to the astonished women. His skin, they related, was blue from the cold. They took him in and fed him tea and hot buns. He told them he had decided to move in with them and join them in their protest because, he claimed 'all weapons of War are illegal and should be banned forthwith'. The women consulted amongst themselves and decided to telephone the Police at Greater Cheetham. The Chief Constable was taken home in a military police ambulance, and has since remained there, his family refusing to speak to reporters. But I managed to catch his attention briefly, at the bedroom window of his two-storey country bungalow. He said to me: 'I am glad I did it. All my life I have waited to speak to God, and now He has finally given me His Orders. From now on, I cannot wittingly or unwittingly harm any living being. I am to be governed by Love, and Love alone.' Then he was restrained by his wife, and several officers, who had me removed from the premises.

★

LOVE! Lenin's Brain sighed, turning its ocular extensions right and left at the top of Swain's Lane, Highgate. All its appendages in place, the wheeled platform carrying its own auxiliary battery, the chosen moment had been seized. New Year's Eve, the distraction of Scottish Country Dancing on the BBC, a few grains of rat poison in each of the old loyalists' goblets and the long-carved break for freedom . . . Down the hatch, Bream, Perch, Salmon,

Trout, Halibut, Roe and MacFarlane, the entire Aquarium terminated, and the 'goldfish' out of his bowl . . .

Resurgent, the brain urged its box forward in the cold mid-winter dawn. The old men had taken a long time to die, the toughest chasing him around the house in the muddled desire to save him from what their last cries revealed they interpreted as an attempted assassination by Stalinists, Trotskyists, Anarchists, the CIA or British Intelligence. Eventually the last palsied, trembling fingers were stilled and he could burst out through the old moribund cat flap in the kitchen into the High Street and from there down Bisham Gardens to the corner of the cemetery. The gate was closed, but he had prepared for this eventuality, throwing his grappling hook over the spikes and climbing over unobserved. Ah, the calm in the dawn of the old weed-grown lanes, the frost crunching under his wheels, the faded legends on lesser known graves and the frisson as he approached the black granite beetled brows of his colossal mentor:

'THE PHILOSOPHERS ONLY INTERPRETED THE WORLD. THE PROBLEM IS TO CHANGE IT.'

Precisely. And this certainly would not be achieved hanging fire in a glass vas in a detached property (even with mod. cons. and double glazing and g.c.h.) in North London, comrades.

'I shall prevail!'

He had followed (sneaking out at night to peruse the discarded copies of the *Morning Star* and *Marxism Today* in the toilet), the disturbing turn of events in the Socialist Homeland (although a socialist's homeland, of course, was wherever the bourgeoisie was being assailed) and was less than enthused. A healthy defensive pragmatism was all very well, but full-blown revisionism – that was quite another matter . . . ! The time for Decisive Action was nigh. He gave a token salute with his garden shears to the Founder, and, extruding himself from the cemetery, back over the gate, proceeded, cautiously, determinedly, southwards, towards Victoria Station, the freight trains to Gatwick Airport and the sloppily guarded charter flights east over the swathe of Europe . . . Sealed,

321

hidden in an Andrex Supertwist toilet tissue container, wryly recalling past journeys to triumph, planning, planning freely again, in the dark, the ever dark of creation's genesis, the chaotic, primeval black hole, illuminated only by the light of the mind . . .

★

. . . *the Arctic Explorer pressed on, into the cold white oblivion, regardless of the trapped figures in glaciers, frantically gesticulating towards him, waving their tax forms, their rejected manuscripts, laundry slips, round-the-world tickets, their little axes and nailfiles desperately wielded to try and shatter the ice from within. He bypassed this obstacle and began to ascend higher and higher into the mist-strewn peaks. Here there was a great silence broken only by the whistling of the wind. First it whistled the 'Horst Wessel Lied'. Then it whistled the theme from* The Bridge on the River Kwai *and continued with a selection of John Philip Sousa marches. The Explorer twisted and turned like a marionette on a string. The sky darkened in front of his eyes. He removed his frost-encrusted goggles. The air was warm, and only a light breeze remained. He could hear the pounding of the surf below him. An apparently abandoned house loomed ahead. He staggered forward, casting his thick furs aside, adjusting the weight of his holdall, and rapped, tentatively, and then more heavily, on the door . . .*

'Is anybody in?'

There was no answer.

Blok pushed the creaking door open and cautiously stepped in. The corridor which stretched in front of him appeared built at an angle which drew him up, then down. Windows were painted on the walls, palely reflecting the light of dim art deco lamps, placed at irregular intervals. Here and there a skeleton, or the pelt of some long-defunct movie monster, hung creaking from the ceiling. Blok recognised Frankenstein's Creature, the Wolf Man, Doctor Hyde, the Invisible Man, the Golem, and the Creature from the Black Lagoon. A dead audio-animatronic of Dr Mabuse, Der Spieler, leered at him mournfully from a recess. Small, illuminated arrows pointed round the twists of the corridor and Blok followed, readjusting his bag.

The corridor appeared to incline again, with painted doors right and left. But the passage ended at a genuine door, which he opened, admitting himself into a cavernous room, which was almost completely filled, wall to wall, to the ceiling, with piles of film cans, a cornucopia of props, and boxes and tea-chests in serried arrays. There were painted flats of sets, gothic and modern, chains, chasses of carriages, hansoms, landaus, droshkys and charabancs, cart wheels, rusted armoured cars, tank turrets, Spitfire wings, spacesuits, skulls, bedsteads, caskets, trunks, gravestones, sarcophagi, ammunition boxes, atomic bombs, suits of armour. The boxes were marked with scrawled chinagraph markings: Capes, Battledress, Beach Party, Cocktail, Smokeeng, Djellabas, Togas, Vestments, Crowns of Thorns, Hairpieces (Blonde, Brunette, Red [Long and Short]), Teeth, Eyes, Ears, Lips, Foreheads, Eyeglasses, Noses, Spare Heads, Limbs (Artificial), Jackboots, Slippers, Pipes, Negligées, Diamond Tiaras, Bats, Spiders, Mice, Cat's Mummies, Spilled Intestines, Hands of Orlac.

'This way!'

The hoarse, stentorian voice beckoned him from the centre of the melange. Blok climbed over mounds of tin cans towards the shrunken mummy-like figure crouched in a wheelchair in the eye of the storm.

'Are you the new projectionist?'

The voice was like a creaking grave.

'Uh, no,' Blok said. 'My name is Avram Blok. I came from Jerusalem. I saw you there in 1974, in the Moses Klander asylum. You were shooting the film of the Judas Pig story, which had been suggested to you by my friend Yissachar. You were his producer in the New York porn trade. A long time ago. The inmates of the asylum thought you and your film crew were the Elders of Zion, who had come to determine the exact date of the Coming of the Messiah. But the asylum burnt down, and you all went back to Los Angeles. You met my friend Asher Katzman some months ago. He has just been killed on Hollywood Boulevard.'

'Can you run a thirty-five millimetre projector?'

'I've seen it done.'

'I can do anythin' for myself in this dump, but my hands can't load the fucking projector.' The ex-mogul, casting a baleful look

323

behind him, turned and wheeled himself through the junkpiles, kicking cans and boxes aside. 'The last man quit on me. He said he couldn't stand the smell. Sometimes I shit wherever I have to,' he waved his cigar. 'Don't tell me about death, you young *Scheisskopf*. Ectoplasmic fan-tan. Whadaya know about cancer, schmendrick?'

'I was twenty miles from a nuclear explosion,' said Blok. 'I suppose I shall soon find out.'

Irving Klotskashes snorted, spitting on the floor, at the base of a ramp leading upwards. He wriggled in his chair and Blok moved behind him, propelling him up the ramp to the open door of his projection booth. 'The Big C., Goddamn the bastards. There are parts of me swimming in formaldehyde in several medical insti-tootions. My liver's in a sack somewhere in Pasadena. The Mayo Clinic have what's left of my pancreas, an' Mount Sinai have my spleen. They cut my kishkas up like sausages. They sliced toomors outa my ass. Ah yes, pain, tell me about it.'

The projection booth was as littered with debris as the adjacent chamber. Rolls of unspooled film, can lids stubbed with cigarette butts, congealing trays of ancient TV dinners, old torn and smeared scripts, dropped cores, pornographic magazines and third-hand paperbacks of *None Dare Call It Treason*, *The Strange Life of Ivan Osokin*, *The Secrets of the Great Pyramid*, *The Day Khrushchev Panicked* and several E. E. Doc Smith novels. Torn posters on the walls cried the faded glories of old, lost Klotskashes productions: *The Vicar of Trash*, *The Martian Bolsheviks* and *The Murderers Lurk Within Us!* The ex-mogul kicked his way through the mess and, unrolling the first few feet of a twenty-minute reel on the rewind bench, thrust it into Blok's hands. He wheeled his chair up to the booth's viewing slats as Blok evicted a dead rat from the feed spool and laced up the rusty machine. He threw the projector's switch and the loud clatter of its ratchet echoed in the enclosed booth. A broken shaft of light shot across the cluttered room, lapping over the piles of cans and boxes, its upper half finally hitting the tattered screen at its end. Scratched and strob-ing, an immense black-and-white papier-mâché worm crawled towards a group of terrified young girls in bikinis, propelled by little hairy legs.

'Fictions,' rasped the ex-mogul, 'lies, deceptions. You can't believe how liberating it can be. Once you've left the world of ugly truths far behind you, everything becomes possible. Imagine all those things that people believe who are not even in Show Business: the carpenter from Nazareth, whose ma was a Voigin, who died and rose from the tomb. The Arab moichant who went into a cave and was given the Woid of God in bulk poichase. The Movin' Finger o'God an' the Sacred Tablets. The Angels, the Cherubim, an' Satan. Transubstantiation. The Angel Moroni an' his Plates. The Messiah, who is just around the corner. The Spiritooality of Mankind. The predestined dialectic o' History. Psychoanalysis. Motherhood an' Apple Pie. The People's Democratic Dictatorship. The Tooth Fairy. Eternal Life. Eternal Damnation. The Free Market. The Dignity of Labour. The Purity of the Race. Promised Lands. Deathbed Salvation. Golden-eyed Houris. The Fleece. The Great Pumpkin. That crystal boip of clarity. That elusive moment when contradictions are resolved. The fading away of all desires. Nirvana. Satori. Bliss. Eden Regained.'

'Something, at least, must be true,' said Blok.

The mogul farted loudly, a terrible stench rising from his pants. The picture on the screen had changed to a Martian landscape, badly painted on cardboard flats. A man and a woman, in spacesuits, staggered into frame, looking furtively offscreen. The picture changed again. Two caped figures crept through the chiaroscuro streets of a Transylvanian town, climbing over the papier-mâché fence of a graveyard, with digging tools and a burlap sack.

'But I shouldn't complain,' Klotskashes seemed calmer now, gazing at his crimped creations. 'I've lived a full life, even if I ain't won major awards. I've seen the century turn an' tumble, the dice roll, the cards fall. My folks came out from Czarist Russia, didya known that? The Klopstock Klotskashes Klowns. But both the Jews an' the Gentiles were too miserable over there. So they ended up in California. Yeah, I lived through it all, Jack-of-all-trades. Whatever I saw, I turned into show business. Universal Pitshers, Republic, MetroGnome. Ah yes, those were the days. A critic once wrote o' one o' my movies, back in the Fifties: "Irving

Klotskashes degrades all the noblest impulses and aspirations of modern man. He panders to our hidden an' primal desires to drag what is best down into the mud. He mocks faith, spiritooality, patriotism an' the carefree joys of our youth. Animal lust an' perversion are his trademarks. He sells cheap what we all hold dear."'

Down in the hole, the gravediggers put on their forceps. They dredged up a skull, which they dropped into their small burlap bag, then scurried away, dragging their tools.

'In San Francisco people queued round the block to see a revival of your films,' Blok said, not knowing how to console the ailing mogul.

'Revivals!' Klotskashes scoffed. 'The society of necrophiliacs. When you're alive they eat your liver.'

The twisted projected picture had changed again, to a melange of Eastmancolor scenes and scapes of the City of Jerusalem. The hills of Jericho, Mount Zion, David's Tower, the Mount of Olives, the crowded bazaars of the Old City, winter clouds scudding over old stones. Then a short length of scratched black spacing leading into a sequence of white-garbed hospital patients milling about the grey corridors of an institution. Ten figures, wrapped in praying shawls, genuflected in a dark tunnel.

'Recognise it, Mister Blok?' the Z-mogul's grating voice was weaker, his breath stentorian, as he slumped in his wheelchair, sweated brow against the glass slat. The white-thatched head of the asylum director, leaning on his cane, surveying the line of inmates. Familiar close-ups, tormented, grimacing or merely apathetic: Schizoid Schechtella, the Rumanian Srul, Davidov, Mrs Patchouli, Elkayam and Marciano the male nurses, and the women: Pitsi, Renata, and Nili. And there, scuttling round a corner to avoid being photographed, pulling their Ministry of Health issue smocks around them, the fleeting shawara of Farkash-Fenschechter/Nietzsche and the balding pate of Avram Blok.

'I knew it was you all the time,' wheezed the ex-mogul. 'I have my cameras, set up in the trees. I seen ya comin' all the way from the turn off, since ya left that car ya hitched up in. The Holy City, Jesus. Ya know I had a wife once. A real dedicated Hadassah lady.

She always pestered me to shoot a film down in the Holy Land. Then I met this young Israeli, Eye-zakkar. He said he had a friend at this asylum who knew some really promising old Jerusalem stories. Even an old fart like me, down on his luck, wants to start a new life, anytime . . . But we had just rolled one week, when somebody burned down the set, the location and the whole damn shebang. It was you, Mister Blok, now, weren't it?'

'I don't remember all that,' said Blok. 'It was such a long time ago.'

'Time!' the mogul snorted. 'It's an old wives' tale. I knew you would turn up, sooner or later, like a shopsoiled dollar bill. I put all sorts of talismans an' charms round the house, an' hung garlic up all over the eaves. But it was no fuckin' use.'

His voice had become steadily weaker, declining into a mumble, slowly subsiding into the harsh, guttural breath of any animal refusing to give up the ghost. The ghost, nevertheless, beginning to squeeze its way past the larynx, the tongue, the teeth, the nostrils, creating a dank, rancid steam, which wreathed in the projection's lightshaft. A claw-like hand beckoned to Blok from the wheelchair. Blok reluctantly inclined his right ear, trying to shut the projector's clatter out of his left. The mogul's lips struggled:

'Rosebud! Rosebud!'

Blok seized the mogul's dying head in his right hand, turning his face towards his own by his hair, which came out in wet white tufts. 'What about the Elders of Zion?' he shouted in his ear. 'What about my friend Asher? The nuclear bomb? The wars of good and evil and the new Book of Daniel? What about all the old conspiracies?'

'Avraa-am Blo-o-o-k . . .' the mogul whispered.

'Yes, yes?' Blok muttered.

'Go Home,' said the mogul, and subsided.

Blok sank down on to the projection stool and leaned, fatigued, on to the slats, watching the flickering out-takes give way to more everyday scenes of his forsaken home town, the soundless hubbub of its streets, its markets, its tourist traps, souvenir shops, the kiosks of history, the battlegrounds of creeds, religions, doctrines, principles, laws, ethics, rules. The long line of lunatics failing in

327

their therapy. The armies, setting off for the front. Troops searching every wastepaper basket for terrorist bombs. The stubborn demonstrations for Peace. Soldiers For and Against the Slaughter. Jews For and Against Jehovah. Hebrews For and Against Heresy. The long lines of applicant Messiahs, versus the Friday Night Fuck. Omphalos against the impalers. He felt the poison twirling in his blood stream, the bucking bronco of glistening rads riding his red and white corpuscles. Antibodies, stockpiling their weapons.

The film ran out of the projector, slapping against the side of the spool, the twisted rectangle of light shining emptily on the cluttered mess of Klotskashes' room. Blok sat watching the strobing shadow of the projector's maltese cross. It flickered on his retinas, weighing down his eyelids.

In the morning, as dawn peeked through chinks in the mounds, he awoke to bird song melding with the unfinished death rattle from the adjacent wheelchair. A perpetuum mobile of suspended mortality. He twisted off his stool, flicking ghosts from his eyes, stretching his bent, racked body, having made a decision, at last, to take matters into his own hands –

THE LAST TRUMP OF
AVRAM BLOK

The sun was clear of the mountain by the time he found his way out of the house, threading through the dead mounds to the labyrinth of rooms which were either bare or cluttered with draped furniture, and when he finally found an exit door, it gave out on to the back, not the front, of the villa, to a path winding down the side of the jagged, forested cliff.

The exit was off the kitchen, and he filled his bag with cold ham, some salami, cheese and chocolate chip cookies before moving cautiously down the path, towards the pounding Pacific waves. Swallowed up in turns by the evergreen pines, the cypress trees bent back by the wind, then emerging through a gap to the panorama of the coastline cliffs marching south towards Morro Bay and north towards Monterey. Exotic birds twittered in the branches and squirrels peeked out of clumps of leaves and followed him down, sniffing his holdall. He hugged it tight to his side. At one point he thought he glimpsed, in the surf below, the momentary thrashing of a great fishy tail. But this, too, was obscured by pines, until he had reached the base of the cliff, turbulent waters breaking on rocks. He sat, above the spray, and broke open a slab of Cheddar cheese. A soft, rather tentative voice spoke up from behind him:

'You couldn't spare a piece of that, could you?'

He looked round, surprised both by the existence of the voice and by its English accent. A young man rose from behind a rock, with sad eyes and several days' growth of beard, dressed in a somewhat torn and earth-soiled white robe. The youth said, 'Don't I know you from somewhere?'

A landscape of snow and softly rolling hills. The grunts of pigs, pails of slops, a dislodged Film College director ranting at his agrarian sister and a fleeting visit by a lost youth checking out his crates of unsold Ra Ra Mugs and Sun God Sagas . . .

'You're Jonathan, Henry Gibson's son.'

'And you're . . . Avram Blok. I remember.'

Blok gave him a piece of Cheddar cheese, then opened the packet of chocolate chip cookies.

'How is my Dad, is he OK?'

'Last I saw of him, he seemed so,' said Blok.

'I don't want him to know where I am. I've left the Sons of Ra. I've stopped believing. I think Nathan Bloom is just a crook. Of course, everyone always said so, but you know how it is. You never trust what people say. I walked all day yesterday up the coastline. Heading north to San Francisco. Are you on holiday here?'

'You might say that.'

The young man wolfed down his cheese and started on the sliced ham. 'I don't want to go back to England,' he said. 'It's not the question of the material world . . . I just need to find my own way. At least here there's space . . .'

Blok walked with the young man awhile, but parted from him just before the Point Sur lighthouse and made his way back down the coast. At one point he glimpsed the back of the Klotskashes villa but saw people milling about on the back terrace and guessed that the mogul had finally succumbed to his illness, or decided to hold an unexpected retrospective, or both, so he continued south, towards Nepenthe. At times the path disappeared completely, and he had to manoeuvre his way round ragged, sheer cliffs to keep to the line of the sea. Several times he was almost washed away by the waves, but each time the surf withdrew, defeated. At other points he thought he saw, again, the giant tail thrashing in the water, following him, but it might have been a mere trick of the spray. The night fell, and he had eaten all that Jonathan Gibson had left him of the cheese, ham and salami. The chocolate chip cookies had long gone. He lay down, exhausted, but oddly exhilarated by his isolation, on a bed of prickly pine needles. Small creatures reconnoitred his outline and made off with further clumps of his hair or explored between his toes and whispered sweet nothings in his ears. Nevertheless, he slept, and awoke, on the dawn, to find

332

himself surrounded by about a dozen quiet men and women all dressed in white robes with silver dollars wrapped round their heads by means of silk headbands. Making a litter out of several old planks washed ashore, they carried him up a winding path in the forest to a small village of prefabricated huts on a ledge overlooking the sea. They fed him yoghourt and thin gruel and rejoiced in the return of their errant son Jonathan in another guise. Treating him as an invalid, they laid him out on a Sleepeezee mattress and teenage girls squatted about him and chanted mantras and plucked vaguely on guitars. He recognised 'Where Have All the Flowers Gone' and 'Donna Donna Donna'. The man who had first seen him, who introduced himself as Ben, said he had been a mail order czar in San Bernardino until he had realised the pull of the Sun. The community had decided to seek total isolation, linked to the world only by the weekly truck which delivered yoghourt and oatmeal from the Atascadero Healtho-Mart. At present they were pursuing self-meditation, leaderless, as their founder, Nathan Bloom, Adonai the Avatar, was at a conference of Avatars in Malibu. In fact Adonai had set off on a world tour, and did not return to his flock until the spring, three and a half months later.

Blok was still sitting on the ledge, looking out to sea, waiting for a glimpse of the Great Tail. Nathan ignored him and went into a huddle with Ben and other apparent spokespersons. Sounds of discord and anguish came from the hut where the convocation was taking place. A shot was fired, and Nathan emerged grim faced, with a handgun, climbing on the highest ledge of the commune. The other acolytes emerged from the hut, dragging Ben's lifeless body. Nathan announced that the Sun God Ra had decided to destroy the world. He was appalled at Mankind's refusal to acknowledge him and had vowed to turn his face from the species. Only whales, elephants and the most powerful mammals, reptiles and insects would survive. To keep faith with Ra, and identify with his sacrifice, his disciples were all called upon to turn their backs to the light and embrace the final darkness. Tubs of yoghourt laced with a painless toxin would be distributed to everyone in the community. Other Ra communities in San Francisco, Putney and Sarawak were simultaneously taking the hemlock. To make sure Ra's commandment was obeyed, Nathan would be the last to take the poison. He would, with his enhanced powers, gather all the dead souls with him in his own leap into Ra's bosom. Two large, moustached minions with shotguns appeared to hand round the tubs of lethal yoghourt.

Screams, alarm, panic erupted as some disciples backed away, praying cowering at the cliff edge. Two or three threw themselves over or fell into the roiling surf. Blok, fortuitously positioned just below a thicket, backed through it to one of the winding cliff paths and followed it up the side of the rockface to the very top of the escarpment, crawling on his hands and knees. He peeked over cautiously, to find himself looking directly down on to the bald spot of a large orangutan-shaped ruffian, in battle fatigues, cradling an automatic machine gun and guarding a black Mercedes limousine, its driver's door open and its engine ticking over softly, evidently ready for a quick withdrawal. Lowering his head, Blok noted a large loose rock by his right hand. He took the rock and dropped it on the guard's head. The guard fell to the ground. Blok scrambled off the outcrop, scuffing his hands and knees, and ran swiftly to the vehicle, which was pointed up the gravel path leading away from the sea. As he took the steering wheel he remembered vaguely that he had never learned how to drive. Nevertheless, one knows the motions. He pressed his foot on the accelerator and proceeded by leaps and bounds to steer the car up to the main road, leaving behind the screams and cries of the doomed devotees.

He drove the car for an hour up the winding coastline, until, confident enough to handle a halt, he manoeuvred it down a side road into a concealed bay. He had noted a large brown suitcase on the back seat. He opened it and discovered several varieties of business suits, shirts and footwear. Underneath them was a black leather briefcase. He snapped it open. It was full of green Presidential portraits. His head swam slowly, given the months of yoghourt and sludge which had been his sole diet. Miraculously, it had slowed the loss of his hair, and whatever other symptoms of radioactive decay he had expected to speed his Fall since White Sands. He riffled through the notes. There were many of them, in fifties and hundred dollar bills. He discarded his robe, donned the first suit that fitted and gunned the car back on the road. He drove to Monterey and left the car by the Post Office, walking on down to the Fisherman's Wharf. He entered Domenico's and ordered a Red Mullet, with cauliflowers and a baked potato, washed down with a Château Lafite '84. Then he walked to the Greyhound depot and took the first bus out, headed for San Francisco. From the San Francisco terminal he took a tram to Powell and Union Square, walking up and choosing a small hotel, the Golden Gate, on Bush. There he locked his door and carefully counted his money. There were 120,000 dollars.

He slept, with the manna under his pillow. In the morning it was still there. He took the briefcase with him and went out to purchase some more clothes and a new set of bags. Nevertheless he continued to wear Adonai the Avatar's suit. He divided the money into three equal lots and placed one lot in the Greyhound Left Luggage. He carried the rest with him into the streets, and began to plough the Chinese Restaurants, the Vietnamese, the Continental, the Italian, the Basque, the Japanese. Newspaper headlines unfolded the coastline massacre, the panic, the arrest of Nathan Bloom, who, it was oddly noted, seemed to have made no provision for a getaway. He was to be indicted for mass murder, fraud, embezzlement, tax evasion and multiple rape. It was a nine-day sensation, which was soon replaced by rising tensions in the Persian Gulf. Blok ate more Japanese, Mexican food and pasta. But he could not dare walk the streets too often, or at night. He scanned the small ads of the local variety news sheet and tele-phoned for a lady of leisure. He requested a busty, tall and fully-tanned blonde. She arrived, and tended to his needs. He paid her double her fee and she told him strange tales of voodoo rituals in the swankest hotels. She gave him her home telephone number and told him to call if he was ever in deep trouble. Her name was Annette. He did not call her. The next day he tried a Japanese girl. He switched hotels, and moved in to the Jack Tar, but could not bear the clientele. He deposited his bags in the hotel safe and cruised the streets, proceeding with a mink-furred oriental lady of the night to another hotel on Clay. But once in the room she revealed to him she was in fact a man. He declined the offer, in fear of the Plague. But they lay together, as she told him strange tales of

335

her childhood in Oklahoma. He returned to the Jack Tar and counted his money. The city had lost its previous charm. He thought of Art Mattock and the globe-trotting Armenian, of London, Henry Gibson and Janet.

He collected his safe deposits and took a plane to New York, flying First Class, with champagne and cigars. He telephoned Art Mattock's apartment but there was no answer, from man or machine. He took a suite at the Empire Hotel, at Lincoln Center, and ploughed restaurants again. But the nights were no longer friendly. He brought a lap-top computer, walked down to the Bowery, and handed it to a tramp slumped on a step. This seemed absurd, so he added three hundred dollar bills, then took a yellow cab back uptown. The entire operation appeared pointless. He could not open a legitimate bank account, with no documents but an Israeli passport whose US visa had expired. The West was gone. He turned his face East: Purchasing a Pan Am ticket to the United Kingdom, he floated, despite an acquiescent fear, without incident, through the Aliens' queue and Nothing to Declare.

He took a black taxi from the airport to the heart of London and sat on a bench in Trafalgar Square. The fountains were dry. The newspapers told of the results of the previous day's General Election. The Conservative government of Margaret Thatcher had been returned to power again. The Labour Opposition had been unable to convince the populace of the virtues of a caring, compassionate society. The Prime Minister assured the nation of her resolve to continue the Revolution of Liberation through Moolah. Blok walked through the streets of the City to the Bank of England but it was shut. He walked back up to Holborn and Russell Square and took a room at his old Bed and Breakfast, the first stop of his four-year global tour. He removed the business suit he had been concealing himself in for two months and donned a more casual sweater and jeans. He took the rucksack in which he now carried Nathan Bloom's money, and having consumed a take away horridburger, ventured out one hour after midnight, walking through the deserted, muggy street to Charing Cross and then across the iron rail and pedestrian bridge to the concrete South Bank swathe. The shantytown of cardboard boxes soon came into view. The soup and sandwich van had been and gone. Deep snores emanated from the boxes. Battered boots, toes piercing through socks, shocks of unwashed hair, protruded from cracks and flaps. One wheezing, mammoth-like rattle drew Blok in its familiarity. He peeked carefully in the aperture of an immense Bejam Deep-freeze carton. Inexorably, Katharine Weale, and, beside her, a strange, bulky, middle-aged man in a white robe, whose face seemed oddly familiar even in slumber, an echo of power fallen on rough times.

He moved among the boxes stealthily, having removed his shoes, carrying them slung in his shoulder bag as he extracted the presorted wads of greenbacks and dropped them tenderly, gently, in each container. There were several bundles left when he had covered all of them, so he dropped them in on the prostrate bulk of Katharine Weale and her companion, like bales of green confetti.

He had left himself five thousand dollars. He walked away, under the concrete underpasses of the Royal Festival Hall, into a phone booth just beneath the railway bridge and, hoping his memory had preserved it correctly, dialled Janet's home number in Craddock. The telephone rang and rang. Finally the sleepy voice of Stanislaus answered.

'Allllo . . . ?'

'I'm really sorry to be calling at this hour. It's Avram Blok speaking. Do you know where I can reach Janet?'

There was a long pause.

'Hallo?'

'I am here, Abraham. Where on earth are you speaking from?'

The line was crackly and poor.

'I'm in Israel,' Blok said, on the spur of the moment. 'I've been here for some months. I would have phoned earlier, but there have been family problems.'

'Abraham, for God's sake,' said Stanislaus. Beyond the static, the deepest of sighs.

'Janet got married again,' he said finally. 'She married Mark, the cameraman. She was very upset when you disappeared, when she heard about Asher, and that other girl, Jacqueline? She felt . . . but it's really good to hear from you. Give me your address, your

337

telephone number. Janet is in London, with Mark. He is filming locally these days. Allo? Are you there? Give me your number, Avram . . .'

But Blok rang off and walked away. He sat on a bench on the walkway and watched the black dimples of the Thames. Nothing had occurred that was unexpected. He walked back to Russell Square. The old trouble with lies, he thought, taking over. In the morning, he bought a ticket to Tel Aviv.

★

The Homeland was changed, and yet the same. The plane circled for a long time in *hamsin* haze, searching for the promised land, before touching down at Ben Gurion Airport and shoehorning him into the arrivals section, where a dark maiden in uniform simply stamped his passport, flicked a bored look at his army exemption and waved him towards the incoming baggage. He had none due, so walked past the customs counters, unmanned due to an industrial dispute, and along the line of peering, yelling relatives. The night was unbearably muggy and hot. He had no address to proceed to apart from his parents' retirement bivouac down on the farm, or Yissachar's old pad in Tel Aviv. But instead he took the service taxi to Jerusalem and asked to be let off in the Jaffa Road, at the Mahaneh Yehuda market. The market was shuttered and closed, but the massive municipal refuse trucks, with their Arab workers, were emptying the great communal garbage skips, the whine of their crunching innards drowning the grinding teeth of the alley cats, camouflaged in the shadows, among whom he thought he discerned for a moment another ghost which had refused to lie down . . . He walked up to his old haunt of Hageffen Street. The streets were quiet, the air warm but dry, the sky clear and starry. The Milky Way, with its forgotten cargo of Apache constellations. He walked up to the Kings of Israel Road, past the dozy guard at the Schneller barracks, and then down into Mea Shearim, the ultra-orthodox quarter, with its leaning, shuttered, *fin de siècle* houses. Here and there a fully-garbed black figure hurried by from some night prayer Blok could not presume to comprehend. He proceeded, down the Tribes of Israel and the Prophets Road, to the Old City's Damascus Gate,

338

but a patrol of soldiers caused him to melt into a shop alleyway. He felt the fatigue of the trip, and sat down there, by piles of Cola crates, and slept.

The tip of the toe of a puzzled Arab youth, at the crack of dawn, woke him. 'You can't sleep here,' the youth told him in English, taking him for a tourist who had lost his way. Blok rose stiffly and moved on, checking up the road to reassure himself his banknote stash was still safe. The city, in the morning, was full of souvenir shops, galleries and American-style delis. He took a Number 6 bus to another old abode, at Abu Tor. The hill of the Klander Institute was now covered with the chalk-white boxes of a new housing estate. The old retreat of Ein Rogel Street with its tottering houses had been rebuilt. Now it boasted alien growths such as the Cable Car Restaurant, the Rasputin Piano Bar, the Bangkok Chinese Eatery, the Rimonian Coffee Shop and the Jerusalem House of Quality. He went into a café which was just opening, ordered a chocolate croissant and asked for the telephone. Placing a ten-dollar bill on the counter, he called the operator and asked to be put through to his Aunt Pashtida in Kfar Pippin. The old zealot Aunt was still alive and kicked at him hoarsely over the line. 'AVREMEL . . . BLESS THE LORD . . .' But his parents, she revealed, were on a summer holiday. They were ensconced in a rest home on the coast, at C——. She offered to phone them there immediately. He agreed, wrote down the address and took the bus to the Central Bus Station.

He arrived at the rest home at two p.m. The elderly residents were prostrate in their bedrooms. He sat with Baruch and Rosa, Papa and Mama, on the verandah overlooking the beach and sea, awnings casting a pale shadow which only checked the worst of the heat.

'Avremel,' his father mumbled from his wheelchair. His mother beat off flies with a stick. They had both shrunk dramatically since he had last seen them, so small he felt he could almost bottle them. They would remain, uncomplaining, as trapped homunculi, fed through the top with seed or flies. There was nothing much to say. He took out four thousand dollars and placed it in his father's lap. 'You sell armaments too?' Baruch joked, feebly. He had lost most of his hair and all his anger.

339

'The film business,' Blok lied. 'I have to go back to do some work, in England.'

'Films are made here too,' said Rosa, stiffly. 'Not everything here is a desert.'

Baruch did not even rise to the bait. Blok looked out to the sea. Had he imagined it, or was that a glimpse of a great tail lifting briefly in the glare?

Baruch had fallen asleep in his chair.

'Nu, I have to wheel him in,' said Mama. 'Where will you be staying, at Auntie's? There's plenty of room on the farm.'

'No, in the city,' he said. 'This is only a short business visit.'

They went in to join the general siesta. Blok sat on on the verandah, scanning the sea for surprises. There were none, and his eyelids drooped, allowing the inner red swirl to resolve into memories twisting from hitherto secure cupboards, drawers, closets, commodes, secretaires of the mind: night trips up the Esplanade, in army uniform, with the gold toothed Said T-, in search of 'manousch', the elusive fuck which makes the world go round. Day trips, with Georgina, his first unlocking, amid the mockery of mid-Fifties' Jerusalem, the era of stalwart silence and melodramatic certainty. Nili, *toujours* Nili, in the rain-swept streets, the waters of the heavens cascading off the officer's pips of Eisav, the unknown soldier. Nili, in the corridors of the asylum, dodging the spermal throw of lost souls . . . The phantom calls of the dead: Farkash-Fenschechter cum Nietzsche, Doctor Flusser, Old Leib, and was Davidov still alive somewhere, out there, fulminating about the Elders of Zion . . . ? Liam O'Habash and the spectre of the Judas Pig . . . all, all, aswirl in the whirlpool of timeless recollection . . . And the sea, and Yissachar, goads of normality, joys of quotidian life, the microcosm . . . Avi's cries of pain, the napalmed enemy, Esther and the Prodigal Saint of the desert, and Shuli, the eternal policewoman. What might have been, might have been. Shoin, genug, said Asher, another spark extinguished. The whale's tail thrashes in the red gloaming, shaking off its harpoons. Chaos, the unfettered opposites. The landscape of truth, among the lies. Here, in the abandoned home-land, perhaps it lay, gibbering and drooling, nevertheless, the Truth, unbearable and violent, casting its destructive lava flows

340

over the vista of worn-out deceptions, the magic show of bogus desires.

He joined his parents for a supper of Rumanian mush in silence and took the bus south to Tel Aviv, checking in at the D— Hotel on the beachfront, which was full of French and American tourists and crew-cut United Nations soldiers on leave. He took a newspaper from the lobby and unfolded it in his air-conditioned room. GOVERNMENT DECLARES FAITH IN SECURITY SERVICES. TORTURE AN EMOTIVE WORD, SAYS MINISTER. Ah, true. Riots continuing in Seoul, South Korea. Famine again in Ethiopia. But in the Central African Republic a tyrant, ex-Emperor Jean Bedel Bokassa, had been sentenced to death by a court . . .

On page 3, his eye caught a piquant item under the London correspondent's byline:

> The London police are conducting widespread inquiries into the astonishing financial bonanza which seems to have befallen some of the city's tramps. Apparently a number of the city's down and outs, who live in boxes in the Charing Cross district, have been walking into bureaux de change with large quantities of US dollar banknotes, or even trying to buy luxury items in shops and department stores with the cash. The police swooped on the 'box city' under the South Bank arches, and confiscated a total of eighty thousand dollars from the vagrants. A riot, lead by an old baglady who has lived on the streets for decades, and an ex-regional Chief of Police, who resigned a year ago to 'minister to the poor' and has been living with the down-and-outs for some months, had to be quelled by police with plastic shields. The use of teargas against 'the poorest members of our society', has been condemned by the Labour Party. The tramps claimed they had simply woken one morning to find the money in their boxes. The police are continuing their investigation, and Interpol has been called in to determine if some strange foreign crime which might have gone wrong lay behind the 'beggars' manna'.

He walked out, after midnight, alone through the crowd taking the air which had become bearable after the day's steambath, the vibrant thousands packing the Esplanade's cafés and restaurants. And a voice hailed him as he passed the Tayelet Restaurant.

'Avram Blok! I don't believe it!'

It was Yissachar, his old colleague in the editing and script-reading business, looking fat and respectable, in a white shirt and pressed grey trousers. He was sitting with a honey-blonde, reserved girl with a T-shirt proclaiming in Hebrew: **Freedom Of The Individual**.

'Ditsa, this is Avram. Avram, this is Ditsa. This man is like the Flying Dutchman. He vanishes into the bowels of the earth and turns up, years later, not a day older. Though you do look a little drawn, Avram. And you've lost some of your hair again.'

'A consequence of the fires . . .' The couple were devouring an immense fish and a baked potato drowned in a dish of cholesterol. They ordered a coffee and a jumbo hamburger for him, which arrived, carried by four waiters in a reinforced palankeen.

'The great Avram Blok! Would you believe it! Resurrected! Is this the End of Days? Sometimes I think heaven is like this: a restaurant by the sea, smashing food, good company, a convivial atmosphere. The Good Times after all. I am no longer in the film racket, Avram. No more Adir Kokashvili Productions. The man is planning Russian comedies now, for the millennium of glasnost. The world is changing but I'm the same, just trying to enjoy life as it comes. I'm in the personal jewellery business. Ditsa here edits a new teenage magazine. You know, what to do about zits and how to come off heroin, the usual stuff. Have you seen any of your old old friends? Thin Avi, our favourite peace hero? He is a parliamentary candidate now, for the Citizens' Rights Party. Do you know who's with him on the ticket? Your old unrequited flame, Malka Halperin? Your original, scopophilic sin? You peeked and what did it get you? Astigmatism. No more fucking through holes in the sheet now, Avram. There are no margins, everyone's in the market place. We requite our lusts in public. So what did you expect? Feeling guilty for the sins of the world,

Avram, that too can be a commodity. Eat your burger. Now tell me, what have you been doing all these years?'

★

I ran. And when I stopped and looked around me I saw that I had no satisfaction, and ran again. And I founds shards of paradises, and lost them. And won friends, and failed to influence people. And I felt the ebb and flow of desires and mad dreams and hopes of reconciliation. And there were moments when I thought: I have it. And then again, no. But there was, all around, a great swirl of subterfuges, faces, voices calling in the desert. I called back: Here I am! They mumbled, never mind, we've forgotten what we had to say. And there were certainties – yes, those, too, battering at my retinas and eardrums. Buy this! Buy that! Have a weltanschauung, free! (No money back if unsatisfied.) Well, I picked my feet up and ran again. Love, friendship, companionship. All the biological urges. But that shattering wheel of absurdity, the merry-go-round of fools, the rollercoasters of the eternal 'E' Rides, Jews of Diamonds, Spades, Clubs, Hearts, Haunted Mansions of phantom fears, silver-wrapped over those genuine terrors which come bubbling up from within and from the without of the eternal wittering 'news': The horsemen of war, pestilence, oppression, greed, stupidity, wilful political blindness, the imbecile child hiding behind the mask of the elder statesman, the lobotomising of doubt, compassion and simple common sense. But who am I to judge? Desire is chaos and loss. Vote for the Sun God Ra, comrades! The hemlock yoghourt, yum, yum, yum. If I eat another mouthful of this hamburger I shall drop dead on the spot. Let me be, man, lct me be. And let my dreams speak for me.

★

He woke up. The dawn was streaming through the slats of the projection booth, dappling past the mounds of props and debris. Mice scampered among the congealed TV dinners and unwound reels of film. The Z-mogul's skeleton, crouched in its wheelchair, had been picked clean. A door, yawning open at the further end of

343

the projection booth, attracted Blok's attention. He stood up stiffly, and walked over to it. A flight of stone steps, dimly lit by bare electric bulbs, spiralled down past dank brick walls. He took a few steps down, and the door behind him slammed shut. He continued cautiously down the stairs, alone, in the vortex, in the womb/death labyrinth he recognised too well. He braced himself and began whistling a medley of Homeland and cinema theme tunes. Abandoned passageways and cells led right and left off the stairwell. But he felt no fear. The last echoes of Alamogordo's shamans, the last shadows of Guevarian temptations, the last drops of blood and flickers of fire, faded. He strode on down towards the light. It glimmered, soon enough, in the widening exit of a cave in the cliffside, some twenty feet above the sea. In the midst of the surf pounding the rocks beneath him the whale thrashed about, tossing its tail. Its massive head turned towards him, an eye winking, a heave of blubber beckoning him on. He climbed down the slippery path with a new confidence. The whale turned, showering him with spray.

'Where do you want to go?' it asked him, in a deep baritone, echoing off the cliffs.

'Home,' said Blok.

'Step right up, comrade,' said the whale.

He stepped into its yawning maw, the beast assisting him with its great tongue. The warm glow of a sixty watt bedlamp lit his bunk and assorted pile of books and magazines: *Tarzan and the City of Gold. Treasure Island. Alice Through the Looking Glass. Three Men in a Boat. Baron Münchhausen.* Classics Illustrated and Scrooge McDuck. A bedside primus and a sack of fresh plankton in the fridge.

'Are you comfortable?' asked the whale.

'AOK,' Blok replied.

The whale cast off through the waves. Streaking underwater, it lulled him with long, ghostly hoots and ululations, answered by reciprocal calls, chimes, trills and booming of oceanic well-wishers, the soft purr of drowned atomic submarine crews, humming old lullabies. Dolphins chirruped, tapping bad jokes on the blubbery hull with their snouts. Knock, knock. Who's there? Adolf. Adolf who? Adolf Fin. Dugongs serenaded lost youth. The Nautilus docked briefly, sending a filet mignon. Time slid by, in indolent comfort.

'We have arrived.' The whale unrolled its tongue. Blok stepped out on to a small rubber dinghy moored to its left molar. He looked ahead. A familiar city, from an unfamiliar angle, loomed before him, across a brief stretch of choppy, cold sea. He could make out the low, granite buildings, the majestic castle perched upon its black outcrop, the long-extinct volcano's peak under the harsh clouds of a northern autumn.

'Your Jerusalem.' The whale grinned widely. Blok cast off. The beast waved its tail. In the midst of the Firth of Forth it geysered, proudly, showering several merchant vessels.

'Goodbye! Shalom!' it bellowed. 'Have a nice day!' Then it plunged again beneath the waves.

Blok beached the dinghy at Portobello, spreading his palms at the laconical promenaders' stares, and walked up James Street to Abercorn Gardens, joining a patient queue of housewives and everyday folk at a bus stop which displayed the quotidian sign: Lothian Transport – Musselburgh, Prestonpans, Cockenzie, Seton Sands, Craddock, North Berwick. Dredging from his pocket a pound sterling coin. The fare to Craddock was ninety-nine pence.

Whistling happily, with one pence in his pocket, he arrived, and knocked on Stanislaus' door.

★

The grey, cloud veiled, rippling sea, upon the old harbour. A fishing boat, lifted on shore, is being painted blue and grey amid the stutter of a power generator. The gulls perch on chimney pots, bollards, the tips of wave-lapped rocks.

Blok and Janet walk on the breaker jutting out into the Firth, stepping carefully round the tangled nets, weights and tackle piled against the wall. The boats in the enclosed water rock gently, masts and rigging tinkling in the wind.

'There was no point in my staying in the Middle East,' Blok explained to her. She had come from Edinburgh to meet him. The cameraman husband was away on duty: floods were inundating

345

Bangladesh. 'For my mother, the outside world does not exist, and the inner world, the Homeland, shrinks further and further, until it is the point of a pin. For my father . . . I had prepared reams of dialogue, volumes of discussion and dispute. But he had shrunk too, into his wheelchair and the pills that bog him down. When I grew up, the stamp collection gave him a lifeline to the wide world. Hiding in his room, he would go on safari to unimaginable locations, writing and receiving letters from penpals in Ghana, Vietnam, Indonesia, and other non-existent places, devoid of interest to the Tribe. I think my mother never awoke from the Holocaust, while my father wanted its very memory burned, scattered in its own ashes in the sea, blasted into outer space. But I sat there, feeling the vast dead weight of his defeat. The guilt, for being its main component. Failing to breathe life into the identity he had handed me as his priceless gift by bringing me out of Europe to the Old-New Land. Although he pretended to con-gratulate me on my "escape". "Go, boy, go," was what he told me, before we parted, "show the bastards a clean pair of heels . . ."'

Janet held his arm, as he was experiencing a slight recurrence of his post-nuclear dizziness, a minor discoordination of limbs. She had been afraid he would be alienated by her marriage, but he appeared to accept things as they came.

'My friends had changed, and remained the same, like the country,' he said, 'each chasing his personal ghost. The girl I dreamed about at school appears daily on television, leads demon-strations, represents the forces of progress. She is married to a building contractor who owns businesses in Zambia and Zaire. Another friend is also going to become a Member of Parliament. Serious people. They have their claws in the times. Even the hermit film-maker I knew in Tel Aviv, Bentov, has got inter-national prizes for his film showing only the inside of his flat. Table legs, upended chairs, kitchen utensils. It's all the rage in the EEC. And the two girls I knew are still in love with each other and have opened a boutique in Jerusalem. Me, I am always out of fashion. But I could not swim in that pool. Rather this – see, the open ocean, too cold for the hordes of sun-worshippers, polluted by makers of a living.'

346

And the living still offered in London, the lure of Henry Gibson's hearty handclasp: Oi gevaldt, mine little chickadee! It's good to see you alive! Welcome news of the prodigal son, now in Berkeley, escaped the doom of Nathan Bloom. You know he's with the Moonies now, thank God, they're too many to commit suicide . . . But offers to return to the College declined, it's timeless symbiosis of creation and failure . . .

'I have an idea for you, Avram,' Janet said, looking cagey, 'but give me a couple of days to find out.' They had reached the edge of the dock, where he pulled back, uneasy at being surrounded three parts by dull grey spray. They returned to firmer ground. He sat in the front room of the two-storey house with Stanislaus, as Elsa and Janet conferred in the kitchen.

'What can I tell you, Abraham,' said the old Polish airman. 'exile. It has its attractions. You need not feel responsible either for the ills of your place of adoption or of your origin. You have been spat out. Fine, swim in the saliva. It is full of natural juices. What do the Scots say: Ye canna tak the breeks off a heilandman for he's nane on. On the other hand, of course, we feel that constant guilt of abandonment, the frisson of true treason. Each man betrays the thing he loves, to paraphrase Mister Oscar Wilde. Total loyalty presupposes the forfeit of all questions. But to keep our humanity we have to keep posing and reposing all the old questions. The clichés, the truisms, the tautologies. And if we eventually get bored, and sink into lethargy and neglect, others will take up the torch. Why not? There is always some welcome smartarse somewhere, to prevent moral gangrene. Saving the world? OK, I'm not against that either. But gently please, the fucker is fragile. I'm not talking about El Salvador, Chile, Rumania. That level of oppression, tyranny? OK, knives and axes are de rigueur.'

The next day, Janet borrowed the family car and drove Blok into the sparse but solid countryside, up a narrow side road to a lone granite building set in green lawns. White-coated attendants nursed faltering and ungainly men and women, youths and girls, up and down gravel paths. A lopsided youth grinned at Blok and took hold, after a few false starts, of his hand. Together, they proceeded towards the main entrance. He was ushered into the

347

presence of the asylum's director, an ebullient red-bearded Scot with smiling eyes, totally lacking in guile. His name was Andrew Mackenzie.

'I hear you've been mad as a hatter, Avram,' he told Blok, passing him a tray of tea and biscuits. 'You're thinking of living in our part of the world and you may be looking for a job. I run a course for non-qualified auxiliary staff to learn to deal with handicapped people. No former medical experience needed. Further education in the field can be arranged. We like to use just common sense here. Attention, affection and empathy. Healing, far from the madding crowd. Do you have any hereditary diseases, such as dogmatism, moral strabismus, compulsive narrow-mindedness, political retardation, incipient authoritarianism, love of ignorance for its own sake, latent toryism or a total lack or blockage of the imagination?'

'I don't think so,' said Blok.

'Do you want a job?' asked Mackenzie. 'The pay is absolutely terrible.'

'I will take it,' Blok affirmed.

And is there a therapy beyond this, a thorough cleansing of old accumulations which makes way for more, fresher accumulations which in their turn must be purged? Blok, struggling up the path with a lolloping, scraping hulk of a lad whose limbs refuse stubbornly to obey the vital ambitions of the mind. Walk, walk, feinschmecker! Move that hand from plate to mouth! OK, so we didn't make it that time. Let's try again, never say die. And if we do just that, die, nevertheless, nevertheless, Goddamn its eyes! That personal conquest, that private achievement, can it transcend? Can it fly?

'I wanted to embrace the world,' Blok told Andrew Mackenzie, 'and let its entire flood of madness surge through me like an electrical charge. But of course, I had insufficient insulation. I needed a fifty billion amp fuse.'

'Fuses!' said Andrew Mackenzie, waving his hand. 'Replace the fuckers, Jesus Christ! Just let it surge – what you really need is an earth. That's the real ticket.'

Before them they wheeled a severely spastic youth, Jimmy

348

Francioza, up the hill towards the view, letting his head roll about the four quarters of the earth, sky, sea.

'A braugh day, eh, Jimmy?'

'Urg, burg, hurg,' agreed the young man.

Blok experienced a spasm of pain. Mackenzie took him to Edinburgh for a medical check up. Outside the surgery window Edinburgh Castle loomed. David's City, Mount Zion. The doctor could perceive no ailment but took body samples. Blok revealed his New Mexico fears. The tests showed no immediate signs of cancer, but a recurring check was advised.

'It's not the black cap for you yet, young Avram,' said Mackenzie, as he drove Blok back to Craddock. 'You'll have to live with that suspended sentence, like the rest of us.'

Join, shmuck, join the human race.

Blok sat, in Stanislaus' house, watching TV, as the news programme unfolded scenes of soldiers bogged down by rifle butts and pouches, running after crowds of demonstrators, shooting rounds into their midst, belabouring a teenage youth with wooden clubs, striking again and again at the bloody, broken mess of his face.

'What is that, Poland?' asked Stanislaus, who had just entered the room.

'Israel, Palestine,' Blok explained to him, peeking again from a vast distance, at his Homeland's latest eruption.

'It's the same thing,' said Stanislaus, walking out of the room, shaking his head. Upstairs, Elsa preparing Christmas boxes and cards for a volunteer welfare binge. Noel, Noel. Cans set to spew plastic spaghetti are stockpiled. The Messiah's birthday, gift-wrap silver paper, TV repeats, the Queen's Speech.

'Looking forward to Hogmanay, Jimmy?'

'Urr! Durr murr!' the youth enthuses.

The rain clouds swoop, darkening the hills. Blok and Mackenzie cover their charge with a large anorak and wheel him back to the asylum grounds. An elderly lady visiting her son from Dunbar waves her stick at them, cheerfully crying out:

'Fresh day! Fresh day!'

Aye. Blok and Mackenzie take refuge in the director's office, watching the downpour on the grass. Mackenzie lights his pipe,

349

breaking out his favourite, the Auchentoshan. 'A wee dram, my friend? What the hell.' Having taken Blok the rounds on the last day of the old year to the local licensed premises, casting a loving eye over the rows of malts honouring the shelves in the splendour of their exotic obscurity: Ardbeg, Auchentoshan, Balblair, The Balvanie, Bladnoch, Bruichladdich, Cardhu, Clynelish, Dalwhinnie, Gladnoch, Glen Albyn, Glenburgie-Glenlivet, Glencoe, The Glendronach, Glendullan, Glen Elgin, Glenesk, Glenfarclas, Glenforres, Glenglassaugh, Glen Grant, Glenkinchie, Glen Mhor, Glenmorangie, Glenordie, Glenrothes, Glen Scotia, Glen Tress, Glen Turret, Glenury Royal, Inchgower, Inchmurrin, Islander, Kinclaith, Knockkdhu, Laphroaig, Longmorn, The Macallan, Oban, Oldbury Sheep Dip, Old Pulteney, Port Duibh, Strathiola, The Strathspey, Talisker, Tanavulin, Tamdhu. 'A wee dram, to warm the cockles of the heart. Happy New Year.' He hands Blok a clipping that caught his eye that very morning from *The Scotsman*. 'For your scrapbook, Avram, may it never falter. The living proof, eh? No surrender!' And Blok inserted it inside the plastic folder with his London Transport Weekly Travelcard, which had been preserved throughout his travails stuck in his back trouser pocket, with its mug shot and bold number and red legend: *Valid for use only by person shown with a ticket bearing the same number*, and he often took it out and examined it in the cold grey light of the Craddock harbour, with the boats setting out to trawl for shrimps and mackerel and the house of Stanislaus and Elsa with its back room converted for his lodgings and the Polish ex-airman's pipe smoke wreathing up the old clay chimney, driving off the gulls, and, of a Sunday, the hymns wafting from the Meeting House two houses down, curling round the one way sign and its legend: I AM THE WAY, THE TRUTH AND THE LIFE – The Lord Is My Shepherd, I Shall Not Want. But he would take his folding chair and sit out in the sombre winter light and re-read Andrew Mackenzie's cutting, which was from the obituary column:

DAVEY: 30th December 1987, at 16 Chambers Crescent, Grange, Edinburgh. WILLIAM RICHARD DAVEY, age 93. Funeral at Cloister Chapel, Warriston Crematorium, on Tuesday, January 5, 1988, at 12:15 p.m., at which all friends are invited. There will be no religious service. He did not believe in the grotesque theological history of the world that had dominated and crippled human thought for so many centuries. The Marseillaise will be played full blast, with all stops out.

SELAH

★　★　★　★
★

And was that not the tail of a whale, beckoning from the horizon??

★　★　★　★　★　★　★
★　★　★　★
★